W9-COV-478

MATHEMATICS

A LIBERAL ARTS APPROACH

HAYDEN SERIES IN MATHEMATHICS

IRVING ALLEN DODES, B.S., A.M., Ph.D.

Chairman, Department of Mathematics
Bronx High School of Science

MATHEMATICS

A LIBERAL ARTS APPROACH

A Textbook in General Mathematics

HAYDEN BOOK COMPANY, INC., NEW YORK

a division of HAYDEN PUBLISHING COMPANY, INC.

LIBRARY OF CONGRESS CATALOG CARD NUMBER 64-10304
Printed in the United States of America

To

Dot, Pam, and Lance

Preface

The content of a general course in secondary school mathematics — or what we prefer to call *the liberal arts approach* to mathematics — has been discussed at great length by local and national committees. Perhaps the most popular versions are still those in the "Second Report of the Committee on Postwar Plans" (*Mathematics Teacher*, November, 1947), in "General Mathematics in Secondary Schools" by the late Professor Reeves (*Mathematics Teacher*, February and March, 1954), and in the *Twenty-Second Yearbook* of the National Council of Teachers of Mathematics, "Emerging Practices in Mathematics Education," in various chapters.

Unfortunately, it is hard to find any actual courses in the field which satisfy the aims stated in these reports. As a lecturer to teachers in graduate courses at the New York University, I never met a teacher who had experienced the joy of teaching a liberal arts course in mathematics. The actual courses varied from *arithmetic* to a kind of diluted algebra and geometry from which merely the most important ingredient, *reasoning*, had been distilled.

In an attempt to improve this situation, I introduced and tested various topics in the general mathematics classes of the Morris High School, New York City. The result of a careful statistical investigation is given in a paper, "Four Investigations in the Improvement of Mathematics Instruction," published in *High Points* (February, 1954). To my surprise and pleasure, I found that certain aspects of mathematics were very interesting to students who did *not* expect to become professional mathematicians or scientists! These aspects were actually the most important ones in mathematics: what mathematics is like, what mathematicians do, how computers work, the basic theory behind measurement (but not measurement by itself), graphs showing time-changes, inequalities, puzzle problems, the basic theory behind experimentation, the use of mathematical instruments, the solution of problems by indirect means, mathematical thinking and logic.

A textbook for these topics was (and, so far as I know, still is) nonexistent. I therefore prepared reams of mimeographed material and tried them on the classes. When something did not "go over," it was discarded. When something had a flaw, it was rewritten — sometimes several times.

The first ten chapters of this book represent that tried and thoroughly tested material. (At least twice as much material was discarded because it was not teachable, or, at least, could not be assimilated.) The last chapter is an *extra* intended for those who become especially interested in mathematical methods.

For whom is the book intended? It is intended for people who do *not* at the present time intend to go into mathematics or science as a profession. It is intended for the citizen who lives in a democracy and wants to see and understand the things going on about him. It bears the same relationship to algebra and geometry as liberal arts English does to journalism. A companion volume is projected for the person who wishes to have a professional background.

When should it be taught? Ordinarily, this subject will occupy the ninth and tenth years, but a reduced course can be taught in one year by selecting chapters — so that this book is used as a source book — or an accelerated course can be taught in one year to a fast group, or in a community college where the aim is a liberal arts aim. This should occasion no great surprise; two years of high school Latin are usually taught in one year at the college level for those who are taking it as a liberal arts course.

Does it prepare a student for the preprofessional course in geometry? No. Preprofessional students should take the preprofessional course. However, you will find (as I did) that students who were not interested before this course, are very interested, and even excited about mathematics, after this course. This kind of exposure seems to appeal to students and they wish to take the regular preprofessional courses.

How does this book differ from other books in general mathematics? There is really no similarity. This book emphasizes the strength and power of mathematics, not the practice and details of manipulation. A nonartist can enjoy a painting by Picasso, and a nonmathematician can enjoy that kind of poetry which is called *mathematics*. If you wish to teach arithmetic, whether of the consumer or the commercial type, this is not the book to use. It does not explain how to write a check or how to fill out an income tax blank. However, in this book (written before the CEEB, UICSM and SMSG studies) you will find the notions of sets, modulo (clock arithmetic), groups, fields, inequalities, linear programming and the theory of games, given in a nonrigorous form, all tested on general groups and guaranteed to be successful.

I have spared no effort to make this book easy to teach. A *Teachers' Manual* containing a discussion of teaching procedures and lesson planning in relation to the material, and giving the answers for the problems and tests, is available.

I do hope that this book will make it possible for teachers to bring to their students the same appreciation of the power and beauty of mathematics which they, themselves, have.

IRVING ALLEN DODES

New York, N. Y.

Contents

Part I: Problems from Algebra

Part II: Problems from Geometry

1

introducing: MATHEMATICS

This book is your friend.

A friend takes you by the hand and introduces you to people and things he thinks you will like. A friend tells you about things you ought to know. A friend stays with you when you need help.

Any friendship goes two ways. Give this book your careful attention and you will be well rewarded.

1 WHAT IS MATHEMATICS?

If you ask the average person what mathematics is, he will usually say, "counting," or "adding and subtracting," or "arithmetic."

Well, it is true that arithmetic is a part, an important part, of mathematics, but it is not the only part. Other areas of mathematics are *algebra*, *geometry*, and *trigonometry*, which you will read about in this book. Then there is advanced mathematics, such as *calculus*, which is studied by engineers.

To do the work in this book, you will need the following:

a loose-leaf notebook with two kinds of paper: lined, and cross-ruled
a 6-in. ruler marked in inches and millimeters
a 12-in. ruler
a 30-60-90° celluloid triangle
a protractor
compasses

Mathematics has many uses. Here are some of them.

1 Mathematics is used for *computing* (kŏm·pūt′ing). This means, for example, *adding* and *subtracting*.

2 Mathematics is used for *measuring*.

3 Mathematics is used to *describe* the universe we live in. For example, mathematics is used to tell where the stars are, how much the earth weighs, how large a virus is.

4 Mathematics is used to *solve* problems, to find out, for example, where to open a gas station, or how much butter to put in a cake.

5 Mathematics is used for *reasoning*, to decide whether or not an argument is *valid* (correct), and whether or not an editorial makes sense.

The following exercises give you a quick look into the type of problems dealt with in this book.

• Test: Section 1

You will not be able to do these problems. Just guess at the answers and check with the correct solutions here. If you finish the book, you will find these problems very easy. *Please do not write in this book.*

Part A. These are questions from Chapters 2, 3, and 4.

1 Find |||∩∩ times |||/|||∩ . (This is how the early Egyptians wrote the numbers.)

2 On an electronic computing machine, $1 + 1 =$ (*a*) 2, (*b*) 5, (*c*) 10.

3 $(-6) \times (-5) =$ (*a*) 11, (*b*) -11, (*c*) 30, (*d*) -30.

4 2.5 in. × 2.5 in. = (*a*) 6.3 sq. in., (*b*) 6.25 sq. in., (*c*) 5.0 sq. in.

5 2.5 in. + 2.5 in. = (*a*) 5 in., (*b*) 5.0 in., (*c*) 5.00 in.

6 In the diagram, point *P* is (*a*) 5, (*b*) 1, (*c*) (3, 2) (*d*) (2, 3).

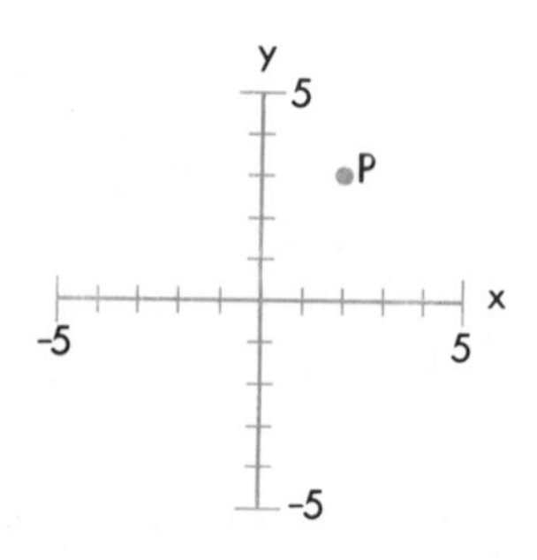

7 The diagram shows how the business of a certain store changed over the years. What do you expect the amount of business will be next year?

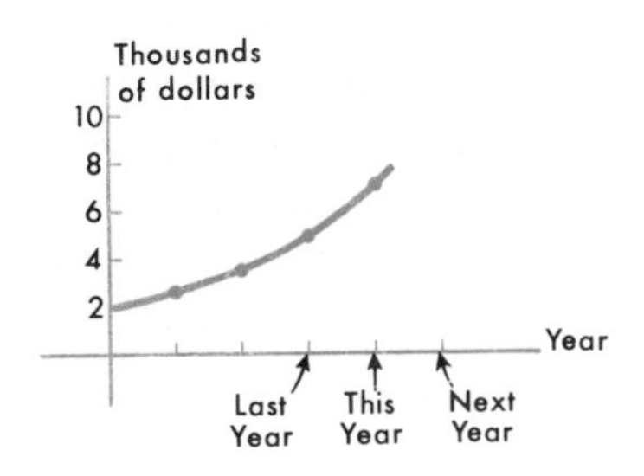

8 What is the smallest pair of whole numbers which satisfy the following two conditions: (*1*) The first is larger than the second; (*2*) the sum of two numbers is less than 8? (*a*) 3 and 2, (*b*) 3 and 3, (*c*) 2 and 1.

Part B. These are questions from Chapters 5, 6, and 7.

1 What is meant by "E = IR"?

2 How long is an oval track 35 ft. long, and 12 ft. wide? (*a*) 420 ft., (*b*) 160 ft., (*c*) 94 ft., (*d*) 47 ft.

3 Think of a number; double it; add 6; subtract 2; divide by 2; subtract the number you started with. The answer is always 2. Why?

4 The producer of a television show wanted to measure its popularity. He called 25 people in various occupations: one teacher, one doctor, one plumber, one housewife, and so on. He collected their opinions and drew his conclusions. Was this a good way?

5 What are: opposite vertical angles, perpendiculars, bisectors, isosceles triangles, altitudes, parallels?

Part C. These questions are from Chapters 8, 9, 10, and 11.

1 What are: regular pentagons, chords, secants, inscribed angles, triangular prisms?

2 How would you find the height of a cloud?

3 Jean's mother said, "Jean, you must eat your vegetables. Vegetables make you healthy. If you don't eat your vegetables, you won't be healthy." Jean's mother might have the correct conclusion, but is this a logical argument?

4 In a poll, 11 people voted that they liked English, and 15 that they liked

social studies. Of these, five stated that they liked both. How many people were interviewed? (*a*) 21, (*b*) 26, (*c*) 31.

5 Adam McLane is conducting a campaign for election as senior president. The facts are as follows: He must provide at least five posters. He cannot have more than 15 posters because there is not enough space to hang them. He wants at least one banner. The school rule is that you cannot use more than 18 posters and banners (together). Each poster convinces 11 people. Each banner convinces seven people. How many of each should he use to get the most votes?

6 What are the chances of getting a "5" in rolling two dice? (*a*) 6%, (*b*) 11%, (*c*) 22%.

7 What are the chances of getting two "heads" in tossing two coins? (*a*) 10%, (*b*) 25%, (*c*) 50%.

8 How many ways can you shuffle three different cards? (*a*) 6, (*b*) 10, (*c*) 15.

9 What are your chances of drawing any flush, ace high, with the ace first, if you are drawing from a full poker deck?

Answers: Test 1

Part A. (*1*) IIII∩∩∩ / IIII∩∩∩ 999 (*2*) c. (*3*) c. (*4*) a. (*5*) b. (*6*) d.

(*7*) $10,000. (*8*) c.

Part B. (*1*) To find the number of volts produced in a network supplied by a battery, multiply the number of amperes (current) by the number of ohms (resistance) in the circuit. (*2*) b. (*3*) Wait until Chapter 5. (*4*) It is not correct. This is explained in Chapter 7. (*5*) Explained in Chapter 7.

Part C. (*1*) Explained in Chapter 8. (*2*) Explained in Chapter 9. (*3*) *No!* See Chapter 10. (*4*) a. (*5*) 15 posters and 3 banners. (*6*) b. (*7*) b. (*8*) a. (*9*) About 69 times out of a million.

2 THE BEGINNING OF MATHEMATICS

Mathematics was born because it was needed. The first mathematician probably had something to do with *art* and *religion*. We know that cavemen, 50,000 years ago, made drawings and sculptures of animals (Fig. 1-1). Some

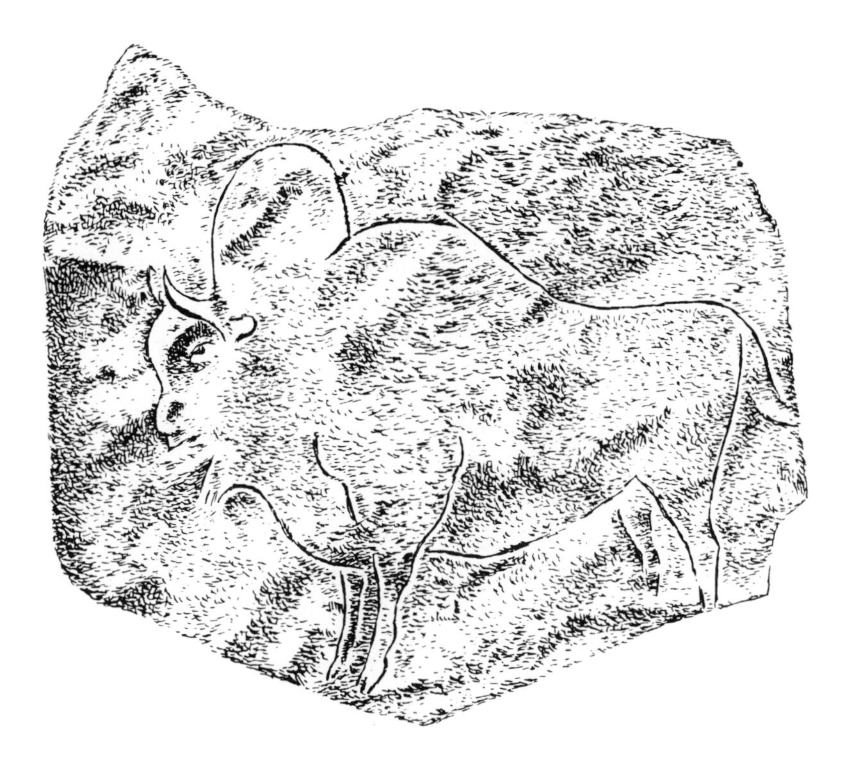

Fig. 1-1. Cave drawing (engraving) of the Upper Paleolithic period. Courtesy *Scientific American.*

of these drawings were made in the darkest part of dark caves, so that it seems logical that the purpose in drawing these was *not* for decoration. They must have been intended for either magic or religion.

The mathematics in these cave drawings is the mathematics of *proportion, perspective,* and *design.*

The second need of mathematics was probably for *counting.* We know that numbers are very old because the names of the numbers are very old. We can, in fact, trace our own number-names to Europe, Greece, and to the cradle of civilization in Asia.

Our table gives a few of the names of the numbers in different languages.

GREEK	LATIN	FRENCH	SPANISH	ENGLISH	GERMAN
oine	unus	un	uno	one	ein
duo	duo	deux	dos	two	zwei (zwo)
treis	tres	trois	tres	three	drei
hepta	septem	sept	siete	seven	sieben

In this table, if you pronounce the words as they are spelled, you will have a good idea of the original pronunciation of the number names. For example, in the first line, our number name for "one" was originally pronounced "oon," which is very similar to the pronunciation of the number-name in other languages. In the second line, "two" was originally pronounced "twoh" or "twah," which sounds like "duo," if you say it fast.

You may be interested in one of the theories as to how our figures "two" and "three" got their present shape.

According to this theory, the European forms of "two" and "three" were originally *horizontal lines,* as shown in the table.

	EUROPEAN		ARABS and PERSIANS	
	Two	Three	Two	Three
original	=	≡	II	III
midway	Z	Ʒ	N	NN
present	2	3	٢	٣

Gradual evolution finally resulted in the edges being joined. In the case of "two," this made a "Z" shaped figure. Over the course of time, loops and curls were added to make it prettier.

The Arabs and Persians had slightly different writing habits. For example, they wrote from right to left, instead of from left to right. They apparently started with *vertical lines* (see table). When they joined the edges, the "two" and "three" came out sideways.

Test: Section 2

These are review exercises for work you had in the lower grades.

Part A. Read the following:

1 2173
2 5326
3 7035
4 5066
5 35,238
6 56,772
7 60,013
8 90,028
9 2,377,4532.16
10 1,581,823.58

Part B. Change to numerical form:

1 Three thousand five hundred seventy three
2 Four thousand one hundred twenty seven
3 Three thousand twenty seven
4 Nine thousand fifty six
5 Twenty-seven thousand two hundred forty six
6 Thirty-eight thousand, three hundred fifty seven
7 Forty thousand twelve
8 Ten thousand eighty eight
9 Five million, two hundred thirty-seven thousand, eight hundred fifteen and twenty-nine hundredths
10 Three million, seven hundred seventy-nine thousand, six hundred fifty, and forty-two hundredths

Part C.

1 How many tenths are there in 27.1?
2 How many tenths are there in 36.45?
3 How many hundredths are there in 2.58?
4 How many hundredths are there in 7.18?

3 EARLY CIVILIZATION

We have already mentioned that in the beginning mathematics was probably connected with the needs of art, religion, and counting.

By the time civilization began in Babylonia, Egypt, and Sumer, certain other needs appeared. For example, there was a need for some way of dividing up land, building canals and reservoirs, making a record of taxes and loans, and figuring out the amount of money owed. In Babylonia, *4000 years ago*, there was already some knowledge of triangles, rectangles, and circles. The Babylonians knew enough mathematics to do simple astronomy.

An achievement which has impressed people for thousands of years was the building of pyramids and obelisks by the Egyptians. The Great Pyramid at Giza, built in 2900 B.C., involved many engineering problems. The structure covered 13 acres of land, and took 100,000 workmen thirty years to complete. Two million blocks of stone, each weighing 2.5 tons, were used. For the roofs of chambers, granite blocks weighing 54 tons each were carried 600 miles and lifted 200 feet.

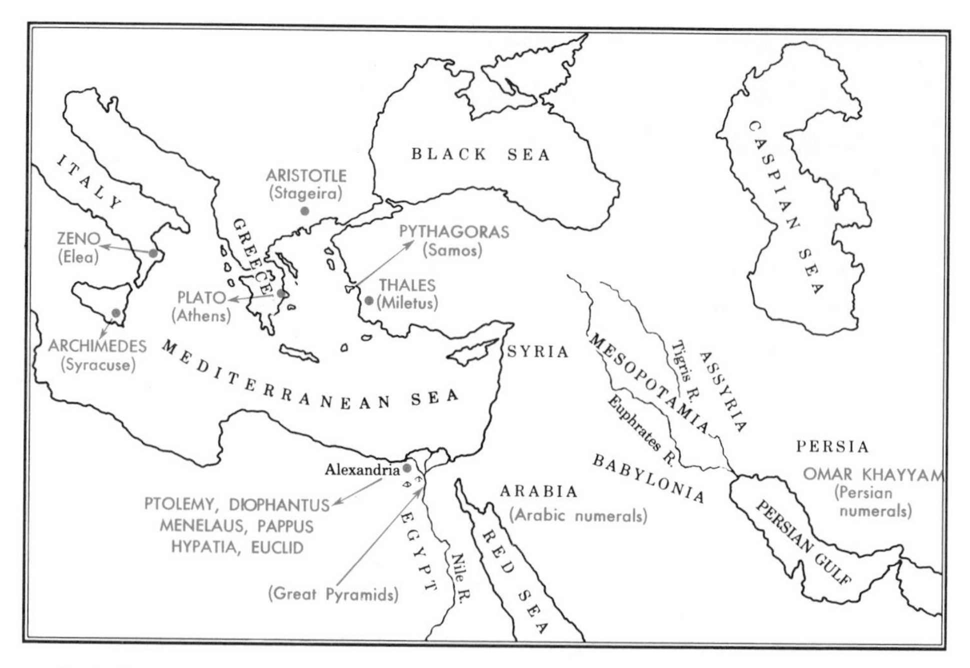

The Mediterranean world is probably the most interesting of all the ancient civilizations. In the areas of Alexandria, Greece, Mesopotamia, Assyria, Babylonia, Chaldea, Persia, and India, mathematics and learning flourished and spread.

The Great Pyramids at Giza, Egypt, built in 2900 B.C. Courtesy *United Arab Republic*.

The Egyptians also had water-clocks, and knew the elementary mathematics of ship building and navigation. They also knew how to solve *mixture problems* (problems about how much of one thing to mix with something else to get what you want).

Test: Section 3

Part A. These questions have to do with the history of mathematics.

1 Why do we think a knowledge of mathematics existed 50,000 years ago?

2 The Giza Pyramid is dated 2900 B.C. How long ago was that?

3 One acre is about 0.6 of a city block. How many city blocks would the Great Pyramid cover?

4 Some of the granite blocks for the Great Pyramid had to be lifted 200 feet. Measure a step in one of the school stairways. Now find out how many steps you would have to lift each block of stone to get 200 feet up.

5 Just North of the Persian Gulf, about this time, in Sumer, lived a people called the *Sumerians*. They charged 30% p.a. interest for a loan. If you borrowed $100 at that rate, how much interest would you have to pay? Do you know the legal limit per year now?

Part B. Review Section: Addition.

1 70 + 30 + 40 + 20 + 70 + 80

2 38 + 15 + 59 + 16 + 82 + 40

3 24 + 32 + 67 + 48 + 75 + 65

4 14 + 28 + 95 + 53 + 84 + 70

5 59 + 19 + 78 + 30 + 54 + 28

6 26 + 43 + 59 + 70 + 41 + 82

7 37 + 21 + 62 + 54 + 18 + 39

8 59 + 77 + 98 + 46 + 75 + 99

9 37 + 428 + 2596

10 655 + 85 + 5020

Part C. Projects.

You can find more information about the cavemen, and the Babylonians, Egyptians and Sumerians in various books on ancient history, or in your local museum or library. Make a report on these.

4 THE FIRST GOLDEN AGE OF MATHEMATICS

The mathematics of Babylonia, Egypt, and Sumer was mostly practical. As civilization advanced, the practical type of problem continued to appear, but became more difficult to solve; a wider knowledge and understanding of mathematics was needed.

About 600 B.C., *Thales of Miletus,* a Greek mathematician, found a way to figure out the distance from a ship to the shore. He also showed how to measure the height of a pyramid by its shadow. Thales was one of the *Seven Wise Men* of the ancient world.

But while practical problems were important, the greatest contribution of the Greek mathematicians was that they realized the importance of asking,

The greatest contribution to early mathematics came from the Mediterranean; Euclid of Alexandria (c. 300 B.C.); Archimedes of Syracuse; Zeno of Elea; Plato (Athens); Aristotle (Stageira); Pythagoras of Samos; Thales of Miletus; Omar Khayyam (Persian numerals); Ptolemy, Diophantus, Menelaus, Pappus, Hypatia. But other countries too, produced brilliant mathematicians: Isaac Newton (England); John Napier (Scotland); Carl Friedrich Gauss (Germany); Nicolai Ivanovitch Lobachevsky (Russia); Abraham de Moivre (France); Seki Kowa (Japan). The background to their work makes fascinating study.

"Why?" They asked many questions about mathematics, some of which were not answered for *hundreds* of years.

In about 450 B.C., the Greek mathematician *Zeno* made up a set of problems called *paradoxes,* because it seemed that they had no answers. Here is one rewritten in modern language:

Achilles and the Tortoise

Achilles can run ten miles an hour, but a tortoise can run one mile an hour. Give the tortoise a head start of ten miles in a race between the two. Now, says Zeno, Achilles can never catch up with the tortoise. Here is the argument.

When the tortoise has gone one mile, Achilles has gone ten miles, so the tortoise is still ahead because it had a head start of ten miles. When Achilles has gone one more mile, the tortoise has gone 0.1 mile, so the tortoise is still ahead. When Achilles has gone another 0.1 mile, the tortoise has gone another 0.01 mile. So far, Achilles has gone 11.1 miles, and the tortoise (including the head start) has gone 11.11 miles, so it is still ahead.

By continuing this race in the same way, you can see that when Achilles has gone 11.1111 miles, the tortoise has gone 11.11111 miles, so the tortoise will always be a short distance ahead.

It seems that fast Achilles will never catch up with the slow tortoise!

Over a thousand years later this problem was solved completely by the work of Newton, Leibniz, and Cantor.

In about 300 B.C., *Euclid,* a professor of mathematics at the University of Alexandria, examined the work which had been done in mathematics up to his time, added some material of his own, and rearranged all the facts in one long, logical sequence. These were published under the title, *Elements.* From the very beginning, this set of books commanded tremendous respect. As a matter of fact, over 1000 printed editions have appeared in the past 1000 years. It is impossible to think of any other work, except the Bible, which has had as much of an effect on the history of civilization.

Test: Section 4

Part A. These questions refer to the history of mathematics.

1 How many years was it between the building of the Great Pyramid and the publication of the *Elements?*

2 Without looking at the text, what did Thales do?

3 What did Zeno do?

4 What did Euclid do?

Part B. Review Section: Addition.

1 930 + 760 + 650 + 990 + 470
2 468 + 503 + 929 + 627 + 569
3 7 + 439 + 78 + 3504 + 936
4 59 + 6 + 437 + 2788 + 64
5 1878 + 35 + 746 + 9 + 3245
6 687 + 934 + 405 + 678 + 396
7 907 + 605 + 808 + 304 + 906
8 254 + 168 + 935 + 647 + 876
9 457 + 321 + 965 + 804 + 438 + 192
10 574 + 231 + 659 + 408 + 843 + 291

Part C. Projects.

Look up the other paradoxes of Zeno and write a report on them.

5 MATHEMATICS: THE HANDMAIDEN OF SCIENCE

Science has always depended on mathematics in one way or another, even if only counting and measuring were involved.

The first man we can definitely call a mathematical scientist, because he used mathematics so cleverly to solve scientific problems, was *Archimedes,* a Greek, born 287 B.C. He lived in the Greek colony of Syracuse on the island of Sicily off the coast of Italy.

Archimedes was possibly the greatest mathematician from that time up until about 300 years ago. He was also the greatest inventor of his time. He knew the principle of the lever and the crowbar. Archimedes is supposed to have made the remark, "Give me a place to stand and to rest my lever on, and I can move the earth!"

Archimedes was a problem-solver. Legend has it, that once, the ruler of Syracuse ordered a goldsmith to make a crown of pure gold. When he received the crown, he suspected that it was not *pure* gold. He thought the goldsmith was cheating him.

After thinking it over, he gave the crown to Archimedes and ordered him to find out whether it was pure gold. This was not easy to find out, especially since Archimedes did not want to destroy the crown while doing it.

One day, as he was in the public pool where the Greeks used to bathe, he noticed that when he got into the water, the level of the water went up. If you put a marble into a glass full of water, some will overflow. This is called *displacement*. How much will overflow? Exactly as much as there was in the space now taken up by the marble.

Archimedes still had the problem of the crown on his mind. Suddenly an idea came to him! He ran out of the public bath-house down the street to

ARCHIMEDES (*c.* 225 B.C.)

his house, shouting, "Eureka! Eureka!", which means, "I have found it! I have found it!"

This is what he did. He filled a bowl with water and put the crown in. As the water overflowed, he caught it in another bowl and weighed it. Then he weighed the crown. This told him how much the crown weighed compared to the displaced water. But it was known that gold (pure) weighed about 19.3 times as much as water, for the same amount. (Other metals have different values: for example, nickel weighs only about 7 times as much as water; lead weighs about 11.3 times, and silver about 10.5 times as much as water, all for the same amount.) So it was easy to tell from this simple experiment whether the crown was pure gold.

The story does not say what Archimedes found out about the crown, but we know that he found an easy way to use mathematics to solve a difficult scientific problem.

Archimedes invented the compound pulley, and the spiral screw still used in some parts of the world to lift water. Becoming interested in a problem, he would sit down and concentrate, forgetting everything else. When Syracuse was attacked by the Romans, he invented a method for using magnifying glasses to set fire to their wooden ships, or so the story runs!

And when after three years, the Romans eventually entered the city, and soldiers broke into his home, Archimedes was sitting, quietly, working on a problem in mathematics. He had just drawn some circles in the sand at his feet and was completely absorbed in his problem.

When the soldier interruped him, Archimedes said, "Don't disturb my circles!"

The soldier killed him. Archimedes was 75 years old.

Test: Section 5

Part **A.** Questions on the history of mathematics.

1 How many years ago was Archimedes born?

2 Using the principle discovered by Archimedes, how could you find the weight of your body compared to an equal weight of water?

3 On a map, find Babylonia, Egypt, Sumer, Greece, and Sicily. What continents have we discussed so far?

Part **B.** Review Section: Subtraction.

1	74 − 39	2	731 − 649	3	613 − 396
4	861 − 138	5	702 − 356	6	809 − 198
7	431 − 119	8	814 − 252	9	561 − 247
10	846 − 385				

Part **C.** Projects.

The Greeks had magnificent schools. Among them were the school of *Plato* and *Pythagoras*. A great many discoveries were made by the students of Pythagoras. Make a report on these.

6 A THOUSAND YEARS OF "ALMOST NOTHING"

After the magnificent achievements of the Greeks, and for over a thousand years, almost nothing of any great importance happened in mathematics and science. There was some interesting work done by the Alexandrian Greeks, *Diophantus* (275 A.D.), *Menelaus* (100 A.D.), *Ptolemy* (150 A.D.), and *Pappus* (300 A.D.), but it was not as profound as the work of Euclid or Archimedes.

There are interesting stories about two mathematicians of the eleventh century: *Omar Khayyam* (a Persian), and *Bhaskara* (a Hindu). Neither did anything very important, although they were the best mathematicians of their time, but their stories show, at least, that mathematicians are just as human as anyone else. They have the same needs and faults as other people.

Bhaskara was an astrologer. He thought that he could read the stars to find out what was best for him to do. He had one daughter named *Lilivati*, which means, "The Beautiful." When she was born, the story goes, other astrologers predicted that she would never be married, but her father, Bhaskara, watched the stars carefully, and finally decided that on a certain day, hour, and minute, three months away, it would be "favorable" for her to marry. As a matter of fact, he said this would be the only moment in her entire life when she could be allowed to enter into marriage.

He told his 12-year old daughter that she would soon be wed, and arranged the marriage to the son of a friend in a nearby town.

When the great day arrived, and all the people had come for the ceremony and feast, Bhaskara carefully arranged the clock to show the exact minute when the ceremony would have to be performed. The clock was a hollow bowl with a small hole in the bottom. This was floated in a tub of water in such a way that the water would slowly leak in. After a certain number of minutes, the bowl was supposed to fill and sink. At exactly this moment, according to the stars, Lilivati could be married.

Lilivati watched her father put the clock into the water. She leaned over it to watch the water seep in. After a while, Bhaskara became quite nervous and asked the astrologer, Vatsaraja, to look at the bowl. Vatsaraja bent over the clock and cried out!

Not a single drop had entered! As Lilivati had leaned over the clock, a small pearl had fallen from her costume and plugged the opening.

By this time, the only "favorable moment" had passed, and because of this superstition Lilivati was never married, after all. To make her feel better, Bhaskara named his arithmetic book after her to make people remember her forever. One of the problems in the *Lilivati Arithmetic Book* begins:

> *"Lovely and dear Lilivati, whose eyes are like a fawn's, tell me, what are the numbers resulting from 135 multiplied by 12?"*

Omar Khayyam was a mathematician and an astronomer but he is remembered chiefly for his poetry, in particular, the *Rubaiyat. Khayyam* means "tent-maker." When Omar was very young, he was a student under an *imam* (teacher) called Mowaffek. He had two close friends called Nizam, and Hasan, who were also students of Mowaffek. The three promised to be friends, forever, and to share their good fortunes.

The first one to be successful was Nizam, who became the Sultan's *vizier* (prime minister). Remembering the friendship pact, he granted each of his friends a request.

Hasan asked for a job in the government, and when it was given to him he tried to take away Nizam's job. The Sultan was so angry that he banished Hasan, who became an outlaw, and finally died running from justice.

Omar was not ambitious. All he wanted to do was study. So he asked for a quiet place where he could study mathematics and science for the rest of his life. This was given to him and he was very successful.

Test: Section 6

Part A. These questions are on the history of mathematics.

1 What is astrology? Does anyone believe in it now?

2 Bhaskara was a great mathematician for his times, but in some respects he did not show much common sense. Explain.

Part B. Review section: Subtraction.

1	5368 − 972	2	5153 − 956
3	6004 − 8	4	1761 − 845
5	8000 − 1356	6	1702 − 356
7	2117 − 1079	8	6126 − 4384
9	32010 − 28017	10	60205 − 50297

Part C. Projects.

Another great mathematician of the time was the Greek lady, *Hypatia.* Find out what she did.

7 THE SIXTEENTH CENTURY

At last, in the 1500's the world began to wake up from a "long sleep." It was just after the discovery of America. It was the time of Shakespeare. *Copernicus* did a good job explaining, in a systematic fashion, the movement of the planets. The first mathematics book was printed in the New World in 1556.

Two interesting mathematicians of that century were *Tartaglia,* or *Nicolo Fontana,* (an Italian) in the first half of the century, and *Napier* (a Scot) at the end of the century.

Nicolo Fontana was born in Brescia (Sicily) in the year 1500. His father was a postal employee. In the year 1512, the French Armies entered Brescia and slaughtered most of the inhabitants. Nicolo's father was killed, and Nicolo was seriously injured. His skull was split in three places and his jaw and palate were cut open. He was left for dead, but his mother

NICOLO TARTAGLIA (1506-1557)

found him and dragged him to a safe place. Having no doctors or medicine, she allowed a dog to lick his wounds, thinking that dogs cured their own wounds that way. In some way, he lived. However, because of the injuries, he was unable to speak clearly, and for this reason, was always called *Tartaglia*, which means "the stutterer."

Tartaglia's mother was so poor that she could not afford to send her son to school. The story goes that he attended school for only 15 days but stole enough books to learn to read. He also learned Latin, Greek, and mathematics, without teachers. Later on, he became a teacher and taught at Verona, Piacenza, Venice, and his own town of Brescia.

At that time, teachers of mathematics were always trying to discover something new in mathematics, but when they succeeded these discoveries were not published. The teachers would save them for two reasons: first, to get more business for their own schools; second, because it was the custom at that time for mathematicians to challenge each other to "duels of problems" where each one would give the other a problem that he hoped the other would not be able to solve.

Tartaglia became famous because he discovered a wonderful method of solving a type of problem called *cubic equations*. He did not let anyone know his method because he planned to publish it in a book some time.

However, he was tricked and cheated. A professor of medicine named *Cardano,* of Milan, begged and begged him to let him know the big secret. He promised not to tell anybody!

Tartaglia finally believed him, and explained his new method. Cardano promptly published it as his own and became famous. To this day, it is called *Cardano's method.* The wrong man became famous.

Perhaps the greatest Scottish mathematician was *John Napier,* a noble-

JOHN NAPIER (1550-1617)

man who was born in 1550 and died in 1617. He invented a short method of multiplying and dividing called the *method of logarithms.* The method took him about 20 years to work out, but it was worth it. All the scientific work for the next 200 years was made possible by this method. Napier also worked on one of the original computing machines which led to the "giant brains" of today.

When John was 13 years old, his father, the Laird of Merchiston, sent him to the Scottish College at St. Andrews. He stayed there for a while, but his uncle persuaded his father that the boy would get better instruction in France. So John was sent abroad to study.

John Napier did not have much to worry about so far as money was concerned. When he was 24, his father built him a castle where he could sit and think about astrology, agriculture, politics, theology, and philosophy. To relax, he did mathematics.

Napier would be surprised to learn that he is famous for his hobby, while no one pays any attention to the work he spent most of his time on.

When his father died in 1608, John Napier became the Laird. At this time he was still working on his method, and in 1614 he published it in a book called *Mirifici logarithmorum canonis descriptio.* Unlike most new ideas, this one met with immediate approval on the part of mathematicians and scientists.

You may be interested to know that the common people in the neighborhood thought John Napier was a magician because he was so wise. They said he got his knowledge by selling his soul to the devil.

Test: Section 7

Part A. These questions refer to the history of mathematics.

1 Why was Nicolo Fontana called *Tartaglia*?

2 Do modern mathematicians or scientists ever hide their discoveries? Discuss the advantages and disadvantages of giving information away.

3 Compare the background of Tartaglia and John Napier.

4 Compare the education of Tartaglia and John Napier.

5 What parts of the world have we "visited" so far? Show on a map.

Part B. Review Section. Multiplication.

1	89 × 6	2	57 × 3	3	638 × 7	4	897 × 6
5	98 × 47	6	47 × 66	7	564 × 73	8	478 × 87
9	315 × 75	10	536 × 20				

Part C. Projects.

Cardano was an interesting rascal. Read some of the things he did. He also did some pretty good mathematics. Some other mathematicians of about this time were *Briggs* and *Kepler*. Find out what they did.

8 THE SECOND GOLDEN AGE OF MATHEMATICS

The 1600's had many great mathematicians and scientists: Galileo Galilei (Italian), Gerard Desargues (French), the Pascal family (French), Pierre de Fermat (French), René Descartes (French), James Gregory (a Scot), Christiaan Huyghens (Dutch), Isaac Newton (English), Gottfried Wilhelm Leibniz (German), Jacques Bernoulli (Swiss), Edmund Halley (English), Evangelista Torricelli (Italian) and André Marie Ampère (French).

You can see that almost all of the Western European countries produced great mathematicians after awakening from their thousand-year sleep!

We shall tell you about two of these: Descartes, and Newton.

René Descartes (ruh-nay day-kart) was born near Tours on March 31, 1596, of a wealthy and noble family. He was such a delicate child that he did not start school until he was 8. When he entered the Jesuit College at La Fleche, the rector, Father Charlet, saw how sickly he was, and advised

RENÉ DESCARTES (1596-1650)

him to stay in bed as late as possible every morning, to preserve his health.

At that time, a man of noble birth joined either the church or the army. When he was 21, René joined the army, and spent some time in Holland. He left the army when he was 25. Remembering how happy he had been in Holland, he retired there when he was 32 years old, and spent 20 years working on philosophy, science, psychology, and mathematics.

It is interesting to hear one of the stories as to how he happened to invent a new branch of mathematics called *analytic geometry*. The story goes that he was lying in bed one morning when he noticed a fly crawling up one wall, over the ceiling and down another wall. You will remember that we said one of the functions of mathematics is to describe the things that happen in the world about us. This is what Descartes tried to do, but he found that no mathematics had been invented at that time which would allow him to describe the path taken by the fly.

So he set about developing a new branch of mathematics. All modern mathematics is based upon this approach, and we shall have more to say about it in a later chapter.

It is rather strange that Descartes did not realize how important this mathematical work was. He published a big book on philosophy, and science, (now forgotten), in which his valuable new method of mathematics was explained in an appendix!

In 1649, when he was 53 years old, Descartes accepted a position at the Court of Queen Christina of Sweden. She was such an unpleasant person, and the weather was so harsh, that Descartes soon broke down. He died of pneumonia on February 11, 1650, at the age of 54.

You may be interested in what Descartes looked like. He was a small man with a large head, a prominent nose and brow, with black hair down to the eyebrows. He had a feeble voice. He was a cold and selfish man and never married.

Isaac Newton, often called the greatest genius the world has ever known, was the son of a farmer in England. He was born on December 25, 1642, after his father had already died. Isaac was supposed to be a farmer, like his father, and left school when he was 14, to learn about farming. However, he spent most of his time inventing things, so when he was 19, his mother sent him to the University of Cambridge, to study chemistry.

One day, Isaac went to a country fair near Cambridge and picked up a book on astrology. For amusement, he tried to read it, and found it was

SIR ISAAC NEWTON **(1642-1727)**

written in mathematical language. Out of curiosity, he obtained a book on mathematics to understand the astrology book, and he became so interested in mathematics that he continued his college work in this field instead of chemistry.

He finished his college course when he was 23. By that time, this great genius had already started the new branch of mathematics called *calculus*.

As things turned out, the college was closed that year and part of the next year because of a plague. Newton went home to the farm, and while at home, worked out most of the *theory of gravitation*.

When Newton returned to college, at the age of 25, he was made a teacher. Two years later, his professor, realizing the greatness of the young man, resigned in Newton's favor. And so Isaac Newton, son of a farmer, became a professor of mathematics at Cambridge University.

He spent 35 years there doing mathematics and science that is so difficult and advanced that people have to study a long time, even now, to understand it.

Newton lived a tremendously full life, too full to study here. He was knighted in 1705, at the age of 63. When he died, on March 20, 1727, he was given a place among the great, in Westminster Abbey.

As a person, Newton was short, rather stout, well-built, with a square lower jaw, brown eyes, a broad forehead and sharp features. His hair turned grey while he was still a young man, and he died with a full head of thick white hair. He was sloppy and very absent-minded. He even forgot to get married; he was engaged to the daughter of the village druggist but forgot about it!

Newton was a very humble man. When praised for his tremendous achievements, he remarked, "If I have seen farther than other men, it is only because I have stood on the shoulders of giants."

Test: Section 8

Part A. These questions are from the history of mathematics.

1 Compare the backgrounds of Newton, and Descartes.

2 Compare the personal qualities of Newton, and Descartes.

3 Descartes' best work was written as an appendix to a big book which is not very important. What other mathematician did his best work as a hobby?

Part B. Review Section: Multiplication.

1	309 × 406	2	308 × 605	3	536 × 209
4	837 × 509	5	924 × 80	6	880 × 60
7	758 × 38	8	694 × 73	9	740 × 890
10	6008 × 506				

Part C. Projects.

Read about some of the other great mathematicians and scientists mentioned, and make a report.

9 THE EIGHTEENTH AND NINETEENTH CENTURIES

These two centuries were so crowded with great work that it is impossible to give a useful summary in a short space. Every little problem seemed to lead to a big discovery.

For example, in 1735, *Leonard Euler* (1707-1783) solved a puzzle called the *Koenigsberg Bridge* problem. The problem was to discover a way to

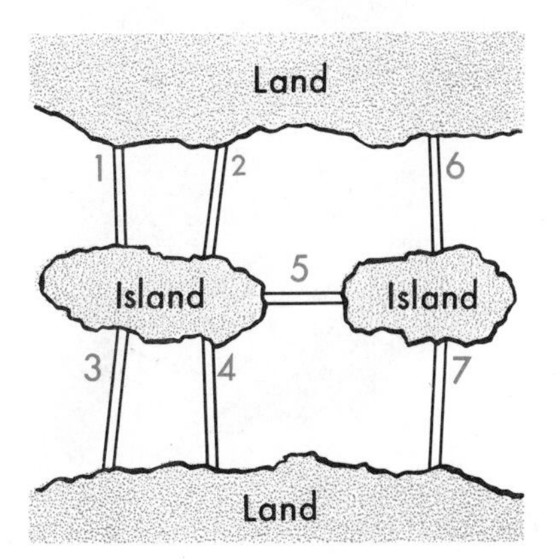

The Koenigsberg Bridge problem.

cross each of the seven bridges without recrossing any one of them. Actually, there is no way to do it, but by the time Euler proved this, he had begun a new branch of mathematics called *topology*.

Another example is the work of *Abraham de Moivre* (1667-1754) who wrote a manual for gamblers called the *Doctrine of Chances*. The mathematics of gambling is exactly like the mathematics for insurance (*actuarial mathematics*) so this work opened the whole field of insurance mathematics.

Things began to move fast in all countries, even in countries which had contributed little up to this time. For example, Russia contributed *Lobachevsky* who did work in a new type of geometry, and Norway contributed *Abel* who laid the basis for a new algebra.

Our most interesting story for this period is the story of *Karl Friedrich Gauss*, a German. Gauss was the last mathematician who seemed to work in every branch of mathematics. For this reason, he is called the *Prince of Mathematicians*. Since his time, no mathematician has been able to learn more than a part of this huge subject. Either the subject has become too wide for one man, or they don't come so smart any more!

At any rate, Karl Friedrich Gauss was born at Brunswick on April 23,

1777. His father was a poor bricklayer, and both parents wanted Karl to be a bricklayer, too.

However, the boy was so outstanding at school that the Duke of Bruns-

CARL FRIEDRICH GAUSS (1777-1855)

wick insisted that he continue his studies, and he paid for his education. The following story is told about his first years in school.

When Gauss was in his third year, he had a very lazy teacher who would give the class an example in addition like this:

$$5286 + 5290 + 5294 + 5298 + 5302 + 5306 + \ldots .$$

and so on, with as many as a hundred numbers. Then the teacher would sit back and relax while the children slaved at the example for hours.

Karl noticed that the teacher always made the problems up in such a way that the numbers were the same amount apart; in this case, each number was four more than the one in front of it.

The custom in this school was that the first one finished would come to the desk, put his slate down on it, then go back to his seat. The next boy who finished would put his on top, and so on.

One day, the teacher had no sooner finished telling the class the numbers when young Karl wrote the answer down on his slate, brought it to the desk, placed it face down, then walked back to his seat. The teacher thought the boy had not even tried to do the addition, and did not even look at the slate until hours later when everyone was finished. When he finally looked at the slates, he found that Karl's answer was correct.

The little boy had figured out a short way of doing the addition. He added the first number to the last number, then divided by two and multiplied by the number of numbers to be added.

For example: to add 1 + 3 + 5 + 7 + 9 + 11 + 15

first: add 1 and 15 = *16*

second: divide by 2, getting *8*

third: multiply by 8 because there are 8 numbers.

The answer is *64*.

The system works just as easily for a million numbers provided they are equally spaced.

When Gauss was 15, he was sent to college. But, by the time he was 18, the teachers admitted that he knew more than they did. He was made Professor of Astronomy at the University of Goettingen in Germany. He made tremendous contributions to mathematics and to science.

He died in Goettingen on February 23, 1855, at the age of 78.

● Test: Section 9

Part A. These exercises have to do with the history of mathematics.

1 Write a report on the life and work of Leonard Euler.
2 Write a report on the life and work of Abraham de Moivre.

Part B. Review Section. Division: check by multiplying.

1	$8\overline{)1920}$	2	$7\overline{)2268}$
3	$24\overline{)2616}$	4	$35\overline{)7245}$
5	$16\overline{)9280}$	6	$32\overline{)8480}$
7	$36\overline{)34{,}704}$	8	$27\overline{)55{,}701}$
9	$92\overline{)214{,}452}$	10	$83\overline{)519{,}331}$

Part C. Projects.

Find out what a Moebius strip is. Make one and do experiments with it. You'll find it interesting.

10 THE PRESENT GOLDEN AGE OF MATHEMATICS

The present is also a Golden Age of mathematics and science. Everything is being investigated mathematically, from the theory of poker to the theory of the universe, from military strategy to the best way of running a business. Machines have even been built to investigate music and language. A good mathematician is able to use his "tools" to explore all these areas.

It is too early to tell who the greatest men of this century are. Among

ALBERT EINSTEIN (1879-1955)
Courtesy "Physics Today".

them will surely be the late Albert Einstein, the late John von Neumann, and Bertrand Russell.

The purpose of this chapter was to show you how mathematics grew, and what sort of person a mathematician is. We hope you have learned that any kind of person can be a mathematician. Some have been white, others have been brown, black or yellow. Some have been young, others old. Abel died when he was 20 years old, in a duel; his greatest work was done the night before he was killed. Napier completed his work when he was an old man. Some mathematicians have been very rich, others extremely poor. Some mathematicians have been very intelligent about everything. Others were superstitious and even a little stupid outside their own fields. Some mathematicians looked like people think a mathematician should look. Others were ugly, or even deformed. No one country has had a monopoly on brains. Mathematicians have come from all countries and all climates.

Some people think that mathematics grows in a dark spot far away from the world. This is not true. Every little and big problem has brought forth mathematics: the fly crawling on the ceiling, the gambler wanting to figure his chances, the people of Koenigsberg asking how they could make a trip on all the bridges, all these little and big problems and puzzles made mathematics.

This is the end of our stories on the subject. The next chapter begins with a new treatment of mathematics, one you have never seen before.

• Test: Section 10

Part A. These questions are on the history of mathematics.

1 Name a mathematician from each of the following countries: Greece, India, Italy, Scotland, France, Norway, England, Persia, Germany, Holland, Switzerland.

2 Write a report on the life and work of Albert Einstein.

3 Write a report on the life and work of John von Neumann.

4 Write a report on the life and work of Bertrand Russell.

Part B. Review Section. Division: check by multiplying (remember to add the remainders)..

1 $7\overline{)1662}$ 2 $8\overline{)4219}$

3 $27\overline{)11,751}$ 4 $31\overline{)21,838}$

5 $46\overline{)23,141}$ 6 $57\overline{)52,700}$

7 $63\overline{)44,555}$ 8 $78\overline{)33,708}$

9 $86\overline{)212,700}$ 10 $94\overline{)337,400}$

Part C. Projects.

Find out what work mathematicians do, how they are "used," in:

a computing centers

b research scientific foundations

c insurance companies.

Fig. 2-1A. In the beginning, man used pebbles.

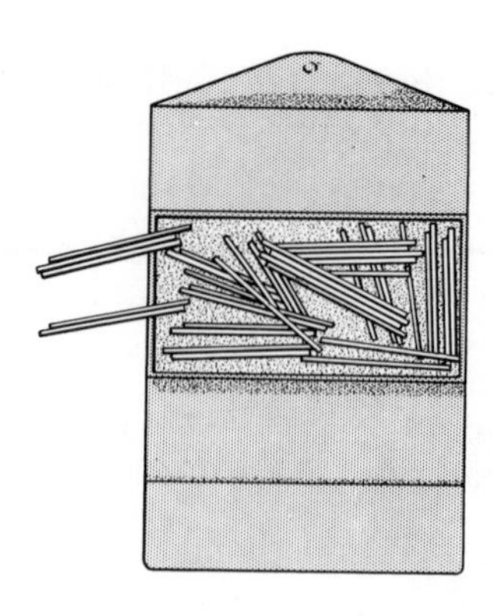

Fig. 2-1B. The Koreans used bone rods.

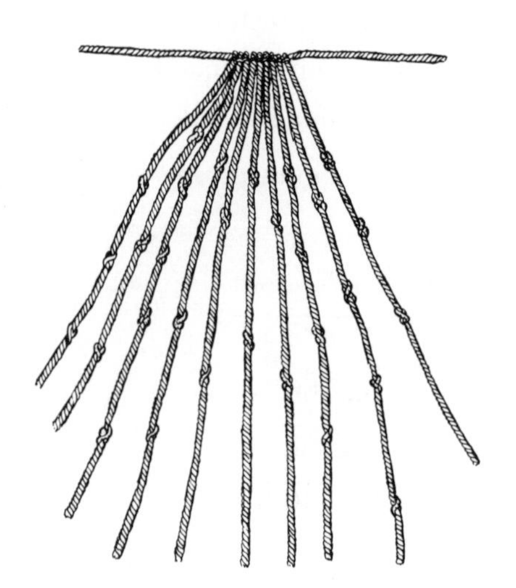

Fig. 2-2. In ancient Peru the quipu was used to record results; a small knot was 1; a big knot, 10.

Fig. 2-3. Tally sticks are almost as old as the notched, split palm leaf, which gave both parties a record.

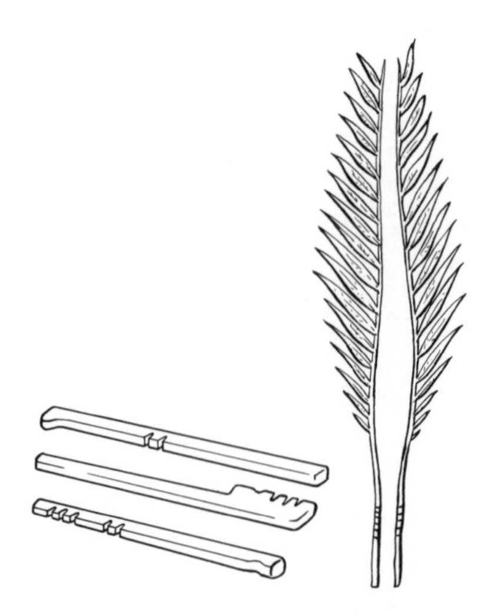

2

the oldest skill: COUNTING

Perhaps you have seen, in the circus, dogs and horses that are supposed to be able to count. Well, maybe they can and maybe they can't. Anyhow, we know for a fact that scientists have been able to train clever birds to count up to six. We also know that in uncivilized parts of the world there are still people who cannot count above *three!* So let us not take counting for granted. It is an important part of civilization.

1 THE BAD OLD DAYS

Except for the very simplest problems, it is useless to count unless you can make some sort of record of the numbers. In very ancient times, people kept records by piles of pebbles or sticks, later by notches in a stick, or a spear or an arrow, and by marks of one kind or another (Figs. 2-1 to 2-4).

A recorded number, such as 23 or 158, is called a *numeral.* The ancient

Fig. 2-4. Aztec numerals. The bottom line shows 20 as the base of Aztec numeration; the principle employed is additive: $2\times8000+400+3\times20+3\times5+3 = 16{,}478$. Courtesy of Florian Cajori, *A History of Mathematical Notations.*

Line	Numbers	Transliteration / numbers
1	53 212̇ 601̇ 35	y w k·ḥm y·wi y·rḫ y·5̇ y·3̇ 3 w·ps y w k·ꜣ ꜣ h y·wi
2	07 5 01 02	wš dd cḥc ꜣp ytp
3	601̇ 35̇ 597̇ 813̇ 03	601 1 1 1
4	01 02̇ 3̇ 1 3̇ 3 3̇ 53	35 2̇ 1 1
5	001 636̇ 813̇ 951̇ 21̇	212̇ 601̇ 35 4̇ 1 2̇ 62 4̇ 1 1
6	3̈ 1 3̇ 3 3̈ 6 3̇ 88	601̇ 35̇ 597̇ 813̇ 03̇ 2̇ 2 1 601̇ 3̇ 3̇
7	08 060.1̇ 035̇ 562̇ 02̇	636̇ 813̇ 951̇ 21̇ 3̇ 2 35̇ 5̇ 5̇
8	4̇ 1 2 4 35	0601̇ 035̇ 562̇ 02̇ 5̇ 1 dmd 2̇ 212̇
9	562̇ 562 4̇ 035 2̇	
10	060.1 dmd 562 4̇	

ỉw·y hꜣ·kwy sp·w 3 3̇ · y 5̇ · y ḥr· y ỉw · y mḥ · kwy pty pꜣ ʿḥʿ dd św

Go down I times 3, ⅓ of me, ⅕ of me is added to me; return I, filled am I. What is the quantity saying it?

1	1	1	4̇	53	1̇06	2̇12	
1	1	2	2̇	3̇0	3̇18	7̇95	53 1̇06
1	1	3̇	1̇2	1̇59	3̇18	6̇36	
3̇	3̇	5̇	2̇0	2̇65	5̇30	1̇060	
5̇	5̇						

1	106
2̇	53
\ 4̇	26 2̇
\ 1̇06	1
\ 5̇3	2
\ 2̇12	2̇
dmd	1
Total	

53	1̇06	2̇12				
20	10	5				35
3̇0	3̇18	7̇95	53	1̇06		
35 3̇	3 3̇	1 3̇	2̇0	10		70
1̇2	1̇59	3̇18	6̇36			
88 3̇	6 3̈	3 3̇	1 3̈			100
2̇0	2̇65	5̇30	1̇060			
53	4	2	1			80
				4̇		2̇65

2̇	530
4̇	265
4̇	265
dmd	1060
Total	

Egyptians, thousands of years ago, had a very pretty numerical system (Fig. 2-5) using pictures called *hieroglyphics* (hi′ẽr•ȏ•glĭf′iks). With these, they could write large or small numbers. Let us try a problem the Egyptian way, and compare it with our own (Fig. 2-6). (The Egyptians read from right to left.)

Problem 1. Find 16 × 23.

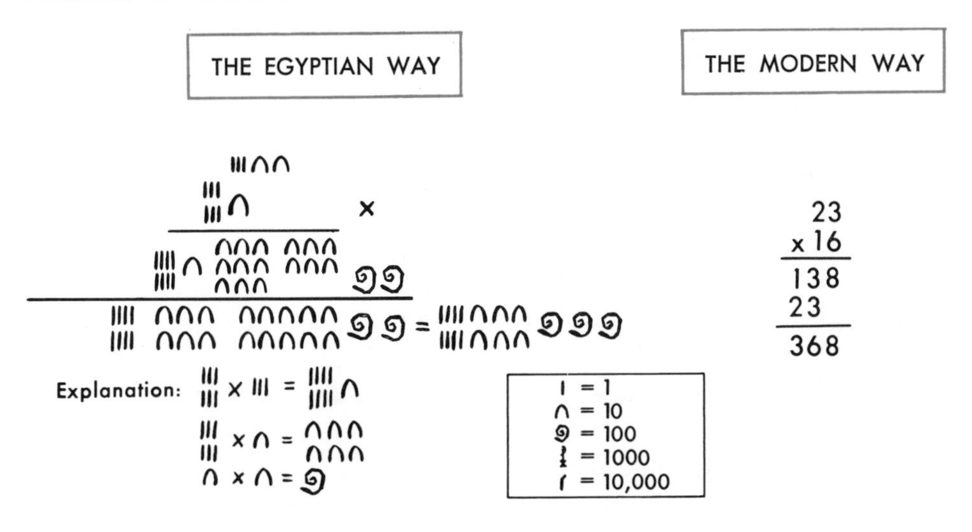

Fig. 2-6. Egyptian method of counting.

Fig. 2-5. THE RHIND PAPYRUS. In 1700 B.C. an Egyptian scribe named A'h-mose set down his "knowledge of existing things all," a document which is now the principal source of what we know of early Egyptian mathematics. The papyrus is a collection of mathematical exercises and practical examples worked out in a syncopated, sometimes cryptic style. Problem 36, for instance, begins: "Go down I times 3, 1/3 of me, 1/5 of me is added to me; return I filled am I. What is the quantity saying it?" The problem is then solved by the Egyptian method. At the top of the opposite page is a facsimile of the problem as it appears in the papyrus. The hieratic script reads from right to left. The characters are reproduced in red and black, as they are written in the papyrus. In the middle of the page is a rendering in hieroglyphic script, which also reads from right to left. Beneath each line of hieroglyphs is a phonetic translation. The numbers are given in Arabic with the Egyptian notation. Each line of hieroglyphs and its translation is numbered to correspond to a line of the hieratic. At the bottom of the page the phonetic and numerical translation has been reversed to read from left to right. Beneath each phonetic expression is its English translation. A dot above a number indicates that it is a fraction with a numerator of one. Two dots above a 3 represent 2/3, the only Egyptian fraction with a numerator of more than one. Readers who would like to trace the entire solution are cautioned that the scribe made several mistakes that are preserved in the various translations. *The illustration and description of Fig. 2-5 are reproduced with kind permission from SCIENTIFIC AMERICAN.*

The Romans, much later in time, were not much better. Their number symbols, or numerals, were just as hard to work with (Fig. 2-7).

Problem 2. Find 52 × 36.

THE ROMAN WAY	*Explanation*	THE MODERN WAY
XXXVI		36
LII		× 52
LXXII	II × I = II	72
MDCCLL	II × V = X	180
MDCCLLLXXII =	II × XXX = LX	1872
MDCCCLXXII	L × I = L	
	L × V = CCL	
	L × XXX = MD	
	CCLLL = CCCL	

Fig. 2-7. Roman numerals were difficult to work with.

Notice that in these old systems greater numbers were written, or "made," by adding smaller ones. For example, LXI meant L + X + I = 50 + 10 + 1, which we write as 61. Our modern system uses *place value*. The numeral 61 means *six tens and one one*. The numeral 583.2 means *five hundreds, eight tens, three ones, and two tenths.*

Test: Section 1

Part A.

1 Translate into modern numerals:

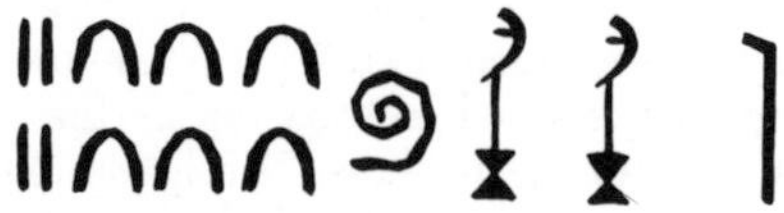

2 Translate into modern numerals:

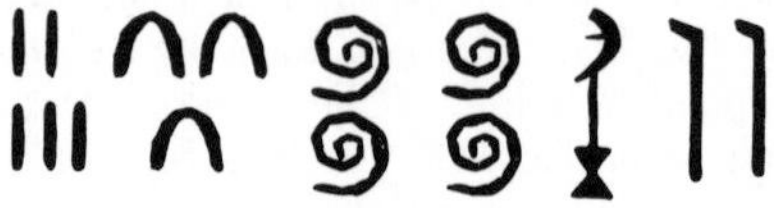

3 Translate into modern numerals: MDCCCLXIV.

4 Translate into modern numerals: MDCCLXXXVIII.

Part B.

1 Add 5785 and 2158 using (*a*) Egyptian, and (*b*) modern numerals.
2 Add 358 and 617 using (*a*) Egyptian, and (*b*) modern numerals.
3 Add 216 and 157 using (*a*) Roman, and (*b*) modern numerals.
4 Add 1034 and 217 using (*a*) Roman, and (*b*) modern numerals.
5 Subtract 285 from 397 using (*a*) Egyptian, and (*b*) modern numerals.
6 Subtract 18 from 39 using (*a*) Egyptian, and (*b*) modern numerals.
7 Subtract 275 from 358 using (*a*) Roman, and (*b*) modern numerals.
8 Subtract 37 from 63 using (*a*) Roman, and (*b*) modern numerals.

Part C.

1 Multiply 65 by 27 in (*a*) Egyptian, and (*b*) modern numerals.
2 Multiply 73 by 29 in (*a*) Egyptian, and (*b*) modern numerals.
3 Multiply 48 by 35 in (*a*) Roman, and (*b*) modern numerals.
4 Multiply 84 by 31 in (*a*) Roman, and (*b*) modern numerals.

2 CLOCK MATHEMATICS: ADDITION

There are so many numbers that it is hard to understand them all at once. Let us limit ourselves to just a few, the numerals on a clock. We will make

Fig. 2-8.
The twelve-hour clock.

a little change for convenience, and start the clock at 0 instead of 12, as in Fig. 2-8.

First, let us see how we add on this clock. If we start at 1 o'clock and add 2 hours, we get 3 o'clock. Mathematically, $1 + 2 = 3$.

If we start at 8 o'clock and add 3 hours, we get 11 o'clock, showing that $8 + 3 = 11$. But if we start at 10 o'clock and add 4 hours, we get 2 o'clock!

This means that in this system 10 + 4 = 2. If we start at 11 o'clock and add 1 hour, we get 0 o'clock! 11 + 1 = 0 in this system.

All these facts are combined into one Timetable for Addition as shown here.

TIMETABLE FOR ADDITION USING THE TWELVE-HOUR CLOCK

+	0	1	2	3	4	5	6	7	8	9	10	11
0	0	1	2	3	4	5	6	7	8	9	10	11
1	1	2	3	4	5	6	7	8	9	10	11	0
2	2	3	4	5	6	7	8	9	10	11	0	1
3	3	4	5	6	7	8	9	10	11	0	1	2
4	4	5	6	7	8	9	10	11	0	1	2	3
5	5	6	7	8	9	10	11	0	1	2	3	4
6	6	7	8	9	10	11	0	1	2	3	4	5
7	7	8	9	10	11	0	1	2	3	4	5	6
8	8	9	10	11	0	1	2	3	4	5	6	7
9	9	10	11	0	1	2	3	4	5	6	7	8
10	10	11	0	1	2	3	4	5	6	7	8	9
11	11	0	1	2	3	4	5	6	7	8	9	10

Using the timetable is easy. To find 8 + 5, locate 8 in the left-hand column, run your finger to the right until it is under the 5, and get the sum, 1. In the same way, 9 + 8 = 5.

With this table, we can point out some of the facts about numbers.

Fact 1. Compare (2 + 7) and (7 + 2). Are they the same? Now try (3 + 9) and (9 + 3). As many as you try, you will see that the result is the same. These are examples of the following important law of addition.

Commutative (kŏm′û·tā′tiv) Principle for Addition. No matter in which direction you add two numbers, the answer is the same either way.

This law is not as obvious as it seems. For example, when a baker mixes the ingredients to make a particular kind of cake, he must add them in a particular order, and mix them in a certain way, not any old way, or the cake will not come out right.

Fact 2. Now compare (2 + 3) + 4, and 2 + (3 + 4). In the first expression 2 and 3 are *associated* by the parentheses, ( ), so that the result is the same as 5 + 4, with the *5* replacing (2 + 3). In the second expression, 3 and 4 are associated, so that the result is the same as 2 + 7, with the 7 replacing (3 + 4).

Looking in the table for 5 + 4, and comparing the result with 2 + 7, we see that the results are the same. This example illustrates another principle of addition.

Associative (ă•sō'shĭ•ā'tĭv) Principle for Addition. In adding sets of numbers, you may "pair off" the numbers in any way you like and the answer will remain the same.

To show that this principle is *not* obvious, notice that (John + Mary) + Bill is definitely not the same as John + (Mary + Bill)!

Fact 3. If you add any two numbers in the Timetable for Addition you will always get a *different* third number for the answer (example: 8 + 5 = 1), except when you are adding 0 (zero) to a number.

Principle of Zero for Addition. Adding zero to a number does not change the result.

Sometimes this principle is useful in simplifying an addition problem in clock mathematics. For example:

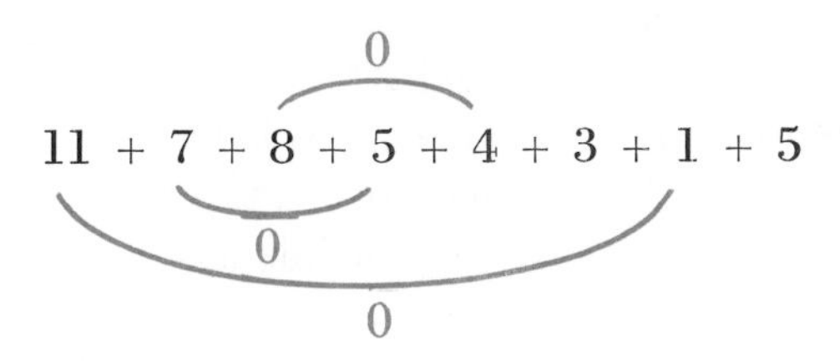

is the same as 3 + 5, or 8, because (11 + 1), (7 + 5) and (8 + 4) all add up to zero in clock mathematics.

Fact 4. The fourth fact is something we have already noticed. In clock mathematics, 11 + 1 = 0, 10 + 2 = 0, 9 + 3 = 0, and so on. These pairs of numbers, (11 and 1), (10 and 2), and so on, are called *negatives* of each other, because the pairs add to zero.

Principle of Negatives for Addition. The sum of a number and its negative is zero.

The four principles are shown on a different "clock" in the following problem.

Problem. Consider a clock with only three hours, marked 0, 1, and 2. (Fig. 2-9).

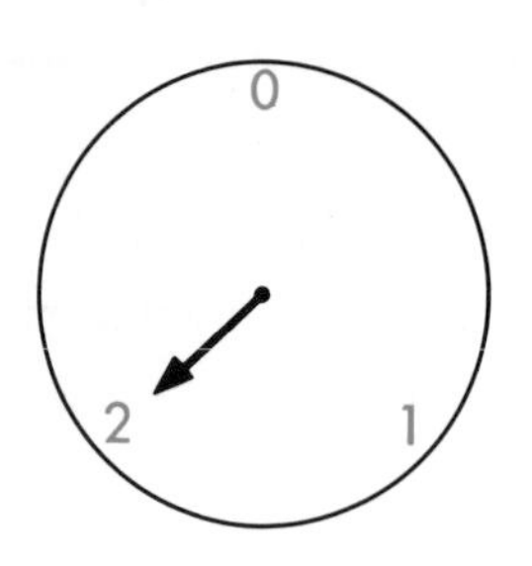

Fig. 2-9.

The three-hour clock.

a Write the addition table for this clock.
b Test the commutative principle by comparing $(1 + 2)$ and $(2 + 1)$.
c Test the associative principle by comparing $0 + (1 + 2)$, and $(0 + 1) + 2$.
d Test the principle of zero by adding zero to each number.
e Test the principle of negatives by finding the negatives of 0, 1, and 2.

Answers:

a. The table is shown here.

+	0	1	2
0	0	1	2
1	1	2	0
2	2	0	1

b. From the table, $1 + 2 = 0$, and $2 + 1 = 0$, so the commutative principle appears to hold.
c. $0 + (1 + 2) = 0 + 0 = 0$, and $(0 + 1) + 2 = 1 + 2 = 0$, so the associative principle appears to hold.
d. $0 + 0 = 0$, $1 + 0 = 1$, $2 + 0 = 2$, so the principle of zero holds.
e. The negative of 0 is 0, the negative of 1 is 2, and the negative of 2 is 1.

Test: Section 2

Part A.

1 Write an addition table for a four-hour clock, using 0, 1, 2, and 3.
2 Test the commutative principle by comparing $(2 + 3)$ and $(3 + 2)$.
3 Test the associative principle by comparing $(1 + 2) + 3$, and $1 + (2 + 3)$.
4 Test the principle of zero by finding $0 + 0$, $1 + 0$, $2 + 0$, $3 + 0$.
5 Test the principle of negatives by finding negatives of 0, 1, 2, and 3.

Part B.

1 Write an addition table for a five-hour clock, using 0, 1, 2, 3, and 4.

2 Test the commutative principle by comparing $(3 + 4)$ and $(4 + 3)$.

3 Test the associative principle by comparing $2 + (2 + 4)$ and $(2 + 2) + 4$.

4 Test the principle of zero by finding $0 + 0$, $1 + 0$, $2 + 0$, $3 + 0$ and $4 + 0$.

5 Test the principle of negatives by finding negatives of 0, 1, 2, 3, 4.

Part C.

Questions 1 - 5 refer to the addition table below. In the table, "LT" means "left turn," and "RT" means "right turn," "AF" means "about face," and "SS" means "stand still." The best way to solve these problems is to have one student call the commands while another one follows them. In each case, take the same starting position, say, facing the blackboard.

+	SS	LT	RT	AF
SS	SS	LT	RT	AF
RT	RT	SS	AF	LT
LT	LT	AF	SS	RT
AF	AF	RT	LT	SS

1 Explain the following: SS + LT = LT, RT + AF = LT, AF + AF = SS.

2 Test the commutative principle by trying some combinations. Does it hold?

3 Test the associative principle by trying some combinations. Does it hold?

4 What corresponds to "zero" in this addition table?

5 LT is the negative of RT. What is the negative of AF?

3 CLOCK MATHEMATICS: MULTIPLICATION

We can investigate the laws of multiplication in the same way as we investigated addition. To save time and space, let us give our clock only five hours (Fig. 2-10) and try to make a timetable for multiplication on this clock.

Multiplication starts as usual: 2×1 hour means "count off" one hour twice. So $2 \times 1 = 2$ hours. In the same way, 2×2 hours $= 4$ hours. This means that you start at the top of the clock and "count off" two hours twice. Now let us try 2×3 hours. Starting from the top of the clock (at 0),

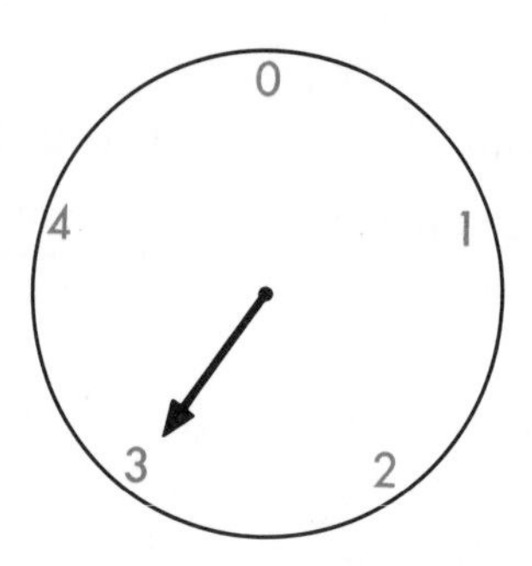

Fig. 2-10.

The five-hour clock.

first we get to 3 o'clock, then to 1 o'clock! In this kind of timetable, $2 \times 3 = 1$! Continuing in the same way, we get the timetable shown here.

×	0	1	2	3	4
0	0	0	0	0	0
1	0	1	2	3	4
2	0	2	4	1	3
3	0	3	1	4	2
4	0	4	3	2	1

The first two facts that we can discover from this multiplication timetable are just like the facts from the addition timetable:

Commutative Principle for Multiplication. You may multiply two numbers in either order and get the same answer.

Example: In the table, $3 \times 2 = 1$, and $2 \times 3 = 1$

Associative Principle for Multiplication. In multiplying sets of numbers, you may "pair off" any way you like.

Example: $(4 \times 3) \times 2 = 2 \times 2 = 4$
$4 \times (3 \times 2) = 4 \times 1 = 4$

The third principle for multiplication is somewhat like that for addition.

Principle of One for Multiplication. Multiplying by 1 does not change the result.

Example: $3 \times 1 = 3$, $4 \times 1 = 4$, and so on.

Lastly, looking at the table, we find that $4 \times 4 = 1$, $3 \times 2 = 1$, $2 \times 3 = 1$, $1 \times 1 = 1$. If two numbers are multiplied and give the result, 1, the two numbers are called *reciprocals* (rê•sĭp′rô•kăl). In the five-hour clock, the following pairs of numbers are reciprocals: (4, 4), (3, 2), and (1, 1). *Zero has no reciprocal.*

Principle of Reciprocals. The product of a number and its reciprocal is 1.

Problem. Suppose the clock has only three numbers, 0, 1, and 2.

a Write the multiplication table.
b Test the commutative principle by comparing (1×2) and (2×1).
c Test the associative principle by comparing $(1 \times 2) \times 2$, and $1 \times (2 \times 2)$.
d Test the principle of one by looking up 0×1, 1×1, and 2×1.
e Test the principle of reciprocals by looking for the reciprocals of 0, 1, and 2.

Answer:

×	0	1	2
0	0	0	0
1	0	1	2
2	0	2	1

a. The table is at the right.
b. $1 \times 2 = 2$, and $2 \times 1 = 2$
c. $(1 \times 2) \times 2 = 2 \times 2 = 1$
$1 \times (2 \times 2) = 1 \times 1 = 1$
d. $0 \times 1 = 0, 1 \times 1 = 1, 2 \times 1 = 2$
e. Zero has no reciprocal. The reciprocal of 1 is 1. The reciprocal of 2 is 2.

● Test: Section 3

Part A.

In Questions 1-8 use the multiplication table for a five-hour clock.

1 Find (*a*) 2×2, (*b*) 3×2
2 Find (*a*) 2×3, (*b*) 3×3
3 Find (*a*) 2×4, (*b*) 3×4
4 Find (*a*) 4×4, (*b*) 4×3
5 Compare (4×3) and (3×4). What is the principle?
6 Compare (2×4) and (4×2). What is the principle?
7 Compare $(4 \times 2) \times 3$, and $4 \times (2 \times 3)$. What is the principle?
8 Compare $(3 \times 3) \times 2$, and $3 \times (3 \times 2)$. What is the principle?

Part B.

In Questions 1-9 use the eight-hour clock worked out for you below.

×	0	1	2	3	4	5	6	7
0	0	0	0	0	0	0	0	0
1	0	1	2	3	4	5	6	7
2	0	2	4	6	0	2	4	6
3	0	3	6	1	4	7	2	5
4	0	4	0	4	0	4	0	4
5	0	5	2	7	4	1	6	3
6	0	6	4	2	0	6	4	2
7	0	7	6	5	4	3	2	1

1 Find (a) 2×6, (b) 4×6
2 Find (a) 3×7, (b) 2×5
3 Find (a) 4×5, (b) 3×7
4 Find (a) 3×4, (b) 5×7
5 Compare (7×3) and (3×7). What is the principle?
6 Compare (6×5) and (5×6). What is the principle?
7 Compare $(2 \times 5) \times 7$, and $2 \times (5 \times 7)$. What is the principle?
8 Compare $(3 \times 4) \times 6$, and $3 \times (4 \times 6)$. What is the principle?
9 We know that zero has no reciprocal. Notice that in this clock, *two* has no reciprocal, either! In other words, there is no number which will multiply 2 and get the answer *1*. Find two other numbers in this table which have no reciprocals.

Part C.

1 Write a multiplication time table for the seven-hour clock, using 0, 1, 2, 3, 4, 5, 6.
2 In this clock, find (a) 3×6, (b) 3×5.
3 Find (a) 2×5, (b) 2×6.
4 Compare (4×5) and (5×4). What is the principle?
5 Compare (3×6) and (6×3). What is the principle?
6 Compare $(6 \times 4) \times 5$, and $6 \times (4 \times 5)$. What is the principle?
7 Compare $(5 \times 3) \times 2$, and $5 \times (3 \times 2)$. What is the principle?
8 Find the reciprocals of 1, 2, 3, 4, 5, 6. Does 0 have a reciprocal?

Fig. 2-11. The "giant brain" electronic computer. *Courtesy IBM.*

4 COMPUTER MATHEMATICS

Now that you know something about clock mathematics, it is easy to learn how the giant brains like the IBM electronic computer (Fig. 2-11), and Univac work.

You may be surprised to learn that these machines can only count up

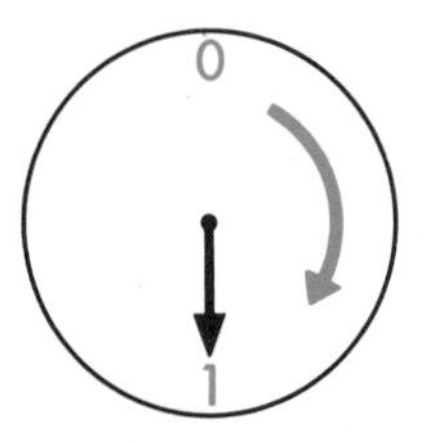

Fig. 2-12. $0 + 1 = 1$.

to 1! In other words, the machine "recognizes" only two numbers: 0, and 1. It uses a two-hour clock with these two numbers on it.

Now, let us see how this works. Suppose the machine is told to add $0 + 1$. Then the clock hand swings down to 1 (Fig. 2-12). So far, so good. Now add 1 to this. We know that in a two-hour clock, $1 + 1 = 0$. This is not very satisfactory to us, however, because when we use a computing machine (especially one that costs half a million dollars) we expect it to add 1 and 1 and get 2.

The method used is quite clever. As the hand swings around to zero, it turns on a "carry" switch that turns on a second clock which reads in

Fig. 2-13. 1 + 1 = 0 and "carry one," or 1 + 1 = 10.

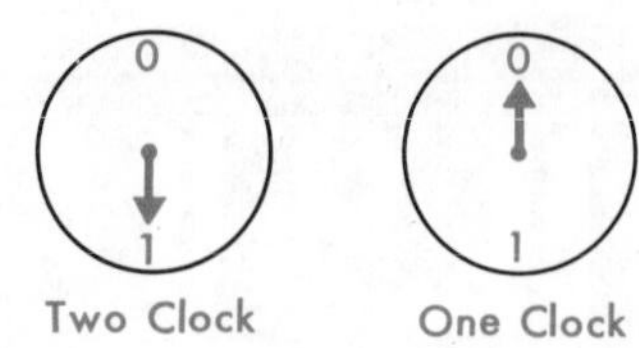

Fig. 2-14. "10" on these clocks means "2" in our usual system.

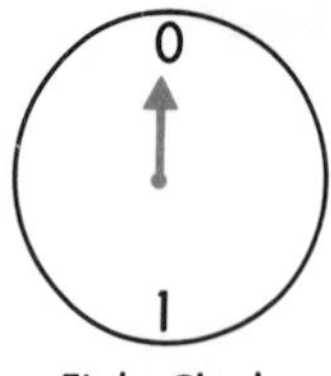

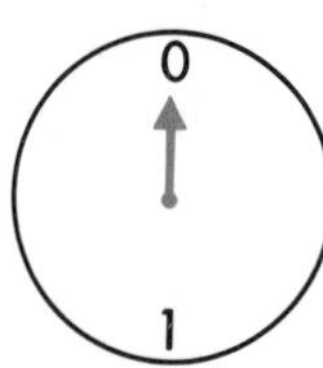

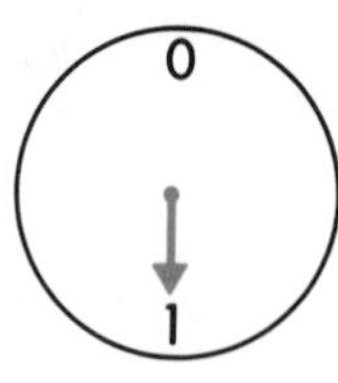

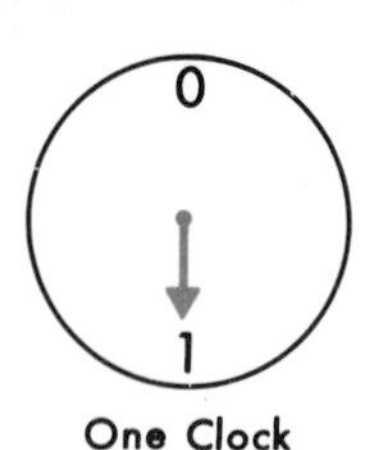

Fig. 2-15. "0011" means "3."

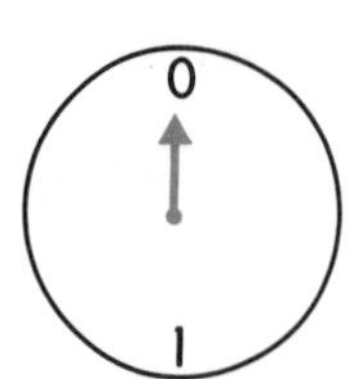

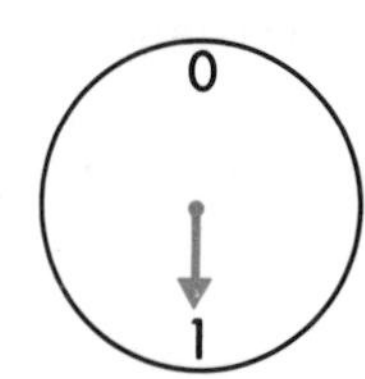

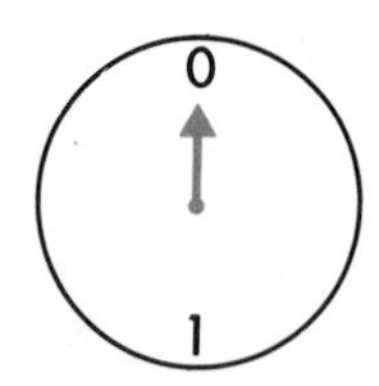

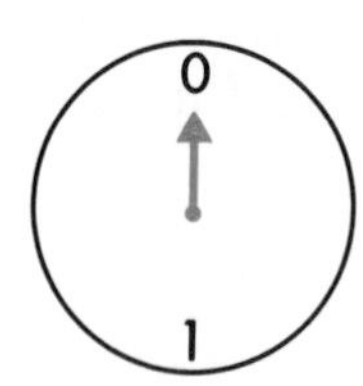

Fig. 2-16. "0100" means "4."

"twos" (Fig. 2-13). Now the two clocks together (Fig. 2-14) read: 1 "two" and 0 "ones". The reading "10" in this system means "2" in our usual system.

The system used in computers is called the *binary system* because the clocks are two-hour clocks. Figure 2-15 shows a 3 in the binary notation, and Fig. 2-16 shows a 4 in the binary system.

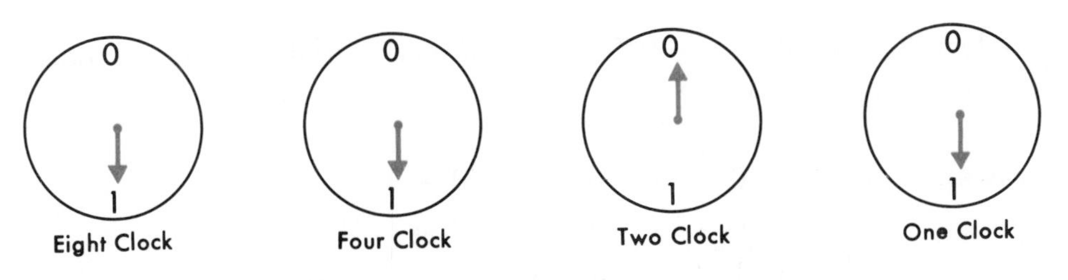

Fig. 2-17. "1101" in binary notation means "13."

Figure 2-17 shows a set of two-hour clocks reading 1101. This means 13, because it represents one 8, one 4, no 2, and one 1.

Problem 1. Sketch the clocks and find what 1011 means in the binary system.

Answer:

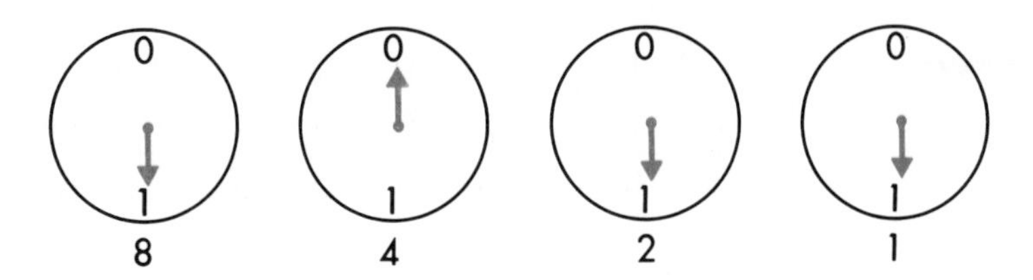

It means 8 + 2 + 1 = 11.

Problem 2. How does seven look in the binary system?

Answer:

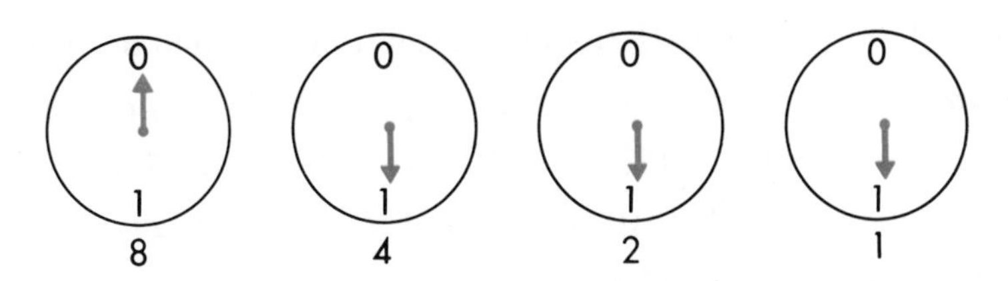

Seven (our system) = 0111 (binary system).

Arithmetic in the binary system is very easy because the counting can only go up to 1.

Problem 3. Add 0101 and 0101, draw the clocks for the result, and translate into decimal notation.

Answer:

$$\begin{array}{rl} 0\ 1\ 0\ 1 & (= 0 + 4 + 0 + 1 = 5) \\ +\ \underline{0\ 1\ 0\ 1} & (= 0 + 4 + 0 + 1 = 5) \\ 1\ 0\ 1\ 0 & (= 8 + 0 + 2 + 0 = 10) \end{array}$$

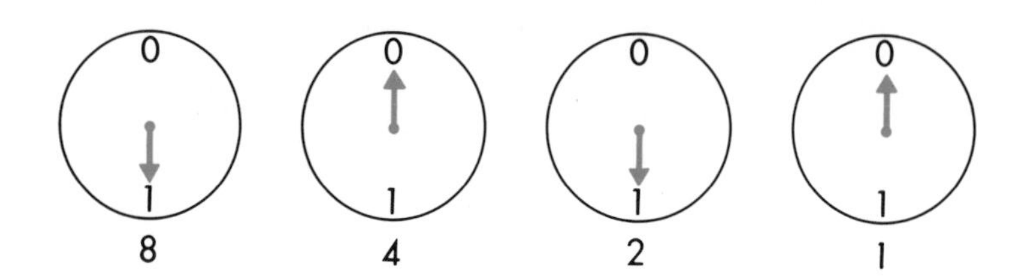

Problem 4. Add 0111 and 1011, draw the clocks for the result, and translate into decimal notation.

Answer:

$$\begin{array}{rl} 0\ 1\ 1\ 1 & (= 0 + 4 + 2 + 1 = 7) \\ +\ \underline{1\ 0\ 1\ 1} & (= 8 + 0 + 2 + 1 = 11) \\ 1\ 0\ 0\ 1\ 0 & (= 16 + 0 + 0 + 2 + 0 = 18) \end{array}$$

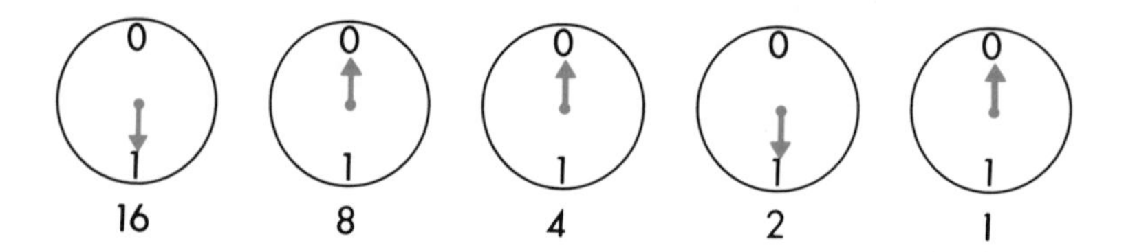

Problem 5. Take 0101 from 0111 and translate into decimal notation.

Answer:

$$\begin{array}{rl} 0\ 1\ 1\ 1 & (= 0 + 4 + 2 + 1 = 7) \\ -\ \underline{0\ 1\ 0\ 1} & (= 0 + 4 + 0 + 1 = 5) \\ 0\ 0\ 1\ 0 & (= 0 + 0 + 2 + 0 = 2) \end{array}$$

Problem 6. Take 0011 from 0101 and translate into decimal notation.

Answer:

$$\begin{array}{rl} 0\ 1\ 0\ 1 & (= 0 + 4 + 0 + 1 = 5) \\ -\ \underline{0\ 0\ 1\ 1} & (= 0 + 0 + 2 + 1 = 3) \\ 0\ 0\ 1\ 0 & (= 0 + 0 + 2 + 0 = 2) \end{array}$$

In this problem, remember that $10 - 01 = 01$ in the binary system.

Problem 7. Multiply 0101 by 0011 and translate into decimal notation.

Answer:

```
          0 1 0 1   (= 0 + 4 + 0 + 1 = 5)
        × 0 0 1 1   (= 0 + 0 + 2 + 1 = 3)
        ---------
          0 1 0 1
        0 1 0 1
      0 0 0 0
    0 0 0 0
    -------------
    0 0 0 1 1 1 1 (= 0 + 0 + 0 + 8 + 4 + 2 + 1 = 15)
```

Test: Section 4

Part A.

Draw the binary clocks and find out what the following numerals mean in decimal notation.

1 0011	**2** 0111	**3** 1001	**4** 1100
5 1101	**6** 0010	**7** 1111	**8** 1011

Change the following from the decimal system to the binary system.

9 12	**10** 9	**11** 5	**12** 11
13 15	**14** 13	**15** 2	**16** 3

Part B. The following numerals are in the binary system:

1 01001 + 01100	**2** 0111 + 1001
3 0111 × 1010	**4** 1011 × 1010

Part C. The following numerals are in the binary system:

1 Take 01 from 10	**2** Take 101 from 111
3 From 11001 take 10101	**4** From 10100 take 01011

5 THERMOMETER MATHEMATICS

Now that we have been introduced to clock mathematics and to the binary system, let us take a closer look at the *decimal system*, the system we use in everyday life.

The decimal system is built on a straight line called the *number line* (Fig. 2-18), which is something like a long thermometer.

On this line, the numeral -10 is called *negative ten,* and means *10 below zero.* In the same way, -23 is called *negative 23,* and means *23 below zero.*

You will notice that the numbers get larger as you go to the right and smaller as you go to the left. In the following table, the first two columns

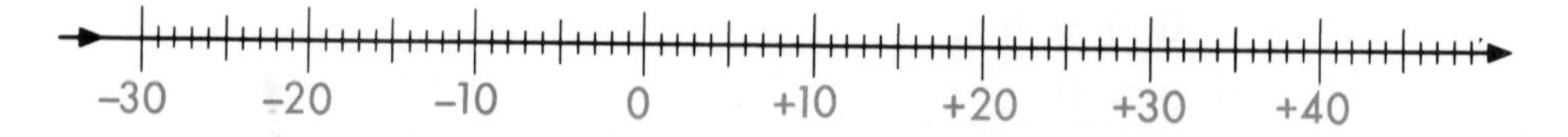

Fig. 2-18. Our number line is like a long thermometer.

are different ways of saying the same thing, while the third column is the way a mathematician writes it.

5 is right of 3	5 is larger than 3	$5 > 3$
3 is right of 1	3 is larger than 1	$3 > 1$
1 is right of 0	1 is larger than 0	$1 > 0$
0 is right of -2	0 is larger than -2	$0 > -2$
-2 is right of -5	-2 is larger than -5	$-2 > -5$

Looking at it another way:

3 is left of 5	3 is smaller than 5	$3 < 5$
1 is left of 3	1 is smaller than 3	$1 < 3$
0 is left of 1	0 is smaller than 1	$0 < 1$
-2 is left of 0	-2 is smaller than 0	$-2 < 0$
-5 is left of -2	-5 is smaller than -2	$-5 < -2$

Notice that the symbol $>$ means *is right of* or *is larger than,* while the symbol $<$ means *is left of* or *is smaller than.* In both cases, the *smaller* or pointed end of the symbol is aimed at the *smaller* of the two numbers.

By the way, -5 means 5 below zero, and $+5$ means 5 above zero. By itself, 5 is the same as $+5$, so that one of these may be written for the other whenever it does not confuse the problem. For example, instead of $5 + 3$, you can write $+5 +3$, but you cannot write 53 because this means something quite different.

Problem 1. Arrange the numerals 5, 2, 7, 1, 0, 11, -30, -20, in correct order.

Answer: $11 > 7 > 5 > 2 > 1 > 0 > -20 > -30$
or: $-30 < -20 < 0 < 1 < 2 < 5 < 7 < 11$

The first arrangement is called in *descending order* because the values are going down as you read from left to right. The second arrangement is in *ascending order.*

You remember that in the binary system, there was a set of two-hour clocks. When one clock was "filled up," the hand on the next clock moved. Well, the decimal system works like a set of clocks, too.

In Fig. 2-19, the number is 5486.27, which means 5 thousands + 4 hundreds + 8 tens + 6 ones + 2 tenths + 7 hundredths, or 5000 + 400 + 80 + 6 + $\frac{2}{10}$ + $\frac{7}{100}$. It is very important to know that 24 means 20 + 4, and 7.6

Fig. 2-19. The ten-hour clocks in the decimal system.

Fig. 2-20. The machinist's scale is a small piece of the decimal number line.

means 7 + $\frac{6}{10}$. In Fig. 2-20, 7.6 in. is shown on a machinist's scale which is, as you can see, a small piece of the decimal number line.

Test: Section 5

Part A. In each of the following, arrange the numerals in (*a*) ascending order, and (*b*) descending order:

1 −5, 1, 6, 3, 8, 11, 12, 0
2 2, −7, 5, 3, 9, 4, 6, 0
3 1, 3, −2, 6, 7, 4, 9, 0
4 27, 13, 0.2, −3, 0
5 15, 17, 11, 5, 0, −9
6 5, −8, 1, 7, 6, 3, 0, 4

In each of the following, explain the meaning of each number by writing the number of thousands, hundreds, tens, ones, tenths, and hundredths:

7 75.68
8 2.14
9 138.50
10 207.02
11 318.91
12 455.73

Part B.

In each of the following, arrange the numerals in (a) ascending order, and (b) descending order:

1 5, 0.02, 3, −0.15, −0.7

2 6, 0.13, −0.70, −0.71, 0.08

3 3, −0.05, −0.5, 0.06, 0.6

4 1, 0, −0.63, 0.13, −0.4

In each of the following cases, explain the meaning of each number by writing the number of millions, hundred thousands, ten thousands, thousands, hundreds, tens, ones, tenths, hundredths, thousandths, ten-thousandths, hundred-thousandths, and millionths:

5 3,501,033.188

6 276.002258

7 0.001445

8 16.2285

6 THERMOMETER ADDITION

Adding in the decimal system is old stuff to you. The numerals are arranged under each other, with decimal points, if any, in a straight line, and then you work row by row.

Problem 1. Add 27.37 and 16.41

Answer:

$$\begin{array}{r} 27.37 \\ +\ 16.41 \\ \hline 43.78 \end{array}$$

What does "adding" mean? Let us go back to 5 + 3. Adding 3 to 5

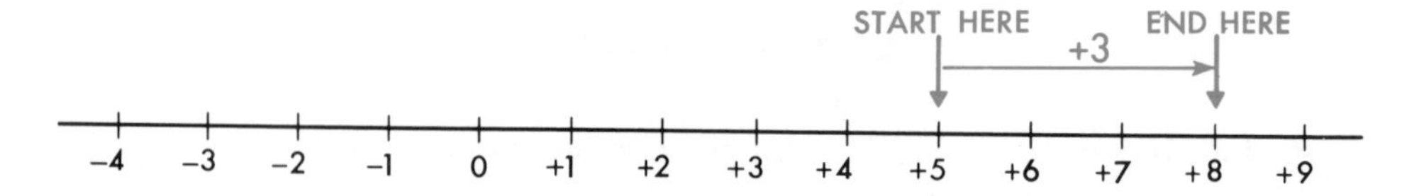

Fig. 2-21. Adding 5 + 3.

means that you *start* at 5 on the number line (Fig. 2-21), and move to the right, 3 places. You *end* at the answer, 8.

The same general idea holds if you start below zero. Suppose the temperature is 10° below zero (or, −10°), and it goes up 7°. This means you have to solve the problem: − 10 + 7. Starting at −10° (Fig. 2-22), move 7 to the right, and end at 3° below zero, or −3°. The mathematician says,

"Negative ten plus seven equals negative three." This is written: $-10 + 7 = -3$.

Suppose the temperature rises three more degrees after it gets to 3° below zero. You can see that this will bring the mercury to zero. In other

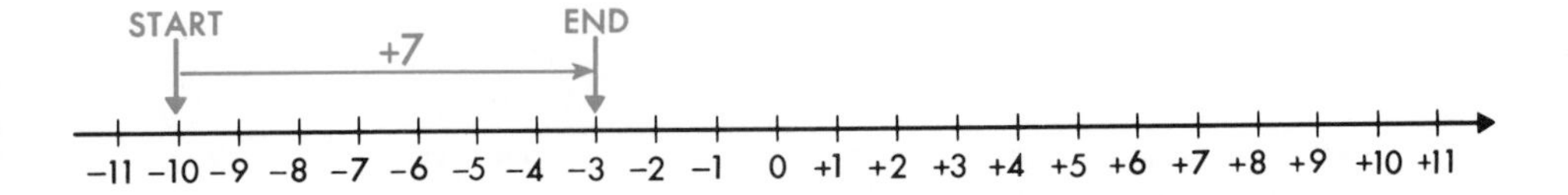

Fig. 2-22. Adding −10 + 7.

words, $-3 + 3 = 0$. This should remind you of the principle of negatives for addition.

Principle of Negatives for Addition. The sum of a number and its negative, is zero.

Now, if the temperature goes up another 5°, the result is shown in the equation: $0 + 5 = 5$. This may remind you of another principle:

Principle of Zero for Addition. Adding zero does not change the result.

Now, let us go to another thermometer which reads 10° below zero

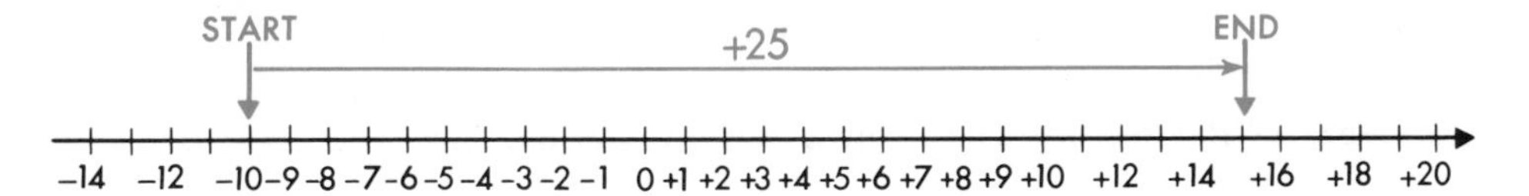

Fig. 2-23. −10 + 25.

(−10°), and heat it up by 25°. What is the new reading? As you see by Fig. 2-23, $-10 + 25 = +15$.

Try a thermometer which reads 5° below zero and *cool* it another 12°. This is like a negative heating because it forces the mercury *down* instead of *up*. Looking at the result (Fig. 2-24), you can see that: $-5 - 12 = -17$.

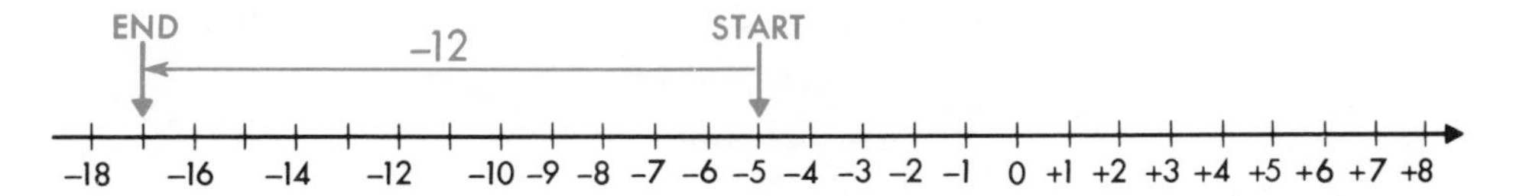

Fig. 2-24. −5 − 12.

The easiest way to do these addition problems is to draw a thermometer and mark the starting and finishing points. After a while you will be able to make the picture in your mind instead of doing it on paper.

Problem 2. Find (a) $6 + 13$, (b) $6 - 13$, (c) $-6 + 13$, (d) $-6 - 13$.

Answers:

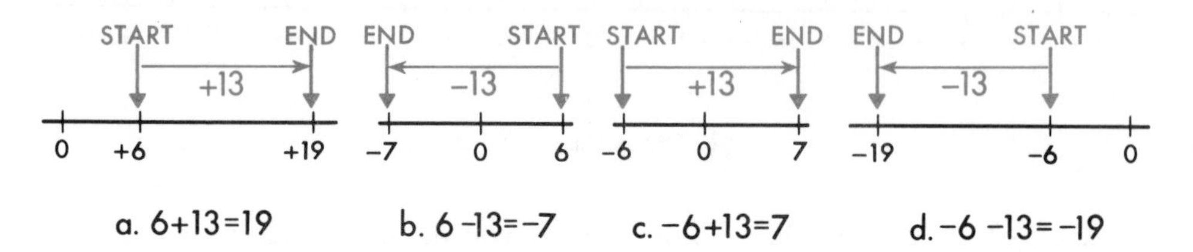

In doing these problems, you are welcome to use the principles previously discussed. For example, the *commutative principle* allows you to add in any direction you like; $-13 + 6$ is exactly the same as $+6 - 13$. Also $-7 + 9$ is the same as $+9 - 7$. Another principle, the *associative principle,* allows you to pair off any way you like. This comes in handy in the following problem:

Problem 3. Add 3, 8, 7, 5, 2, 5, 6.

Answer: "Pairing off" as shown, the answer is 36.

$$3 + 8 + 7 + 5 + 2 + 5 + 6$$

10 10 10

Problem 4. Add 3, 7, -9, 4, -3, 9, -7, 2.

Answer:

$$3 + 7 + (-9) + 4 + (-3) + 9 + (-7) + 2$$

0 0

0

The answer is 6.

Test: Section 6

Part A.

Use diagrams to do the problems (1) through (6).

1 $5 - 7$	2 $8 - 15$	3 $-4 - 6$
4 $-9 - 11$	5 $-3 + 6$	6 $-5 + 8$

7
```
  17.63
  21.86
  17.95
   3.71
  61.75
+ 41.24
```

8
```
   51.54
   28.92
   71.59
    1.06
  207.12
+  38.81
```

9
```
  121.615
    0.426
    9.875
    5.001
  769.291
+   0.691
```

10
```
  18.11823
  19.2969
  41.5406
   2.5000
   3.0569
+ 24.1557
```

11
```
  223.41
   18.69
   73.54
   18.77
  156.23
+  17.98
```

12
```
  1752.61
    28.41
    57.83
   156.91
  1257.45
+    0.70
```

Part B.

Do the following by pairing off any way you find convenient.

1 $5 - 7 + 9$	2 $6 - 11 + 7$	3 $-8 - 9 - 3$
4 $-4 - 8 - 2$	5 $-5 + 7 - 8$	6 $-10 + 12 - 4$
7 $8 + 6 - 12$	8 $10 + 7 - 15$	

Part C.

1 $5.7 - 6.8$	2 $3.5 - 4.7$	3 $-5.7 - 6.8$
4 $-3.5 - 4.7$	5 $-5.7 + 6.8$	6 $-2.9 + 0.7$

7 THERMOMETER SUBTRACTION

You already know about one kind of subtraction. For example, take 4 from 7. This means: *start* on the number line at 7 (Fig. 2-25), *go back* 4 places, *end* at 3, so that $7 - 4 = 3$.

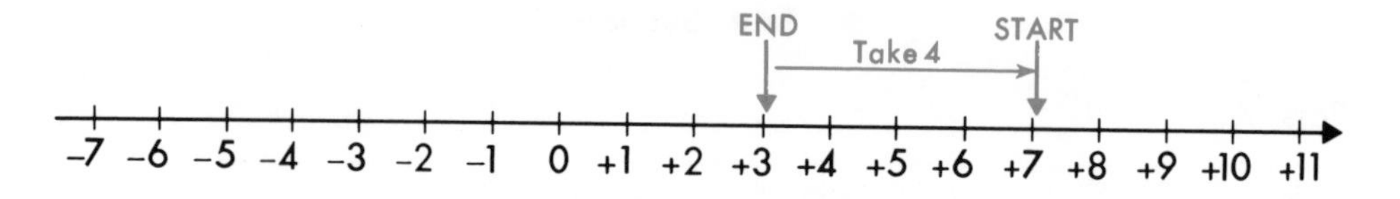

Fig. 2-25. Take 4 from 7.

Notice that *taking away* is the *negative of adding*, so that you get the same answer if you

take 4 from 7 add −4 to 7

This leads to a general rule called the *definition of subtraction.*

Definition of Subtraction. To take a number (the *subtrahend*) from another number (the *minuend*), add the negative of the subtrahend. (The answer is called the *difference.*)

Problem 1. Take 8 from 12.

Answer: The negative of 8 is −8.

$-8 + 12 = 4$

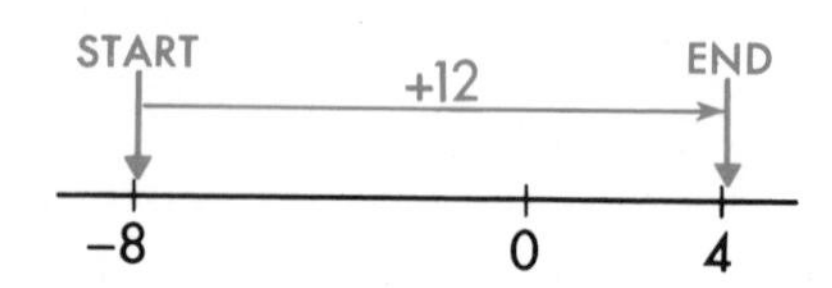

Problem 2. Subtract 9 from 5.

Answer: The negative of 9 is −9.

$-9 + 5 = -4$

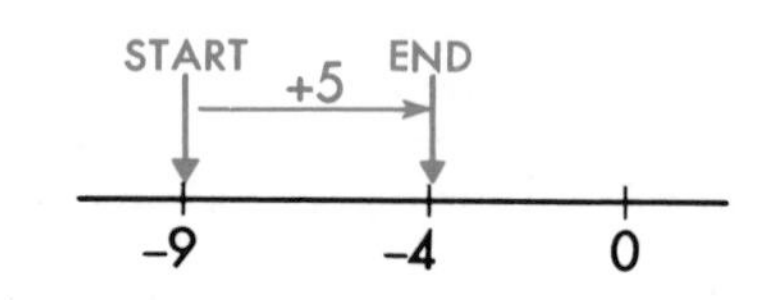

Problem 3. Take −5 from 7.

Answer: The negative of −5 is +5.

$5 + 7 = 12$

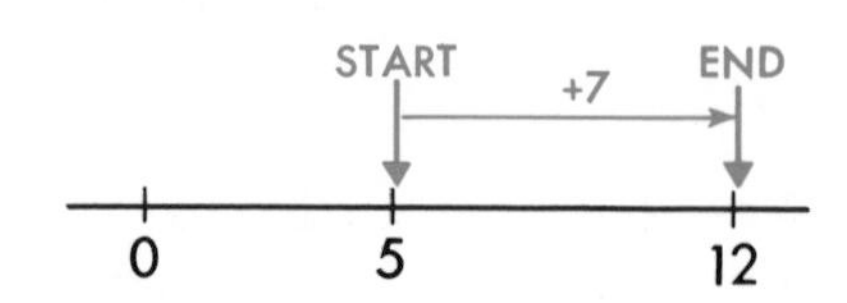

Problem 4. From −2, subtract −3.

Answer: The negative of −3 is +3.

$-2 + 3 = 1$

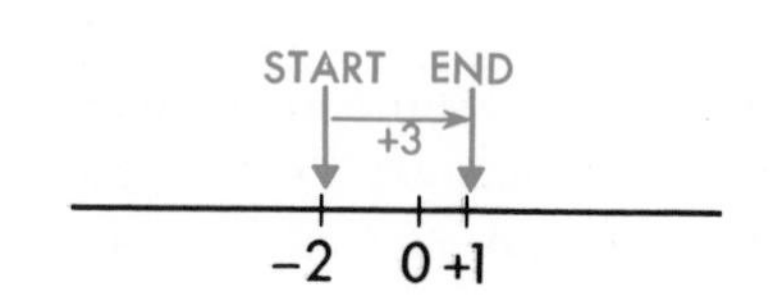

Test: Section 7

Part A.

1. Take 5 from 7
2. Subtract 8 from 12
3. Take 3 from 9
4. Subtract 2 from 11
5. From 16, take -3
6. From 13, take -5
7. Take -7 from 15
8. Take -2 from 10
9. Take 8 from -5
10. Subtract 11 from -8
11. Take 12 from -2
12. Subtract 20 from -16
13. From -8, take -3
14. From -5, take -8
15. Take -7 from -7
16. Take -2 from -9

Part B.

1. Take 5 from the sum of 8 and 10
2. Take 7 from the sum of 2 and -5
3. Take -8 from the sum of -3 and 7
4. Take -10 from the sum of -4 and -8
5. Take 6 from the sum of 6 and 7
6. Take 5 from the sum of 8 and -4
7. Take -9 from the sum of -5 and 3
8. Take -12 from the sum of -8 and -9

8 MULTIPLICATION OF THERMOMETER NUMBERS

When you have to multiply 3×6, you can do it by method *A* or method *B* (Fig. 2-26). It does not make much difference, because you know both methods so well. Of course, you will always get the same answer.

Let us think about $3 \times (-6)$. We already know that $-6-6-6$ (Fig. 2-27) is -18 by method *A*; so the answer *must* come out the same way in method *B*.

$$\text{A}\quad \begin{array}{r} 6\\ 6\\ \underline{6}\\ 18 \end{array} \qquad \text{B}\quad \begin{array}{r} 6\\ \underline{\times 3}\\ 18 \end{array}$$

Fig. 2-26. Three times six.

$$\text{A}\quad \begin{array}{r} -6\\ -6\\ \underline{-6}\\ -18 \end{array} \qquad \text{B}\quad \begin{array}{r} -6\\ \underline{\times 3}\\ -18 \end{array}$$

Fig. 2-27. Three times negative six.

Do you remember the *commutative principle for multiplication*? That you can multiply two numbers in *either* order? In other words, if $3 \times (-6) = -18$, then $(-6) \times 3 = -18$, too.

The two rules for multiplication already illustrated are as follows:

The + + Rule for Multiplication. When you multiply two + numbers, the product is +.

Example: $7 \times 8 = 56$, or $(+7) \times (+8) = (+56)$

The + − Rule for Multiplication. When you multiply a + and a − number in either order, the result is −.

Example: $7 \times (-8) = -56$, $(-6) \times 9 = -54$

There is one more combination: something like $(-5) \times (-4)$. Is this $(+20)$ or (-20)? Here is how we reason it out:

Line 1: $(+5) \times (+4) = +20$ by the + + rule
Line 2: $(+5) \times (-4) = -20$ by the + − rule
Line 3: Therefore $(-5) \times (-4) = +20$ by a new rule

Explanation. Notice that in line 1, the answer was +. In line 2, we changed from $(+4)$ to (-4), and this *one* change caused the answer to change from $+20$ to -20, also *one* change. This gives us a *hint*: a *change of sign causes a change in the result.*

Using the same thinking, we changed another sign in the problem when we went from line 2 to line 3. We changed from $(+5)$ to (-5). Now there should be a change in the result, too. That is why the result goes from -20 (line 2) to $+20$ (line 3). The rule is as follows:

The − − Rule for Multiplication. When you multiply a − number by a − number, the result is a + number.

Example: $(-6) \times (-4) = +24$

You may be interested in the fact that mathematicians can actually prove these three rules that we guessed at. They are called *laws of signed numbers*. A "signed" number is a number with a + or a − before it.

Test: Section 8

Part A.

1	12×25	2	6×15	3	13×6
4	7×92	5	-12×25	6	-6×15
7	-13×6	8	-7×92	9	$12 \times (-25)$
10	$6 \times (-15)$	11	$13 \times (-6)$	12	$7 \times (-92)$
13	$-12 \times (-25)$	14	-6×-15	15	$-13 \times (-6)$
16	$-7 \times (-92)$				

Part B.

1	6.8×4.7	2	3.5×9.8
3	$(-4.7) \times 2.7$	4	$(-3.9) \times 8.5$
5	$7.7 \times (-6.1)$	6	$5.8 \times (-3.3)$
7	$(-9.3) \times (-4.7)$	8	$(-6.9) \times (-3.8)$

9 DIVISION OF THERMOMETER NUMBERS

You may remember that in multiplying on the five-hour clock (p. 37), we found that $4 \times 4 = 1$, $3 \times 2 = 1$, and so on. The pairs of numbers that had products equal to 1, were named *reciprocals.*

In the decimal system, $3 \times 2 = 6$ (not *1*), and $4 \times 4 = 16$. So these numbers are *not* reciprocals in the decimal system. Are there reciprocals in the decimal system? Yes; here are some:

$1 \times 1 = 1$	$(-1) \times (-1) = 1$
$2 \times \frac{1}{2} = 1$	$(-2) \times (-\frac{1}{2}) = 1$
$3 \times \frac{1}{3} = 1$	$(-3) \times (-\frac{1}{3}) = 1$
$\frac{2}{3} \times \frac{3}{2} = 1$	$(-\frac{2}{3}) \times (-\frac{3}{2}) = 1$
$\frac{4}{7} \times \frac{7}{4} = 1$	$(-\frac{9}{5}) \times (-\frac{5}{9}) = 1$

The rules for finding reciprocals in the decimal system are:

Reciprocal Rule for Whole Numbers. The reciprocal of a *whole number* is the *fraction*: 1 divided by the whole number.

Examples: The reciprocal of 16 is $\frac{1}{16}$

The reciprocal of -35 is $-\frac{1}{35}$

Reciprocal Rule for Fractions. The reciprocal of a *fraction* is the *inverted* fraction.

Examples: The reciprocal of $\frac{3}{4}$ is $\frac{4}{3}$

The reciprocal of $-\frac{3}{5}$ is $-\frac{5}{3}$

Now let us talk about division for a minute. Suppose we divide 8 by 2. The answer is 4. Now, instead of doing this, *multiply* 8 by the *reciprocal* of 2. This means: $8 \times \frac{1}{2}$. The answers are exactly the same.

This is an example of an important rule called the *definition of division.*

Definition of Division. Dividing by a number is the same as multiplying by its reciprocal.

Examples.

5 divided by 3 $= 5 \times \frac{1}{3} = \frac{5}{3}$

6 divided by $\frac{2}{3}$ $= \overset{3}{\cancel{6}} \times \frac{3}{\underset{1}{\cancel{2}}} = 9$

$\frac{5}{6}$ divided by $\frac{3}{4}$ $= \frac{5}{\underset{3}{\cancel{6}}} \times \frac{\overset{2}{\cancel{4}}}{3} = \frac{10}{9}$

8 divided by (-2) $= \overset{4}{\cancel{8}} \times \left(-\frac{1}{\underset{1}{\cancel{2}}}\right) = -4$

(-9) divided by $\left(-\frac{3}{4}\right)$ $= (-\overset{3}{\cancel{9}}) \times \left(-\frac{4}{\underset{1}{\cancel{3}}}\right) = 12$

Notice two facts: (1) you cannot divide by zero, because zero has no reciprocal; (2) the + +, + −, and − − rules for division are the same as those for multiplying, because division, as explained in this section, is just a way of multiplying.

Test: Section 9

Part A.

In Questions 1–16, write the reciprocals:

1 7	**2** 9	**3** 15	**4** 12
5 -3	**6** -7	**7** -4	**8** -10
9 $\frac{2}{3}$	**10** $\frac{3}{5}$	**11** $\frac{5}{7}$	**12** $\frac{1}{3}$
13 $-\frac{6}{5}$	**14** $-\frac{3}{7}$	**15** $-\frac{15}{11}$	**16** $-\frac{5}{8}$

In Questions 17–32, do the divisions by converting to multiplications.

17 8 divided by 2
18 5 divided by 15
19 12 divided by 4
20 16 divided by $\frac{1}{2}$
21 -8 divided by 2
22 -5 divided by 15
23 -12 divided by 4
24 -16 divided by $\frac{1}{2}$
25 8 divided by (-2)
26 5 divided by (-15)
27 12 divided by (-4)
28 16 divided by $(-\frac{1}{2})$
29 -8 divided by (-2)
30 -5 divided by (-15)
31 -12 divided by (-4)
32 -16 divided by $(-\frac{1}{2})$

Part B.

1 $\frac{2}{3}$ divided by $\frac{3}{4}$
2 $\frac{3}{5}$ divided by $\frac{9}{15}$
3 $\frac{4}{5}$ divided by $\frac{8}{21}$
4 $\frac{5}{6}$ divided by $\frac{10}{6}$
5 $-\frac{2}{3}$ divided by $\frac{3}{4}$
6 $-\frac{3}{5}$ divided by $\frac{9}{15}$
7 $-\frac{4}{5}$ divided by $\frac{8}{21}$
8 $-\frac{5}{6}$ divided by $\frac{10}{6}$
9 $\frac{2}{3}$ divided by $(-\frac{3}{4})$
10 $\frac{3}{5}$ divided by $(-\frac{9}{15})$
11 $\frac{4}{5}$ divided by $(-\frac{8}{21})$
12 $\frac{5}{6}$ divided by $(-\frac{10}{6})$
13 $-\frac{2}{3}$ divided by $(-\frac{3}{4})$
14 $-\frac{3}{5}$ divided by $(-\frac{9}{15})$
15 $-\frac{4}{5}$ divided by $(-\frac{8}{21})$
16 $-\frac{5}{6}$ divided by $(-\frac{10}{6})$

Part C. Find the reciprocals of the following:

1 $2\frac{1}{2}$ **2** $3\frac{3}{5}$ **3** $4\frac{1}{4}$ **4** $7\frac{5}{8}$

In Questions 5 – 8, do the divisions by converting to multiplications.

5 $2\frac{1}{2}$ divided by $5\frac{3}{4}$
6 $3\frac{1}{3}$ divided by $1\frac{5}{6}$
7 $7\frac{5}{8}$ divided by 4
8 $5\frac{2}{3}$ divided by $3\frac{8}{9}$

10 DISTRIBUTIVE PRINCIPLE

How many ways can you write "eight"? Well, here are some of them: acht (German), huit (French), octo (Latin), ocho (Spanish), 8, $\frac{16}{2}$, (4×2), $(6 + 2)$, $(7 + 1)$, $(-4) \times (-2)$, and an endless number of other ways.

Let us pay attention to the *sum*, $(6 + 2)$. We know that $3 \times 8 = 24$.

What is $3 \times (6 + 2)$? It must be the same: 24. Now, notice that

$$\begin{array}{r} 3 \times 6 = 18 \\ 3 \times 2 = 6 \\ \hline 18 + 6 = 24 \end{array}$$

In other words, $3 \times (6 + 2) = (3 \times 6) + (3 \times 2)$. This is an example of a very important principle of mathematics.

Distributive Principle. If a number multiplies a sum (or difference) the result is the same whether you add (or subtract) first, or multiply first.

Problem 1. Verify the distributive principle for $8 \times (2 + 7)$.

Solution: Adding first: $8 \times (2 + 7) = 8 \times 9 = 72$
Multiplying first: $8 \times (2 + 7) = (8 \times 2) + (8 \times 7)$
$= 16 + 56 = 72$

Sometimes, the distributive principle is useful in doing problems mentally.

Problem 2. Multiply 6 by 27.

Solution: $6 \times 27 = 6 \times (20 + 7) = (6 \times 20) + (6 \times 7) = 120 + 42$
$= 162$

Problem 3. Multiply 15 by 99.

Solution: $15 \times 99 = 15 \times (100 - 1) = 1500 - 15 = 1485$

The opposite of *distributing* is called *factoring*. Here is an example of factoring.

Problem 4. Find $(8 \times 85) + (8 \times 15)$.

Solution: $(8 \times 85) + (8 \times 15) =$
$8 \times (85 + 15) =$
$8 \times 100 = 800$

Problem 5. Find $(12 \times 27) + (12 \times 13)$.

Solution: $(12 \times 27) + (12 \times 13) =$
$12 \times (27 + 13) =$
$12 \times 40 =$
480

Test: Section 10

Part A. Verify the distributive principle.

1 $9 \times (30 + 2)$
2 $9 \times (20 + 8)$
3 $12 \times (10 + 3)$
4 $12 \times (10 + 5)$
5 $8 \times (7 + 5)$
6 $8 \times (2 + 9)$
7 $15 \times (3 + 7)$
8 $15 \times (4 + 6)$
9 $25 \times (10 + 10)$
10 $25 \times (12 + 8)$

Part B. Use the distributive principle to multiply the following:

1 $12 \times 12 = 12 \times (10 + 2)$
2 $12 \times 14 = 12 \times (10 + 4)$
3 $8 \times 17 = 8 \times (10 + 7)$
4 $8 \times 23 = 8 \times (20 + 3)$
5 $15 \times 25 = 15 \times (20 + 5)$
6 $15 \times 16 = 15 \times (10 + 6)$
7 $22 \times 99 = 22 \times (100 - 1)$
8 $17 \times 99 = 17 \times (100 - 1)$
9 $8 \times 999 = 8 \times (1000 - 1)$
10 $13 \times 999 = 13 \times (1000 - 1)$

11 BIG NUMBERS AND INFINITY

The numbers on our thermometer become increasingly great as we go to the right. Go far enough, and you will reach the following "big numbers."

What It Is	*How To Say It*	*Numeral*	*Scientific Notation*
Number of students in a large high school	Three Thousand	3000	3×10^3
Population of Puerto Rico in 1950	Two million two hundred thousand	2,200,000	2.2×10^6
Population of New York in 1950	Fourteen million, eight hundred thousand	14,800,000	1.48×10^7
Number of miles from the earth to the sun	Ninety three million	93,000,000	9.3×10^7
Number of words spoken on the earth since the first word was spoken (at a guess!)	Ten thousand million million	10,000,000,000,000,000	1×10^{16}

One of the reasons for *scientific notation* is to make it easier to write very large numbers. The rule for writing these numbers is easy.

Rule for Scientific Notation for Big Numbers. (1) Put a decimal point after the first figure. (2) Count the number of figures from the new decimal point to the old one. (In the case of a whole number its decimal point is at the end.) (3) Use this count as an *exponent*. The "exponent" is the little number positioned above the 10, to the right.

Problem 1. Change 2 35,000,000 to scientific notation.

Answer: 2.35×10^{8}

Problem 2. Change 1 000 to scientific notation.

Answer: $1. \times 10^{3}$

Problem 3. Change 1 00 .35 to scientific notation.

Answer: 1.0035×10^{2}

To change back from scientific notation to the usual decimal notation, use the following rule:

Rule for Decimal Notation. Move the decimal point to the right as many places as the "number" of the "exponent." Attach zeros to fill the empty spaces.

Problem 4. Change 5.7×10^{5} back to decimal notation.

Answer: 5 70000

Problem 5. Change 2.75×10^{3} back to decimal notation.

Answer: 2 750

You may wonder what the *greatest* number is. Well, there is no greatest number. For any number that one person names, another person can add one and get a greater number! The mathematician says that there is an "infinite number" of numbers.

The whole idea of infinity is a difficult one, but we can talk about it a little, and compare ordinary numbers with infinite numbers.

When you take half an ordinary positive number, you always get a smaller number. For example, one half of twelve is six; and one half of six is three.

Let us try taking half of all the whole numbers. To do this, we line up all the whole (*odd and even*) numbers (line 1 below), and underneath them in line 2, all the *even* numbers:

Line 1:	1	2	3	4	5	6	7	8	9	10	11	12 and so on
Line 2:	2	4	6	8	10	12	14	16	18	20	22	24 and so on

Now, we know that there are half as many even numbers as there are whole (odd and even) numbers, because only every other number is an even number. Therefore, one would expect line 2, to have only half as many numbers as line 1.

However, if you compare line 1 and line 2, you will see that there are just as many even numbers as whole numbers, because there is one even number for every whole number! In other words, the number of *whole* numbers is exactly the same as the number of *even* numbers. Paradoxically, the *infinite* number of numbers is equal to one half of itself!

This example shows the peculiar behavior of infinite numbers. They will not obey the rules of ordinary arithmetic!

• Test: Section 11

In Questions 1–10, change the numbers to scientific notation.

1 The radius of the earth is 3963 miles at the Equator.

2 The earth weighs 6,595,000,000,000,000,000,000 tons.

3 The earth has 57,470,000 square miles of land.

4 The earth has 139,480,000 square miles of ocean.

5 Mt. Everest, the highest mountain in the world, has a height of 29,003 feet.

6 The greatest known sea depth is 34,219 feet.

7 The average distance from the earth to the moon is 238,854 miles.

8 The sun weighs 329,390 times as much as the earth.

9 The speed of light is 186,000 miles per second.

10 There are about 100,000,000,000,000,000,000 grains of sand in Coney Island Beach, New York City.

In Questions 11–20, change the numbers back to the decimal form.

11 The diameter of the sun is 8.64×10^5 miles.

12 The diameter of Mars is 4.26×10^3 miles.

13 The diameter of Saturn is 7.49×10^4 miles.

14 The diameter of the moon is 2.16×10^3 miles.

15 The distance from the sun to Mars is 1.42×10^8 miles.

16 The distance from the sun to Neptune is 2.79×10^9 miles.

17 A wavelength of 1.25×10^3 meters corresponds to a frequency of 2.40×10^2 kilocycles.

18 Avogadro's number, used throughout physics and chemistry, is 6.0247×10^{23}. It refers to the number of atoms in a specified weight of material.

19 The speed of sound in dry air is 1.087×10^3 feet per second.

20 Multiplied by itself three times (5.5×10^2) is about 1.66×10^8.

3

THE MATHEMATICS OF SCIENCE AND TECHNOLOGY

Mrs. Average had just rented an apartment, and decided to carpet the living-room. She sent her husband to ask the superintendent what the dimensions were. He reported that they were 16 ft. 3 in. × (by) 18 ft. 6 in.

"Well," said Mrs. Average, thinking aloud, "three inches is one quarter of a foot, or 25%, and six inches is half a foot, or 50%. That makes the room 16.25 ft. × 18.5 ft. What do we do now?"

"Easy," replied Mr. Average, "we multiply the two, and that will tell us how many square feet of carpet we need."

```
16 ft. 3 in. = 16.25  ft.
18 ft. 6 in. = 18.5   ft.
               ----------
                8125
              13000
              1625
              ---------------
              300.625  sq. ft.
```

Fig. 3-1. How they worked out the number of square feet.

The two of them figured out (Fig. 3-1) that there were 300.625 sq. ft. At $2.98 per square foot, the bill for the carpet was supposed to come to $895.86250.

"What in the world does that mean?" asked Mrs. Average.

"I don't know," replied her husband, "we'll have to let the man at the store figure it out."

Of course, the method they used was nonsense. What, they *had* to do was buy carpeting 17 ft. × 19 ft. and cut it to size. The bill came to about $962.54 plus tax.

Like most people, Mr. and Mrs. Average had never learned the difference between the mathematics of *exact* numbers and the mathematics of *approximate* numbers. In this chapter we will study exact and approximate numbers and the difference between them.

1 EXACT AND APPROXIMATE NUMBERS

Early in the history of mankind, the savage probably learned to count, at least a little. The *natural* or *counting* numbers are 1, 2, 3, 4, . . . and so on.

Fig. 3-2. Counting gives you exact numbers.

These are the *exact* numbers; you get them when you *count* things (Fig. 3-2). For example, the following conditions give you *exact* numbers:

There are two windows in the room
There are 30 students in the class
There are seven days in a week

Any number obtained by any other method is an *approximate* number. ("Approximate" means "not exact.") This kind of number is the result of a

Fig. 3-3. Measuring gives you approximate numbers.

measurement (Fig. 3-3), not a counting process. The following conditions give you *approximate* numbers:

The desk is 6 ft. long. (Use of a ruler.)
His temperature is 98.6°. (Use of a thermometer.)
The bottle holds one quart. (Use of a volumetric burette.)
It takes ten minutes to get there. (Use of a watch.)
The room requires six rolls of wallpaper. (Use of a folding rule.)

Notice, however, that the following is an *exact* number:

I bought six rolls of wallpaper.

In dealing with numbers, it is important to be able to tell the difference between a result obtained after measuring, and one obtained after counting. The sentence, "This room requires six rolls of wallpaper," tells that someone measured the room, then figured out how many rolls were needed. In the other sentence, "I bought six rolls of wallpaper," the clerk went to his stockroom and actually counted up to six.

Sometimes, it is not so easy to tell whether a number is exact or approximate. For example, the sentence, "The population of the United States is 180 million people," seems to indicate that someone actually counted these people. However, if ten people were counted every second, it would take more than six months to count up to 180 million. During this time, the count would change because of births, deaths, and other factors, such as travelers. No; this number is not exact. It is *based* on counting, but it is a kind of estimate. It is an *approximate* number.

Remember: When you consider numbers, think of how they were obtained. If they were obtained by an *actual count*, they are *exact*. Otherwise they are *approximate*.

Test: Section 1

In the following, decide whether the numbers are exact or approximate.

1 The sun is 93 million miles from the earth.

2 He ran the 100-yard dash.

3 There are 100 cents in 1 dollar.

4 There are 12 inches in 1 foot.

5 There are 50 states in the United States of America.

6 There were once 13 colonies in America.

7 At the last meeting of the Mathematics Club, every seat was taken. There were 42 seats, so there must have been 42 people.

8 There were 100 people at the dance.

9 The temperature is 8° below zero.

10 Scientists have decided that the temperature at which water freezes should be called 32° Fahrenheit.

11 This thermometer has 180 degree marks.

12 There are 5280 feet in 1 mile.

13 He is 16 years old.

14 An American is entitled to vote when he is 21 years old.

15 I weigh 120 pounds.

16 There should be 32 stitches in each line of knitting for this sweater sleeve.

17 To make a pie crust, take 2 cups of flour and 1 tablespoonful of shortening.

18 The foreman said, "Cut this down to 0.378-in. diameter."

19 This air-conditioner needs 110 volts and draws 12.3 amperes.

20 "Officer, I was only doing 35 miles an hour!"

2 READING APPROXIMATE NUMBERS

Most approximate numbers occur in the reading of an instrument, such as a ruler or a thermometer, although others come by "estimate." In the case of a measurement, the word *precision* refers to the smallest measurement that can be made on the instrument.

For example, an ordinary ruler can be read directly to eighths as shown in Fig. 3-4, but if you have a good eye, you can read it to the nearest six-

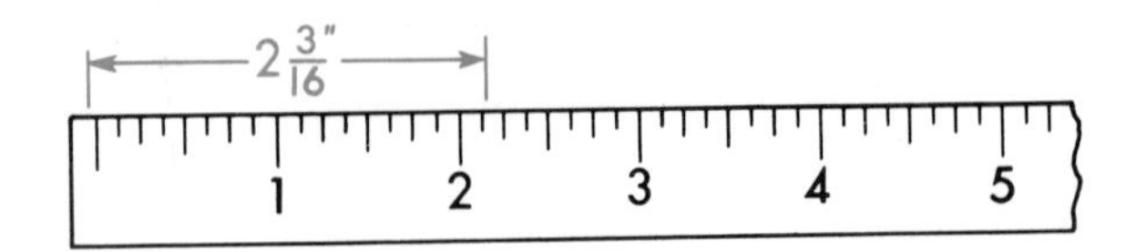

Fig. 3-4. An ordinary ruler can be read directly to eighths and estimated to sixteenths.

teenth, without much trouble. In other words, you can get a measurement such as $2\frac{3}{16}$ in. with this ruler. The *precision* of the ordinary ruler is $\frac{1}{16}$ in., meaning that this is as far "down" as it can be read.

The machinist uses a more precise rule which may be marked down to $\frac{1}{64}$ in. (Fig. 3-5) or even to $\frac{1}{100}$ in. (Fig. 3-6). Without reading between the marks, the machinist can read with a *precision* of $\frac{1}{64}$ in. with one of them, and $\frac{1}{100}$ in. with the other. He will get greater precision if he reads between the marks.

Even more precise measurements of length can be made with instruments

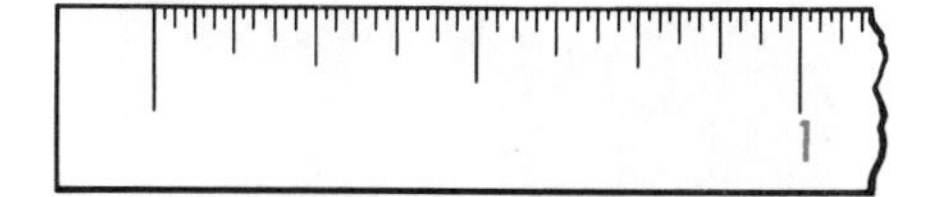

Fig. 3-5. Machinist's steel rule marked in 64ths.

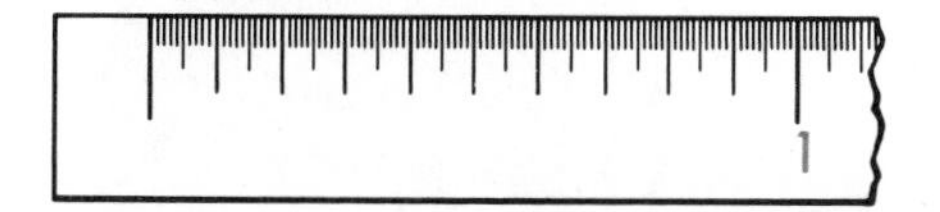

Fig. 3-6. Machinist's steel rule marked in 100ths.

such as the micrometer caliper (Fig. 3-7) which can be read directly with a precision of $\frac{1}{1000}$ in., and the vernier micrometer caliper (Fig. 3-8) which can be read directly with a precision of $\frac{1}{10,000}$ in.

Other instruments exist for measuring with very great precision such

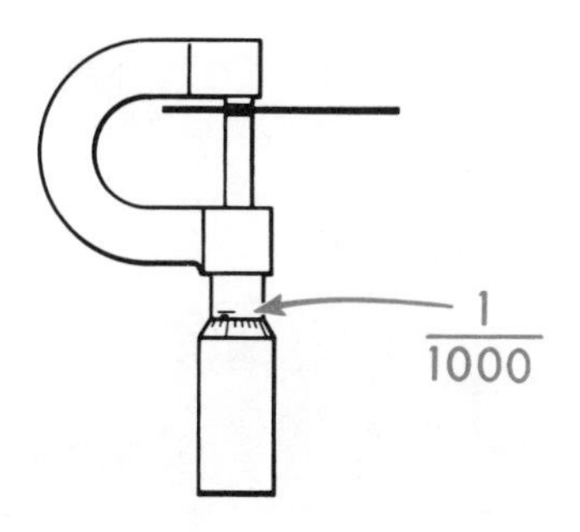

Fig. 3-7. Micrometer caliper.

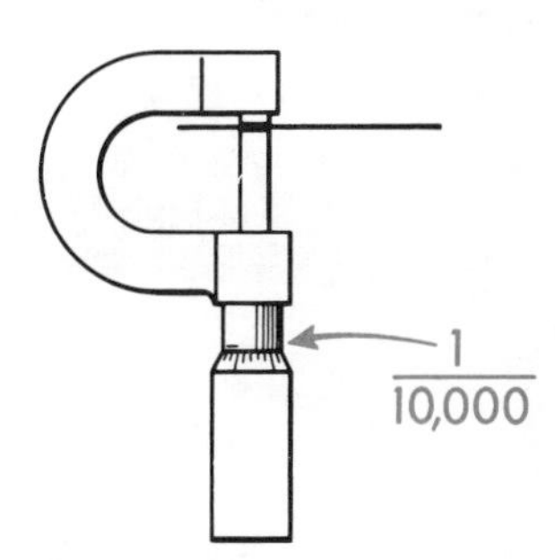

Fig. 3-8. Vernier micrometer caliper.

things as the amount of sugar in your blood, your blood pressure, the weight of a sample of uranium, the amount of butter fat in milk, and so on. The widely differing range of measuring devices is shown in Fig. 3-9.

It is not the purpose of this book to describe the use of measuring instruments. However, it should be clear that the precision of a measurement depends upon the type of instrument used. And in every case, the handling of the numbers depends upon the amount of approximation.

Suppose a machinist announces a measurement of 2.37 in. Looking at the *last* figure given (which is in hundredths place) we see that the precision was $\frac{1}{100}$ in. To put it differently, this was the smallest mark used in the measurement. Now, how precise is this measurement?

If you went back to the machinist and asked him, he might say, "I measured it with my steel rule. It came out between 2.36 in. and 2.37 in., but closer to 2.37." Or he might say, "It seemed to be right between 2.36 in., and 2.37 in. When I'm in doubt, I always take the higher of the two, so I took 2.37 in. as the measurement."

100 FEET
1000 FEET

(1)

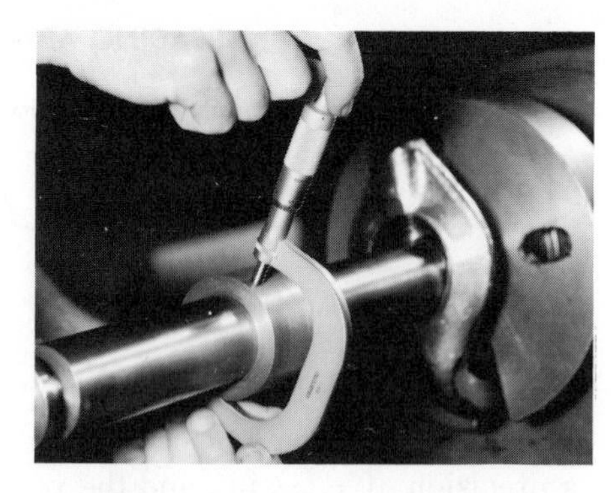

(2)

VOLTS D.C.
WESTON ELECTRICAL INSTRUMENT CORP.
ZERO
CORRECTOR

(3)

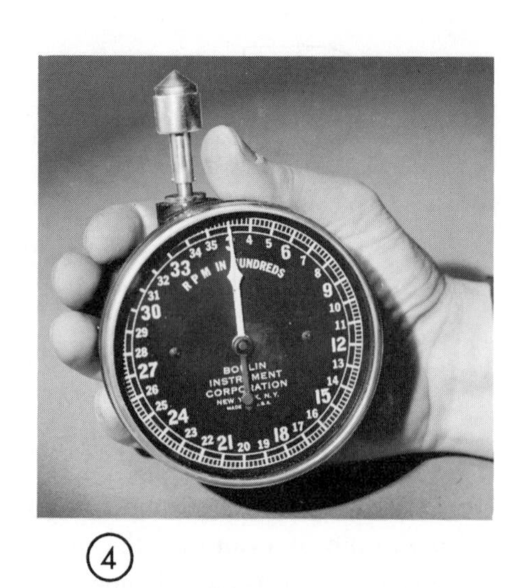

(4)

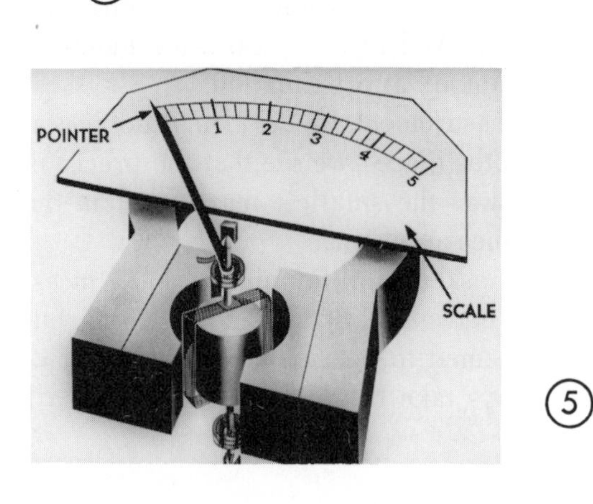
POINTER
SCALE

(5)

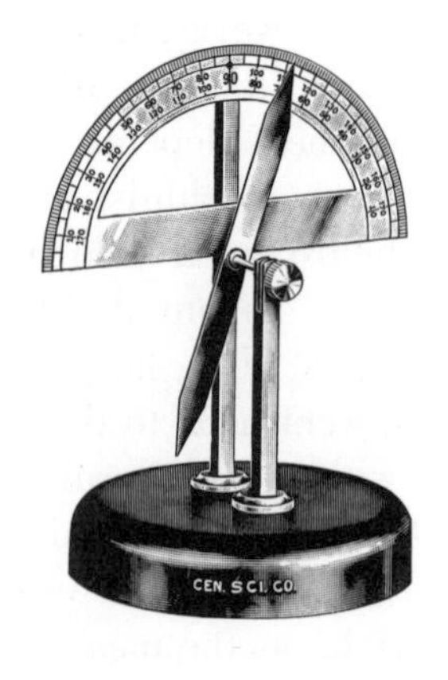
CEN. SCI. CO.

(6)

As you can see, the *last* figure written in a measurement may be in doubt by as much as one half the unit of precision. For example:

The measurement	*Is read as*	*Has a precision of*	*Is in doubt by*
3.5 ft.	Three and five *tenths* ft.	One tenth of a ft.	One twentieth of a ft.
3.50 ft.	Three and fifty *hundredths* ft.	One hundredth of a ft.	One two hundredth of a ft.
72.3°	Seventy-two and *three* tenths degrees	One tenth of a degree	One twentieth of a degree
1.27 min.	One and twenty-seven *hundredths* min.	One hundredth of a min.	One two-hundredth of a min.

If the measurement is expressed in "ruler fractions," the same rule holds:

The measurement	*Has a precision of*	*Is in doubt by*
$3\frac{1}{2}$ in.	$\frac{1}{2}$ in.	$\frac{1}{4}$ in.
$3\frac{2}{4}$ in.	$\frac{1}{4}$ in.	$\frac{1}{8}$ in.
$15\frac{5}{16}$ in.	$\frac{1}{16}$ in.	$\frac{1}{32}$ in.

You may be a little surprised to see that $3\frac{1}{2}$ in. is in doubt by $\frac{1}{4}$ in., while $3\frac{2}{4}$ in. is in doubt by only $\frac{1}{8}$ in. We must admit that most people think that $3\frac{1}{2}$ is the same as $3\frac{2}{4}$, but it is not. Three and a half means that the measurement was taken to the closest "half mark," but three and two quarters means that it was measured to the closest "quarter" mark. At least, that is what it means among scientists!

←

Fig. 3-9. Typical measuring devices.

1. Barometric-type airplane altimeter. *Kollsman Instrument Corp.*
2. Using a large micrometer caliper to measure the diameter of a shaft.
3. Portable triple-scale laboratory-type d-c voltmeter. *Weston Electrical Instrument Co.*
4. Tachometer (scale graduated in hundreds of rpm). *Boulin Instrument Corp.*
5. Meter movement. *Westinghouse Electric Corp.*
6. Magnetic dip needle. *Central Scientifc Co.*

Test: Section 2

In parts *A* and *B*, answer three questions: (1) How do you read it? (2) What is the precision of the measurement? (3) How much is it in doubt by?

Part A.

1 14.7 ft.
2 23.5 ft.
3 76.18°
4 29.50°
5 4 hr. 26 min.
6 8 hr. 10 min.
7 2.027 in.
8 1.489 in.
9 24.1 sq. in.
10 38.8 sq. mi.

Part B.

1 14.70 ft.
2 23.50 ft.
3 4 hr. 26 min. 0 sec.
4 8 hr. 10 min. 0 sec.
5 24.10 sq. mi.
6 138.62 sq. mi.
7 $5\frac{1}{2}$ in.
8 $7\frac{3}{4}$ in.
9 $14\frac{7}{8}$ sq. in.
10 $29\frac{11}{16}$ sq. in.

Part C.

1 Compare the measurements: $5\frac{1}{2}$ in. and $5\frac{4}{8}$ in.
2 Compare the measurements: $3\frac{7}{8}$ ft. and $3\frac{14}{16}$ ft.
3 Compare the measurements: $2\frac{1}{2}$ hr. and 2 hr. 30 min.
4 Compare the measurements: $3\frac{1}{5}$ hr. and 3 hr. 12 min.

3 FRACTIONS TO DECIMALS, AND BACK AGAIN

In practical work, especially if a computing machine is being used, it is always more convenient to use *decimal fractions* such as 2.50 in., rather than *numbers with fractions,* such as $2\frac{1}{2}$ in. For this reason it is important to know how to change from fractions to decimals and back again, because measurements sometimes come out in fractions (even though we'd rather have decimals), and sometimes have to be given in fraction form (even though we have the answer in decimal form).

If you remember that $\frac{3}{4}$ can be read as *3 divided by 4,* it is easy to find out what the decimal is by doing the division.

Problem 1. Find the decimal equivalent of $\frac{3}{4}$.

Solution:

```
    0.75
 4)3.00  <----  use as many
   2 8x         zeros as you
   ---          need
     20
     20
     --
```

Answer: $\frac{3}{4} = 0.75$

Problem 2. Find the decimal equivalent of $\frac{5}{16}$.

Solution:

```
     0.3125
 16)5.0000  <----  use as many
    4 8xxx         zeros as you
    ---            need
      20
      16
      --
       40
       32
       --
        80
        80
        --
```

Answer: $\frac{5}{16} = 0.3125$

In general, the rule for converting a fraction into its decimal equivalent is as follows:

F to D Rule. Do the division, attaching a decimal point and as many zeros as you need.

Problem 3. Find the decimal equivalent of $\frac{19}{64}$.

Solution:

```
      0.296875
 64)19.000000  <----  use as many
    12 8              zeros as you
    ----              need
     6 20
     5 76
     ----
       440
       384
       ---
        560
        512
        ---
         480
         448
         ---
          320
          320
          ---
```

Answer: $\frac{19}{64} = 0.296875$

Problem 4. Find the decimal equivalent of $8\frac{19}{64}$.

Solution: The fraction part, $\frac{19}{64}$, is done *separately* as in Problem 3. The answer is 8.296875.

Problem 5. Find the decimal equivalent of $\frac{1}{3}$.

Solution:

```
      0.33333  etc.
   3)1.00000   <----  use as many
     9xxxx            zeros as you
     --               need
      10
       9
      --
       10
        9
       --
       etc.
```

Answer: *This one cannot be written as a decimal because the division never ends*

To change back from decimals to fractions, you simply reverse the process, and *multiply* instead of *dividing*.

Problem 6. Convert 0.296875 into the denomination sixty-fourths.

Solution:

```
  0.296875
       ×64
  --------
   1187500
  1781250
  --------
 [19].000000
```

Answer: $0.296875 = \frac{19}{64}$

Problem 7. Convert 5.296875 into the denomination: sixty-fourths.

Solution: The decimal part is done *separately* as in Problem 6. The answer is $5\frac{19}{64}$.

D to F rule. Multiply the *decimal part* of the number by the *denomination.*

• Test: Section 3

Convert the fractions into decimals, and the decimals into fractions.

1 $\frac{5}{8}$	**2** $\frac{7}{8}$	**3** $\frac{11}{16}$
4 $\frac{15}{16}$	**5** $3\frac{9}{32}$	**6** $2\frac{11}{32}$
7 $5\frac{17}{32}$	**8** $8\frac{19}{32}$	**9** $10\frac{21}{64}$
10 $11\frac{37}{64}$		

11 0.375 into eighths

12 0.250 into eighths

13 0.3125 into sixteenths

14 0.4375 into sixteenths

15 2.96875 into thirty-seconds

16 8.84375 into thirty-seconds

17 5.71875 into thirty-seconds

18 7.625 into thirty-seconds

19 6.703125 into sixty-fourths

20 9.546875 into sixty-fourths

4 ROUNDING OFF

It costs 10¢ for a ruler good enough to measure $\frac{7}{16}$ in. A good mechanic will pay $25 or more for an instrument to measure $\frac{7}{16}$ in. A scientist will pay thousands of dollars for instruments to measure $\frac{7}{16}$ in. Now, what is the difference?

The answer is that the expensive instruments are more precise. When you measure $\frac{7}{16}$ in. with a ruler, you can say, "According to this ruler, which has a precision of $\frac{1}{16}$ in., the measurement is $\frac{7}{16}$ in., but I may be out by half a sixteenth. When the mechanic measures with the micrometer, he can say, "My micrometer has a precision of one thousandth of an inch, so I may be wrong by one half of one thousandth of an inch." The scientist may use a precision of a millionth of an inch, or even better, and be in error by half of that.

You can see that it makes a great deal of difference how the approximate number was measured. To avoid misinformation, the mathematician tells you how *sure* he is by *rounding off* decimal fractions in a way that we will discuss in a minute.

A measurement like $\frac{7}{16}$ in., all by itself, does not tell you how precise the measurement is, but if it is put in decimal form, you can use the following method:

0.4375 means, "I am sure of 0.437 but not of the last figure."
0.438 means, "I am sure of 0.43 but not of the last figure."
0.44 means, "I am sure of 0.4 but not of the last figure."

In each case, all but the last figure is *sure*. The last figure is a kind of guess, or estimate. Now suppose Mr. Beginner says to you, "How shall I write this number: 15.2573 square inches? I'm sure of the first figures, but the last two are doubtful." How should this be written?

Simple; let us emphasize the *sure* part: *15.25*73. We need one extra figure. The correct, scientific way to write it, is 15.257 sq. in. The "3" that was dropped is called the *first figure dropped,* and the "7" that was kept is called the *last figure kept.*

Now, Mr. Beginner says, "Here's another one: 17.3894°. I am sure of the first three figures."

We start the same way. Emphasize the *sure* part: *17.3*894°. We need one extra figure. Shall we write "17.38°"? This would mean that the *first figure dropped* is a "9." This is a rather big figure to throw away, even if it is doubtful. For the sake of safety, we write the answer as "17.39°" instead of "17.38°."

The rule for *rounding off* is as follows:

R O Rule. First write the sure figures. Then write one more. If the first figure dropped is 5 or more, add one to the last figure kept.

Problem 1. Rewrite 27.14368 sure to three figures.

Solution:

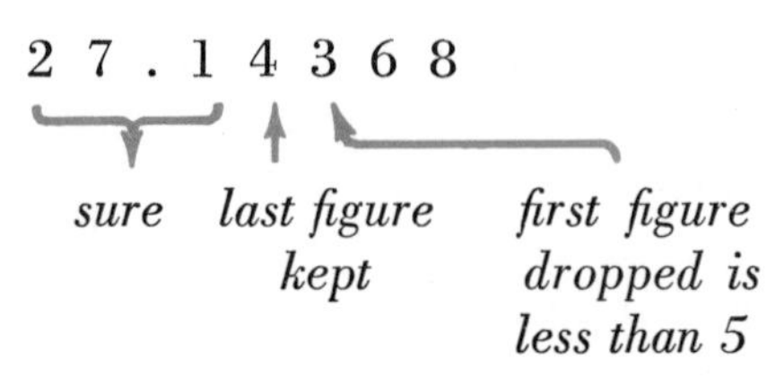

Answer: 27.14

Problem 2. Round off 81.6227 to the nearest tenth.

Solution: This means that the tenths figure is the last one kept.

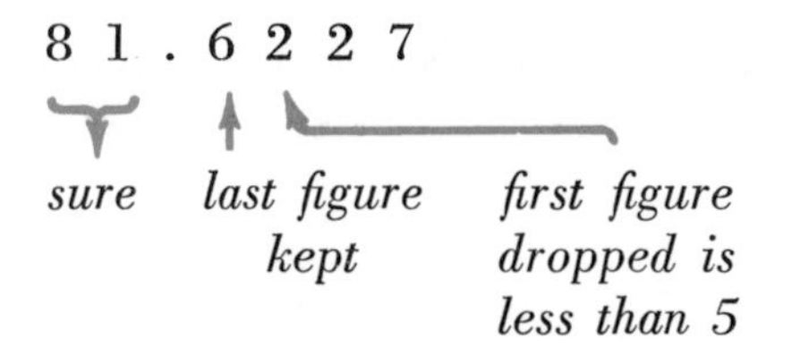

Answer: 81.6

Problem 3. Round off 35.6877 sure to hundredths.

Solution:

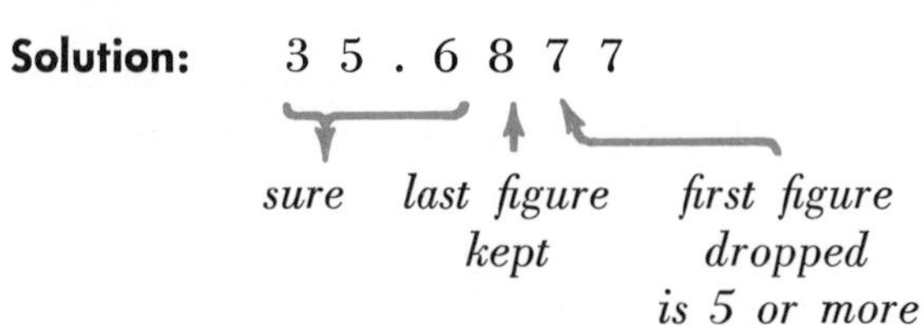

Answer: 35.69

Problem 4. Round off 73.855 to the nearest whole number.

Solution: This means that the units digit is the last figure kept.

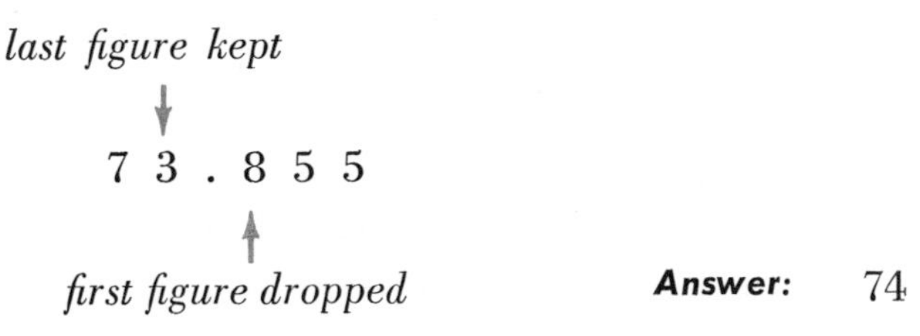

Answer: 74

Problem 5. Find $\frac{7}{16}$ in. correct to the nearest thousandth.

Solution:

```
     0.4375
 16)7.0000
    64xxxx
     60
     48
     120
     112
       80
       80
```

Answer: 0.438 in.

Problem 6. Find $\frac{7}{16}$ in. correct to the nearest hundredth.

Solution: We could divide completely (as in Problem 5), then round off by dropping the two last figures, but this is a waste of time. Instead, simply divide until there is only *one* figure to drop off. This saves time:

```
     0.437
 16)7.000
    6 4xx
     60
     48
     120
     112
       80
```

Answer: 0.44 in.

R O Division Rule. In converting fractions to decimals, carry out the division until you have one extra place (the first figure dropped).

Test: Section 4

Part A. In each of the following measurements, tell (*a*) which are the sure figures, (*b*) what is the precision of the measure, (*c*) by how much may the measurement be in error?

1 27°
2 38°
3 14.5 ft.
4 22.7 ft.
5 356.48 sq. in.
6 218.73 sq. in.
7 186.1 lb.
8 93.6 lb.
9 3.55 sec.
10 12.63 sec.

Part B. Round off each of the following as directed:

1 85.177 miles sure to tenths
2 68.248 miles sure to tenths
3 950.62 yd. to the nearest tenth
4 812.88 yd. to the nearest tenth
5 71.184 in. to the nearest hundredth
6 66.776 in. to the nearest hundredth
7 27.489° to the nearest degree
8 16.518° to the nearest degree
9 23.72 hr. to the nearest hour
10 37.48 hr. to the nearest hour

Part C. Convert each of the following fractions to a decimal rounded as directed:

1 $\frac{3}{8}$ nearest hundredth
2 $\frac{5}{8}$ nearest hundredth
3 $\frac{9}{16}$ nearest hundredth
4 $\frac{11}{16}$ nearest hundredth
5 $\frac{3}{32}$ nearest hundredth
6 $\frac{21}{32}$ nearest hundredth
7 $\frac{5}{7}$ nearest thousandth
8 $\frac{3}{7}$ nearest thousandth
9 $\frac{17}{64}$ nearest thousandth
10 $\frac{23}{64}$ nearest thousandth

5 ADDING AND SUBTRACTING APPROXIMATE NUMBERS

We have already mentioned the fact that a fraction, all by itself, usually does not tell how precise the measurement was. The following "rule of thumb" is useful for converting ruler fractions to decimals:.

If the ruler is marked to	*Round off to*
quarters or eighths	nearest tenth
sixteenths	nearest hundredth

This is a very rough rule, but it will save you from getting into the mess that Mr. Dedrong got himself into. Wanting to buy molding for his wall, this is what he did.

First, he took a yardstick (marked in $\frac{1}{4}$-in. intervals) and found the distance to be 7 ft. $5\frac{3}{4}$ in. from one end of the wall to a pipe. He did not know exactly what to do about the pipe, so he decided to guess at about 3 or 4 in. There was a little bit of wall on the other side of the pipe, so he borrowed a machinists' scale and found the remaining distance was 7.58 in.

7 ft.	5.75 in.
	3.50 in.
	7.58 in.
7 ft.	16.83 in.

or

8 ft. 4.83 in.

or

8 ft. $4\frac{27}{32}$ in.

By this time, he felt pretty proud of himself and thought of himself as a great engineer. He converted $5\frac{3}{4}$ in. to 5.75 in., "3 or 4 in." to 3.50 in., then added it all up. When he finished he converted back to fractions and got the "answer" shown at the left.

You can see that there are many things wrong with this whole job. First, a measurement on a ruler marked to quarters cannot be rounded off to hundredths. The best you can do is *tenths.*

Second, the 3.50 in. for the guess around the pipe is even worse. The approximate number, *3.50,* promises that the error will be less than half of a hundredth of an inch! He was lucky if his guess was within half an inch!

Lastly, the final result, with a precision of $\frac{1}{32}$ in. (and a promise that the approximate number is in error by less than $\frac{1}{64}$ in.) is obviously ridiculous. Even the measurement around the pipe could have been wrong by half an inch.

The story — not too far away from what some people do — illustrates the general rule for adding and subtracting approximate numbers.

Adding and Subtracting Approximate Numbers. No result can have greater *precision* than its *weakest* measurement.

Therefore, all results should be rounded off to avoid misinformation about the strength of the answer.

Problem 1. Add the following measurements: 17.566 lb., 2.43 lb., 3.8173 lb. and 120.8 lb.

Solution:

```
 17.566
  2.43
  3.8173
120.8
--------
144.6133 lb.
```

Answer: 144.6 lb.

Problem 2. Add the following measurements: 2.3155 oz., 1.728 oz., 2.500 oz.

Solution:

```
2.3155
1.728
2.500
------
6.5435 oz.
```

Answer: 6.544 oz.

Note that if 2.50 oz. had been written in place of 2.500 oz., the correct answer would have been 6.54 oz., instead of 6.544.

Problem 3. Take 2.663 ft. from 38.7 ft.

Solution:

```
38.7
 2.663
------
36.037 ft.
```

Answer: 36.0 ft.

Notice that the answer is 36 ft. and 0 tenths of a foot. This answer is therefore in doubt by one half of one tenth of a foot. The answer, "36 feet," means that the answer was measured to the *nearest foot*, and may therefore be in error by as much as one half of this precision, or six inches. There is a big difference between 36 feet and 36.0 feet, so far as a scientist or technician is concerned!

• Test: Section 5

Part A. What is the result in each of the following?

1 35.684 feet + 27.61 feet + 135.8822 feet

2 47.60 feet + 37.817 feet + 163.244 feet

3 175.0 inches + 63.4 inches + 73.77 inches

4 736.89 inches + 4.128 inches + 3.114 inches

5 96.4 miles − 37.51 miles

6 82.33 miles − 17.6 miles

7 143.7781 hours − 29.413 hours

8 163.8 hours − 75 hours

9 35.77 feet + 76.142 feet − 81.1622 feet

10 85.18 feet + 39.044 feet − 17.3817 feet

Part B. Find the perimeters (the sum of the lengths of the sides).

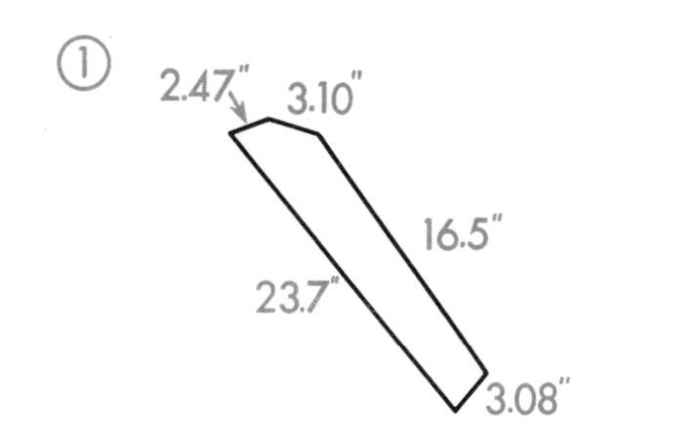

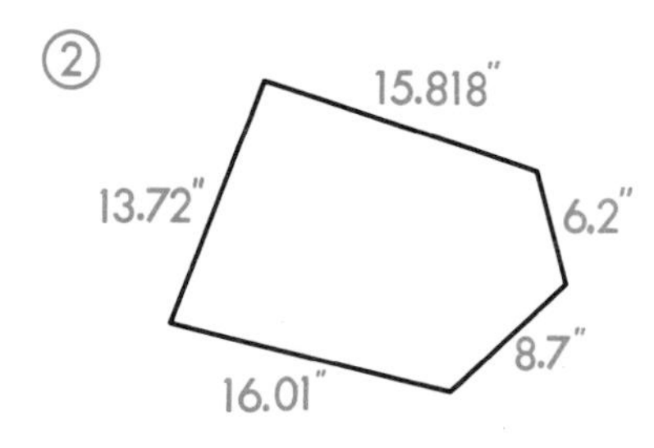

Part C. In the following, the kind of ruler used to make the measurements is indicated. Convert the fractions to decimals, then find the correct answer.

1 Ruler marked to eighths: $3\frac{1}{2}$ in + $2\frac{3}{4}$ in. + $5\frac{3}{16}$ in.
2 Ruler marked to eighths: $4\frac{3}{8}$ in. + $5\frac{7}{16}$ in. + $3\frac{1}{4}$ in.
3 Ruler marked to sixteenths: $5\frac{7}{32}$ in. + $4\frac{3}{16}$ in. + $8\frac{1}{4}$ in.
4 Ruler marked to sixteenths: $11\frac{19}{32}$ in. + $5\frac{9}{16}$ in. + $2\frac{1}{8}$ in.

6 MULTIPLYING DECIMALS

Not one person out of a thousand knows the area of a closet floor 5.3 ft. × 7.6 ft. (Fig. 3-10). If you just multiply them, as you probably did in the lower grades, you will get 40.28 sq. ft. Let us see how sure this result is.

$$\begin{array}{r l} 5.3 & \text{ft.} \\ \times\ 7.6 & \text{ft.} \\ \hline 318 & \\ 371 & \\ \hline 40.28 & \text{sq. ft.} \end{array}$$

The measurement, 5.3 ft, is sure for the 5, but doubtful for the 3. In other words, it may be in error by one half of one tenth of a foot.

The true measurement may be as *high* as 5.35 ft.

The true measurement may be as *low* as 5.25 ft.

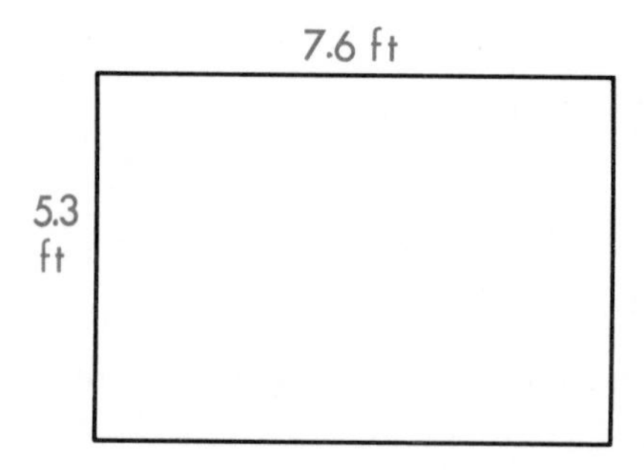

Fig. 3-10. What is the area?

The same sort of thing holds for the 7.6 ft. measurement:

The true measurement may be as *high* as 7.65 ft.

The true measurement may be as *low* as 7.55 ft.

Now suppose that the true measurements are 5.25 ft. by 7.55 ft. (Fig. 3-11). Then, multiplying the two sides, we get an area of 39.6375 sq. ft.

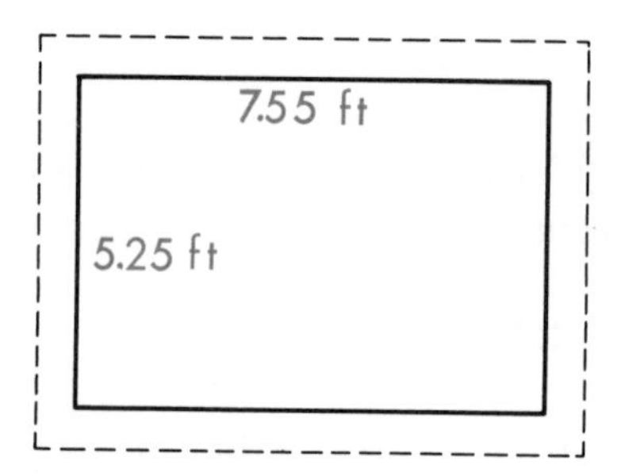

Fig. 3-11. Suppose the true measurement is 5.25 × 7.55 ft.

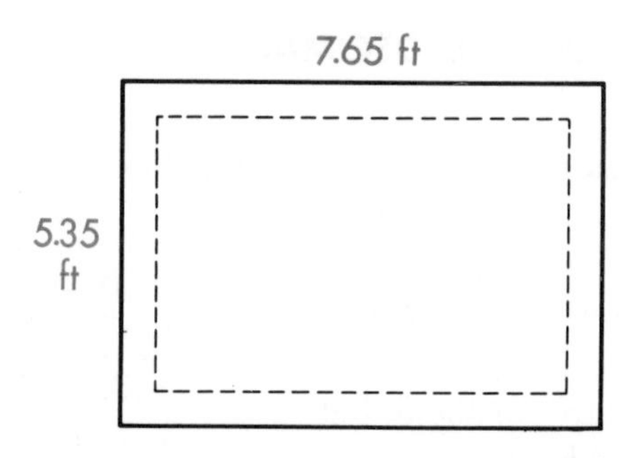

Fig. 3-12. Suppose the true measurement is 5.35 × 7.65 ft.

On the other hand, the true measurements may be 5.35 ft. by 7.65 ft. (Fig. 3-12). In this case, if the two numbers are multiplied the result is 40.9275 sq. ft.

This shows that when you measure a floor and get the values 7.6 ft. × 5.3 ft., the area may be anywhere between 39.6375 sq. ft. and 40.9275 sq. ft. *Actually, we can write only two figures.* It would be ridiculous to write the third figure. The correct answer is 5.3 ft. × 7.6 ft. = 40 sq. ft. This means that we are sure of the first figure and doubtful about the second.

In the same way, it is wrong to say that 2.78 in. × 3.64 in. is 10.1192 sq. in. The correct answer is 10.1 sq. in. (three figures).

Before telling you the rule, it is necessary to learn a new definition about numbers.

Significant Figures. These are all figures counting from left to right, but *omitting* the left-hand zeros. The number of significant figures is called the *accuracy* of the number.

Problem 1. What is the accuracy of each of the following numbers:

a 2.78 **b** 27.8 **c** 2780.5 **d** 0.2764
e 0.00081773

Solution: (*a*) 3 s.f. (*b*) 3 s.f. (*c*) 5 s.f. (*d*) 4 s.f. (*e*) 5 s.f.

Now you are ready for the rule.

Rule for Multiplying Approximate Numbers. When multiplying approximate numbers, the result is as *accurate* as the *least* accurate number.

Problem 2. Find 3.76 × 0.02258

Solution: 3.76 has 3 s.f., 0.02258 has 4 s.f., so the answer must have only 3 s.f.

$$3.76 \times 0.02258 = 0.0849008$$

Answer: 0.0849

Problem 3. Find the wattage of an electric motor which takes 115 volts and draws 0.2763 amperes (wattage = voltage × amperage).

Solution: 115 volts has 3 s.f., and 0.2763 has 4 s.f., so the answer must have only 3 s.f.

$$115 \text{ volts} \times 0.2763 \text{ amperes} = 31.7745 \text{ watts}$$

Answer: 31.8 watts

Problem 4. In a certain month, 28 men worked an average of 195.2 hours each. What was the total number of man-hours of labor?

Solution: This is a tricky problem, because 28 men is an *exact* number, obtained by counting. It does not limit the accuracy of the answer. Therefore, the answer has as many s.f. as 195.2, namely four s.f.

$$195.2 \text{ hours} \times 28 \text{ men} = 5465.6 \text{ man-hours}$$

Answer: 5466 man-hours

Problem 5. A machine has a rectangular side which measures 195.2 in. by 28 in. What is the area of the side?

Solution: This problem has the same numbers as Problem 4, but in this case 28 is really an approximate number. The result after multiplying is 5465.6 sq. in., but this has to be rounded off to two s.f. What shall we do? We write 5500 (2 s.f.) to indicate that only two significant figures are allowed. The other two zeros are necessary to act as *place-holders*. In other words, if they were omitted, the result would be 55, which is a ridiculous answer.

Answer: 5500 sq. in. (2 s.f.)

Problem 6. Find 87.72 yd. × 17.6 yd.

Solution: The result of multiplying is 1543.872.

Answer: 1540 sq. yd. (3 s.f.).

● Test: Section 6

Part A. Find the products of the following.

1 2.5 × 3.1   2 7.4 × 6.8   3 1.92 × 3.77

4 2.57 × 4.06   5 2.97 × 1.4   6 3.76 × 2.8

7 4.388 × 12.0   8 6.285 × 15.0   9 88.7 × 0.00812

10 73.1 × 0.00562

Part B.

1 Fifteen men worked an average of 37.6 hours on a certain job. What was the total number of man-hours?

2 Seventeen men worked an average of 44.8 hours on a certain job. What was the total number of man-hours?

3 Find the wattage of a TV set that takes 112 volts and draws 14.2 amperes.

4 Find the wattage of an air-conditioner rated at 207 volts and drawing 25.5 amperes.

5 How many miles are traveled in 120.5 hours if the rate of speed is 57.3 mph?

6 An airplane travels at 163.0 mph. for 70.8 hours. How far does it go?

7 DIVIDING APPROXIMATE NUMBERS

You may remember, from the previous chapter, that *division* is the same as *multiplying by a reciprocal.* The rules for division are exactly the same as those for multiplication.

Problem 1. A man used 11.2 gallons of gas traveling 205.8 miles. How many miles per gallon did he get on this trip?

Solution: After moving the decimal point, the division looks like the example shown below. The answer *appears* to be 18.375 mpg.

However, these are approximate numbers. The 11.2 is doubtful in the last figure, and may be anywhere between 11.15 and 11.25. The 205.8 may be anywhere between 205.75 and 205.85.

```
         18.375
   112)2058.000
       112
       ---
        938
        896
        ---
         420
         336
         ---
          840
          784
          ---
           560
           560
           ---
```

Suppose the true amounts are 205.85 and 11.15. Then:

$$205.85 \,/\, 11.15 = 18.461883 \ldots.$$

Suppose the true amounts are 205.75 and 11.25. Then:

$$205.75 \,/\, 11.25 = 18.288888 \ldots.$$

so that it would be wrong to write the answer 18.375, as though we were sure of all but the last figure.

Answer: The correct answer is *18.4 miles per gallon,* which indicates that the 18 is sure, but the .4 is in doubt.

Rule for Dividing Approximate Numbers. The general rule for division of approximate numbers is that the result is as *accurate* as the *least* accurate number.

Problem 2. To find the resistance (ohmage) of an electrical circuit, divide the voltage by the amperage. If the voltage is 75 volts, and the amperage is 23.63 amperes, how many ohms of resistance are there?

Solution: Divide 75 by 23.63. ***Answer:*** (Rounded off) 3.2 ohms.

In using the rule, be sure to decide whether the numbers are *exact* or *approximate*. In the following two problems, $\frac{1}{2}$ and 7 are exact numbers and are not limited by the rule.

Problem 3. Find $\frac{1}{2}$ of 2.7738 lb. **Answer:** 1.3869 lb.

Problem 4. Find 7×14.6 min. **Answer:** 102 min.

● Test: Section 7

1. Find half of 2.7618 pounds.
2. Find half of 3.8157 pounds.
3. Find a quarter of 27.8 miles
4. Find a quarter of 36.9 miles.
5. A family travels 3020.7 miles and uses 162.5 gallons of gas. How many miles are they getting per gallon?
6. A family travels 1764.8 miles and uses 151.0 gallons of gas. How many miles are they getting per gallon?
7. What is the resistance of a circuit if it uses 0.6236 amperes on a 110-volt line?
8. What is the resistance of a circuit if it uses 0.2570 amperes on a 220-volt line?
9. What is the rate of speed of a plane that travels 2012 miles in 3.27 hours?
10. What is the rate of speed of a plane that travels 1578 miles in 4.20 hours?

8 REINTRODUCING FRACTIONS

We have already mentioned that practical people usually avoid working with fractions because of the problem of *precision* and *accuracy*. However, there are times when it is convenient to use fractions, especially if the fractions are made up of small numbers like $\frac{2}{3}$ or $\frac{5}{7}$. No one would like to work with a fraction like $\frac{243}{377}$, and that kind is almost always changed to a decimal.

The following problems review *reduction of fractions.*

Problem 1. Reduce $\frac{3}{12}$ to lowest terms.

Solution: $\dfrac{\overset{1}{\cancel{3}}}{\underset{4}{\cancel{12}}} = \frac{1}{4}$ Divide the numerator and the denominator by the same number, 3.

Problem 2. Reduce $-\frac{8}{12}$ to lowest terms.

Solution: $-\dfrac{\overset{2}{\cancel{8}}}{\underset{3}{\cancel{12}}} = -\frac{2}{3}$ Divide the numerator and the denominator by the same number, 4.

Sometimes, people find it easier to reduce fractions in more than one step, as in the following:

Problem 3. Reduce $\frac{30}{36}$ to lowest terms.

Solution: $\boxed{\dfrac{\overset{15}{\cancel{30}}}{\underset{18}{\cancel{36}}}} = \frac{15}{18}$ $\boxed{\dfrac{\overset{5}{\cancel{15}}}{\underset{6}{\cancel{18}}}} = \frac{5}{6}$

The easiest thing to do with fractions is to multiply them.

Rule for Multiplying Fractions. To multiply two fractions means to multiply numerator by numerator and denominator by denominator.

Problem 4. Find $\frac{2}{3} \times \frac{4}{5}$.

Solution: $\frac{2}{3} \times \frac{4}{5} = \boxed{\dfrac{2 \times 4}{3 \times 5}} = \frac{8}{15}$

Sometimes the problem can be simplified as shown in the next problem.

Problem 5. Find $\frac{2}{3} \times (-\frac{6}{7})$.

Solution: Using the + − rule, the answer will be −.

$$\frac{2}{3} \times \left(-\frac{6}{7}\right) = -\boxed{\frac{2 \times \overset{2}{\cancel{6}}}{\underset{1}{\cancel{3}} \times 7}} = -\frac{4}{7}$$

The reason that you can reduce the fraction is that 2 × 6 is the same as 6 × 2 by the *commutative principle for multiplication.* In other words, $\frac{2}{3} \times \frac{6}{7}$ is the same as $\frac{6}{3} \times \frac{2}{7}$. But you do not have to worry too much about this. Just remember to *simplify multiplication problems as soon as you can.*

Problem 6. Find $(-\frac{10}{21}) \times (-\frac{28}{15})$.

Solution: Using the − − rule, the answer will be +.

$$\left(-\frac{10}{21}\right) \times \left(-\frac{28}{15}\right) = \boxed{\frac{\overset{2}{\cancel{10}} \times \overset{4}{\cancel{28}}}{\underset{3}{\cancel{21}} \times \underset{3}{\cancel{15}}}} = \frac{8}{9}$$

The only other problem that arises is one in which there are whole numbers such as 3, or mixed numbers such as $3\frac{1}{2}$. In each case, the first thing to do is to convert these to the usual fractional form.

Converting Whole Numbers to Fractions. Write the number as a fraction with a 1 in the denominator.

Problem 7. Convert 8 to fractional form.

Solution: $\frac{8}{1}$

Problem 8. Find $8 \times \frac{3}{2}$.

Solution: $8 \times \frac{3}{2} = \frac{8}{1} \times \frac{3}{2} = \boxed{\frac{\overset{4}{\cancel{8}} \times 3}{1 \times \underset{1}{\cancel{2}}}} = \frac{12}{1} = 12$

The following problems show how to convert a mixed number to fractional form:

Problem 9. Convert $4\frac{3}{5}$ to fractional form.

Solution: $4\frac{3}{5} = \frac{23}{5}$ → numerator is $(4 \times 5) + 3$ → denominator remains the same as original

Problem 10. Convert $8\frac{1}{7}$ to fractional form.

Solution: $8\frac{1}{7} = \frac{57}{7}$ → numerator is $(8 \times 7) + 1$ → denominator remains the same as the original

Converting Mixed Numbers to Fractional Form. The new denominator is the same as the old denominator. The new numerator is found by (1) multiplying the whole number by the old denominator, then (2) adding the old numerator to this.

Problem 11. Find $(-2\frac{1}{4}) \times (3\frac{1}{3})$.

Solution: Converting both mixed numbers to fractional form, we get:

$$\left(-\frac{9}{4}\right) \times \frac{10}{3}$$

Using the rule for multiplying fractions, the answer is $-\frac{15}{2}$, or $-7\frac{1}{2}$.

Test: Section 8

Part A. Reduce the fractions to lowest terms.

1 $\frac{4}{6}$ 2 $\frac{10}{15}$ 3 $\frac{9}{12}$ 4 $\frac{10}{14}$

5 $\frac{24}{27}$ 6 $\frac{12}{32}$ 7 $\frac{16}{36}$ 8 $\frac{10}{22}$

9 $\frac{40}{15}$ 10 $\frac{35}{10}$

Part B. Multiply the fractions.

1 $\frac{3}{4} \times \frac{5}{6}$ 2 $\frac{5}{7} \times \frac{2}{3}$ 3 $\frac{12}{32} \times \frac{40}{15}$

4 $\frac{16}{36} \times \frac{27}{24}$ 5 $\frac{10}{15} \times \frac{10}{22}$ 6 $\frac{10}{14} \times \frac{35}{10}$

7 $(-\frac{4}{6}) \times \frac{15}{40}$ 8 $\frac{9}{12} \times (-\frac{36}{16})$ 9 $(-\frac{6}{15}) \times (-\frac{5}{12})$

10 $(-\frac{7}{32}) \times (-\frac{16}{5})$

Part C. Convert to fractional form, then multiply.

1 $3 \times 4\frac{1}{2}$ 2 $6 \times 2\frac{1}{2}$ 3 $5 \times 8\frac{1}{10}$
4 $2 \times 5\frac{1}{4}$ 5 $1\frac{1}{3} \times 1\frac{1}{5}$ 6 $2\frac{2}{3} \times \frac{15}{40}$
7 $(-\ 2\frac{1}{2}) \times 2\frac{2}{5}$ 8 $4\frac{4}{7} \times (-\ \frac{5}{16})$ 9 $(-\ 1\frac{2}{5}) \times (-1\frac{1}{2})$
10 $(-\ 2\frac{1}{4}) \times (-\ \frac{24}{27})$

9 DIVIDING FRACTIONS

You already know that *dividing* is the same as *multiplying by a reciprocal,* so all the rules of the previous section apply. The following problems show how to use these rules.

Problem 1.
Find $\frac{2}{3} \div \frac{5}{4}$.

Solution:

$$\frac{2}{3} \div \frac{5}{4}$$

$$\frac{2}{3} \times \frac{4}{5}$$

$$\boxed{\frac{2 \times 4}{3 \times 5}}$$

$$\frac{8}{15}$$

Problem 2.
Find $\frac{2}{3} \div (-\ \frac{6}{7})$.

Solution:

$$\frac{2}{3} \times (-\ \frac{7}{6})$$

$$\boxed{-\frac{\overset{1}{\cancel{2}} \times 7}{3 \times \underset{3}{\cancel{6}}}}$$

$$-\ \frac{7}{9}$$

Problem 3.
Find $(-\ \frac{10}{27}) \div (-\ \frac{15}{28})$.

Solution:

$$(-\ \frac{10}{27}) \times (-\ \frac{28}{15})$$

$$\boxed{\frac{\overset{2}{\cancel{10}} \times \overset{4}{\cancel{28}}}{\underset{3}{\cancel{27}} \times \underset{3}{\cancel{15}}}}$$

$$\frac{8}{9}$$

Problem 4.
Find $(-\ 2\frac{1}{4}) \div 3$.

Solution:

$$(-\ \frac{9}{4}) \div (\frac{3}{1})$$

$$(-\ \frac{9}{4}) \times (\frac{1}{3})$$

$$\boxed{-\frac{\overset{3}{\cancel{9}} \times 1}{4 \times \underset{1}{\cancel{3}}}} \quad -\ \frac{3}{4}$$

Problem 5.

Find $8 \div \frac{3}{4}$

Solution:

$$\frac{8}{1} \div \frac{3}{4}$$

$$\frac{8}{1} \times \frac{4}{3}$$

$$\boxed{\frac{8 \times 4}{1 \times 3}}$$

$$\frac{32}{3}$$

$$10\frac{2}{3}$$

Problem 6.

Find $2\frac{1}{2} \times 3\frac{7}{8} \div \frac{5}{16}$.

Solution:

$$\frac{5}{2} \times \frac{31}{8} \times \frac{16}{5}$$

$$\boxed{\frac{\overset{1}{\cancel{5}} \times 31 \times \overset{\overset{1}{\cancel{2}}}{\cancel{16}}}{\underset{1}{\cancel{2}} \times \underset{1}{\cancel{8}} \times \underset{1}{\cancel{5}}}}$$

$$31$$

Test: Section 9

Part A. Find the quotients.

1 $\frac{3}{4} \div \frac{6}{5}$ 2 $\frac{2}{3} \div \frac{7}{5}$ 3 $\frac{40}{15} \div \frac{32}{12}$

4 $\frac{16}{36} \div \frac{24}{27}$ 5 $\frac{10}{15} \div \frac{22}{10}$ 6 $\frac{10}{35} \div \frac{10}{14}$

7 $(-\frac{4}{6}) \div (\frac{40}{15})$ 8 $(\frac{9}{12}) \div (-\frac{16}{36})$ 9 $(-\frac{6}{15}) \div (-\frac{12}{5})$

10 $(-\frac{5}{16}) \div (-\frac{7}{32})$

Part B.

1 $1\frac{1}{3} \div \frac{5}{6}$ 2 $2\frac{2}{3} \div 2\frac{2}{3}$ 3 $3\frac{2}{5} \div \frac{2}{5}$

4 $1\frac{7}{8} \div 2\frac{1}{2}$ 5 $4\frac{1}{16} \div 7\frac{1}{2}$ 6 $1\frac{3}{5} \div 1\frac{1}{2}$

7 $(-2\frac{3}{4}) \div 1\frac{1}{8}$ 8 $(5\frac{1}{3}) \div (-4\frac{4}{7})$ 9 $(-3\frac{4}{5}) \div (-38)$

10 $(-6) \div (-1\frac{3}{8})$

Part C.

1 $2\frac{2}{3} \times 3\frac{1}{9} \div 1\frac{1}{6}$ 2 $3\frac{3}{4} \times 1\frac{5}{8} \div 6\frac{1}{2}$

3 $5\frac{1}{7} \times 6\frac{3}{4} \div 1\frac{2}{7}$ 4 $6\frac{2}{3} \times 1\frac{5}{7} \div 4\frac{2}{7}$

5 $3\frac{1}{7} \times 2\frac{1}{2} \div 3\frac{3}{4}$ 6 $4\frac{1}{8} \times 2\frac{1}{2} \div 3\frac{1}{7}$

7 $(-2\frac{5}{8}) \times 1\frac{2}{3} \div 4\frac{2}{3}$ 8 $(1\frac{15}{16}) \times (-1\frac{1}{8}) \div (3\frac{7}{8})$

9 $(-5\frac{1}{2}) \times (-2) \div 3\frac{1}{7}$ 10 $(-10\frac{3}{4}) \times (-6) \div 28\frac{2}{3}$

10 COMBINING FRACTIONS

To understand the rules for combining (adding and subtracting) fractions, we must know what the two parts of a fraction mean.

Think of the fraction $\frac{3}{4}$. The *denominator*, 4, tells you that we are talking about the *denomination*, fourths or quarters. The *numerator* counts (or *enumerates*) how many of the denomination we have. The fraction, $\frac{3}{4}$, could just as well be written "3 fourths."

If two or more fractions have a *common denomination* (the same denominator), they are easy to add or subtract.

Problem 1. $\frac{3}{4} + \frac{9}{4}$, or, 3 fourths + 9 fourths.

Solution:

$$\frac{3}{4} + \frac{9}{4} = \frac{3+9}{4} = \frac{12}{4}$$

or 12 fourths

Combine the numerators
Keep the denominator

Problem 2. Take $\frac{5}{8}$ from $\frac{3}{8}$, or, 3 eighths − 5 eighths.

Solution: $\frac{3}{8} - \frac{5}{8} = \boxed{\frac{3-5}{8}} = -\frac{2}{8}$, or, (−2) eighths

Problem 3. $\frac{15}{16} - \frac{9}{16} + \frac{13}{16}$, or 15 sixteenths − 9 sixteenths + 13 sixteenths.

Solution: $\frac{15}{16} - \frac{9}{16} + \frac{13}{16} = \boxed{\frac{15-9+13}{16}} = \frac{19}{16}$

You notice that 3 fourths + 9 fourths "behaves" just like 3 pencils + 9 pencils. That is, you get 12 of them. The rule is:

Rule for Adding or Subtracting Fractions of the Same Denominations. Add or subtract the numerators. The denomination remains the same.

Now, what happens if the denominations are *not* the same? Simple; we make them the same. This must be done without changing the *value* of the fraction. For example, $\frac{1}{2}$ in. is the same as $\frac{2}{4}$ in., even if it does not look the same; and $1 is the same *in value* as four quarters, $\frac{4}{4}$, even if it does not seem to be.

The method we use to change the *form* of a fraction is based upon the:

Principle of 1 for Multiplication (1). Multiplying by 1 does not change the value of a number.

Now, if you use the fact that $1 = \frac{2}{2} = \frac{3}{3} = \frac{4}{4} = \frac{5}{5}$ etc., we can rewrite the principle as follows:

Principle of 1 for Multiplication (2). Multiplying by 1, or $\frac{2}{2}$, or $\frac{3}{3}$, or $\frac{4}{4}$, etc., does not change the value of a fraction.

Problem 4. Change $\frac{3}{4}$ mile to *eighths.*

Solution: $\frac{3}{4}$ mi. $\times$ $\boxed{\frac{2}{2}}$ $= \frac{6}{8}$ mi.

Problem 5. Change $\frac{2}{3}$ foot to *twelfths.*

Solution: $\frac{2}{3}$ ft. $\times$ $\boxed{\frac{4}{4}}$ $= \frac{8}{12}$ ft.

Now we have enough information to handle any kind of problem involving combining fractions, even if the denominations are not the same.

Problem 6. $\frac{2}{3} + \frac{5}{6}$.

Solution:

Long Way: CD = 6

Convert $\frac{2}{3}$ into sixths, first

$$\frac{2}{3} = \frac{2}{3} \times \frac{2}{2} = \frac{4}{6}$$

$$\frac{2}{3} + \frac{5}{6}$$

$$\frac{4}{6} + \frac{5}{6}$$

$$\frac{4 + 5}{6}$$

$$\boxed{\frac{\overset{3}{\cancel{9}}}{\underset{2}{\cancel{6}}}}$$

Short Way: CD = 6

$$\frac{2}{3} + \frac{5}{6}$$

3 → 6, 6 → 6

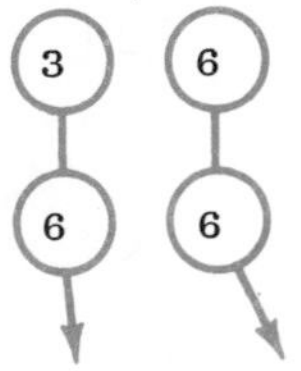

$$\frac{(2 \times 2) + (5 \times 1)}{6}$$

$$\frac{4 + 5}{6}$$

$$\boxed{\frac{\overset{3}{\cancel{9}}}{\underset{2}{\cancel{6}}}}$$

Both ways → $\frac{3}{2}$ = $1\frac{1}{2}$

The short way does the same thing as the long way but does it faster. It does not matter which you use. Here are the steps:

a. Divide the denominator into CD, a *common denominator*

b. Multiply the result by the numerator. This is the "new" numerator

Problem 7. $\frac{5}{6} + \frac{3}{8}$.

Solution: In this problem, both denominations will have to be changed. We could use forty-eighths (as in Method 1), but twenty-fourths (Method 2) will do the job just as well. When a *common denominator*, CD, is made *as small as possible*, the result is called *the least common denominator, LCD.* It makes no difference whether CD is an *LCD* or not, but it is a little shorter if you have an LCD, because then the result will not have to be reduced as often.

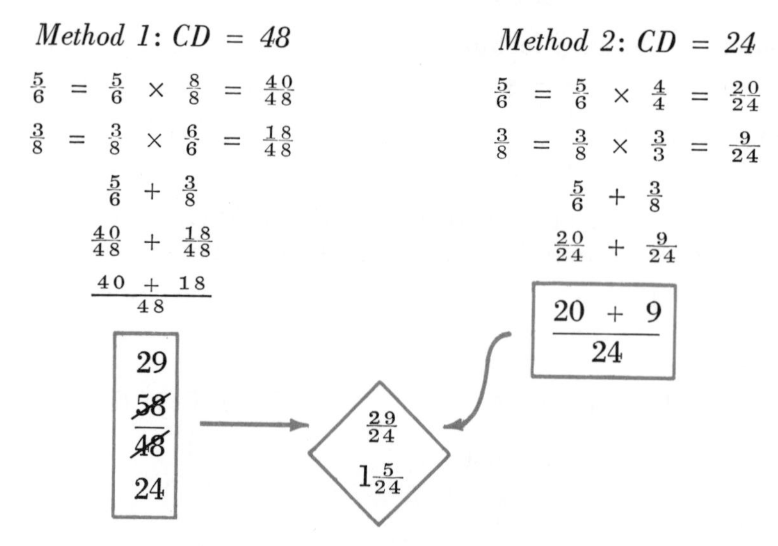

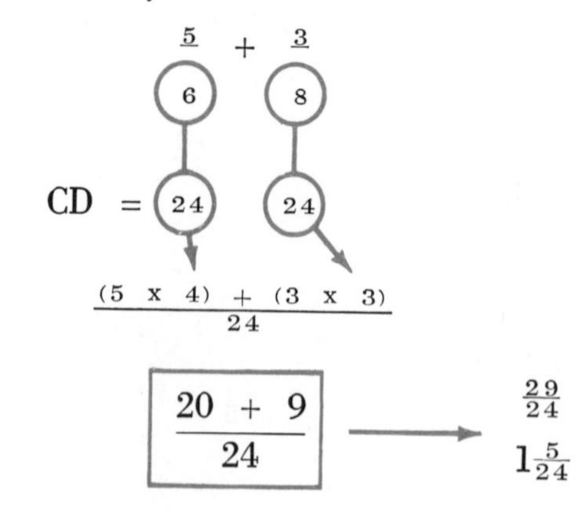

Problem 8. $\frac{2}{9} + 1\frac{1}{6} - \frac{5}{12}$.

Solution: All these denominations can easily be changed to thirty-sixths. Other possibilities are seventy-seconds and 108ths, but thirty-sixths are the LCD's.

Method 1 (Long Way): LCD = 36

$$\frac{2}{9} = \frac{2}{9} \times \frac{4}{4} = \frac{8}{36}$$

$$1\frac{1}{6} = \frac{7}{6} \times \frac{6}{6} = \frac{42}{36}$$

$$\frac{5}{12} = \frac{5}{12} \times \frac{3}{3} = \frac{15}{36}$$

$$\frac{2}{9} + \frac{7}{6} - \frac{5}{12}$$

$$\frac{8}{36} + \frac{42}{36} - \frac{15}{36}$$

$$\boxed{\frac{8 + 42 - 15}{36}}$$

$$\frac{35}{36}$$

Method 2 (Short Way): LCD = 36

$$\frac{2}{9} + \frac{7}{6} - \frac{5}{12}$$

LCD = 36 36 36

$$\frac{(2 \times 4) + (7 \times 6) - (5 \times 3)}{36}$$

$$\boxed{\frac{8 + 42 - 15}{36}}$$

$$\frac{35}{36}$$

Test: Section 10

Part A.

1 $\frac{3}{4} + 1\frac{1}{4}$

2 $1\frac{1}{2} + 3\frac{1}{2}$

3 $\frac{6}{7} + \frac{2}{7}$

4 $\frac{1}{9} + \frac{7}{9}$

5 $\frac{2}{3} - \frac{5}{3}$

6 $\frac{3}{5} - \frac{7}{5}$

7 $-\frac{8}{10} + \frac{7}{10}$

8 $-\frac{5}{3} + \frac{2}{3}$

9 $-\frac{9}{16} - \frac{7}{16}$

10 $-\frac{17}{32} - \frac{12}{32}$

Part B.

1 $\frac{1}{2} + \frac{3}{4}$

2 $\frac{1}{3} + \frac{5}{6}$

3 $\frac{2}{15} - \frac{1}{5}$

4 $\frac{3}{16} - \frac{1}{4}$

5 $-\frac{3}{8} - \frac{5}{16}$

6 $-\frac{5}{32} - \frac{1}{4}$

7 $\frac{1}{2} + \frac{1}{4} - \frac{1}{16}$

8 $\frac{3}{8} - \frac{5}{16} + \frac{1}{32}$

9 $-\frac{1}{7} + \frac{11}{14} - \frac{9}{28}$

10 $-\frac{3}{5} + \frac{7}{15} - \frac{11}{30}$

Part C.

1 $1\frac{3}{4} - 3\frac{2}{5}$

2 $2\frac{5}{6} - 5\frac{1}{7}$

3 $3\frac{5}{8} + 2\frac{5}{6}$

4 $2\frac{7}{8} + 1\frac{1}{6}$

5 $5\frac{11}{12} - 3\frac{13}{15} + 1\frac{7}{20}$

6 $3\frac{5}{12} - 1\frac{4}{15} + 2\frac{3}{20}$

7 $2\frac{1}{2} - 1\frac{1}{6} + 1\frac{3}{10}$

8 $3\frac{5}{6} - 3\frac{1}{2} + 2\frac{7}{10}$

9 $1\frac{4}{15} - 2\frac{5}{21} + 3\frac{1}{35}$

10 $2\frac{7}{15} - 3\frac{8}{21} + 1\frac{4}{35}$

4

TWO-DIMENSIONAL NUMBERS

When Mr. Al Gebra got off the train, he asked a bystander where the museum was.

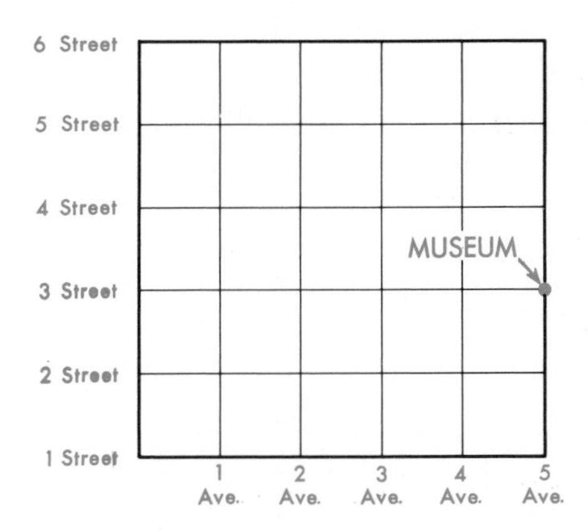

Fig. 4-1. Finding the museum at (5.3).

"Oh, that's on Fifth," said the man.

Al was puzzled. "Where?" he asked.

"On Fifth and Third," the man answered.

"Fifth and Third what?"

The bystander turned to him in surprise and said, "You must be a stranger in town. In this town, we always name the avenue first, then the street. The museum is on Fifth Avenue and Third Street."

"Thanks," said Mr. Gebra.

1 COORDINATES

A network of lines like those in Fig. 4-1 is called a *lattice* (lăt′ĭs). Any position in the lattice can be located by *two* numbers if you know which number refers to the horizontal lines and which number to the vertical lines. These two numbers are called *coordinates* (kō·ôr′dĭ·nāts) and are written in parentheses, like this: (5, 3). By agreement among mathematicians, the *first coordinate*, called the *x value*, locates the vertical line of the lattice, and the *second coordinate,* called the y *value,* locates the horizontal line of the lattice. Notice that you have to know both numbers to locate a specific point on the lattice. One number alone will only locate a line (such as Fifth Avenue, or Third Street).

Problem 1. Give the coordinates of the points marked A, B, C, D, and E, in the figure.

Solution:

A: (1, 2)
B: (2, 2)
C: (3, 1)
D: (3, 4)
E: (4, 3)

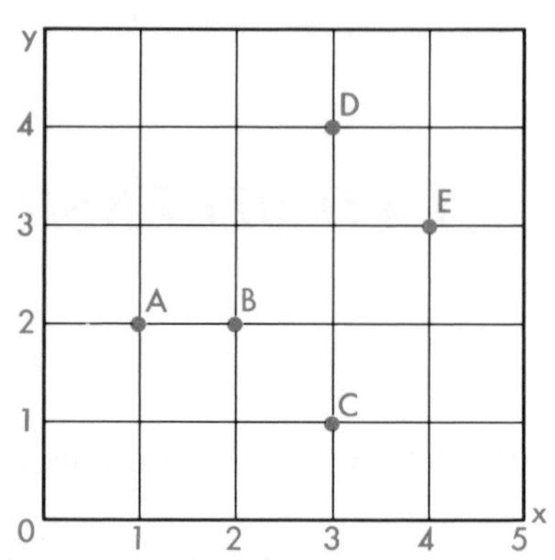

Problem 2. Make a lattice on graph paper and find the following:

a The line for an x value of 3

b The line for a y value of 4

c The point (2, 5).

Solution:

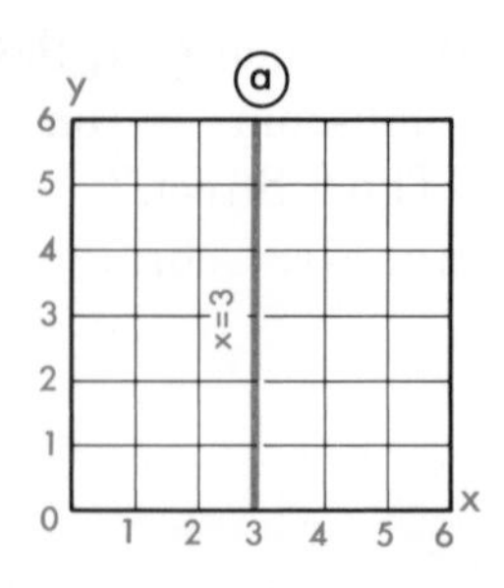

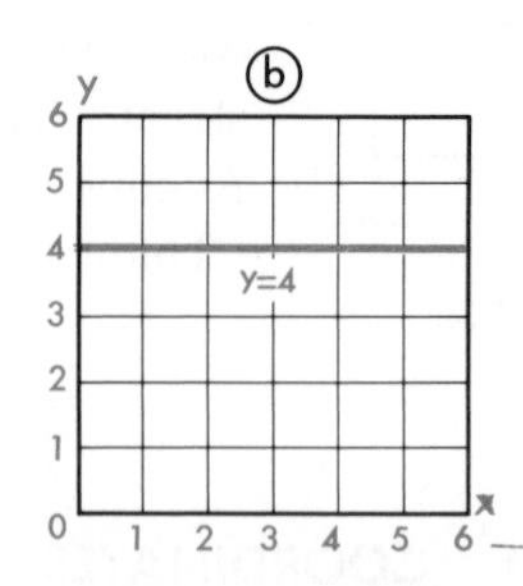

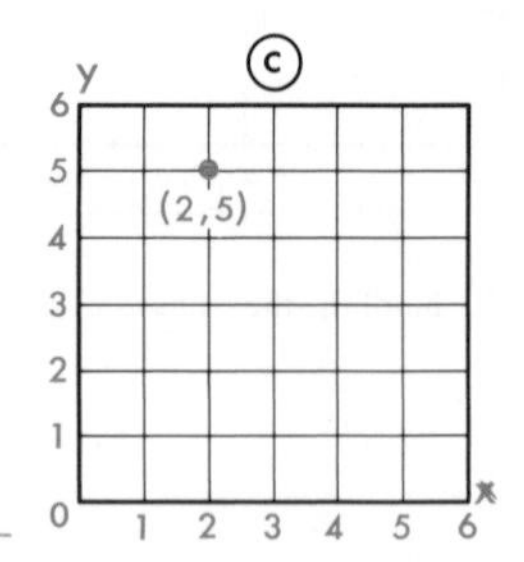

Notice that $x = 3$ means that the first coordinate, or the x value, is 3. If you just say, $x = 3$, and nothing else, you do not "fix" the value of y. The value of y depends on where you are on the $x = 3$ line. It is like saying, "I live on the Equator." This does not tell exactly where you live.

These illustrative problems are just samples of the possibilities of the coordinate method for locating lines and points. You can make the lattice as big as you like by using a greater number of lines (Fig. 4-2). The two number lines are called *axes.* The horizontal number line, called the *X-axis,* locates the vertical lines; the vertical number line, called the *Y-axis,* locates the horizontal lines. The point where the two axes meet is called the *origin.*

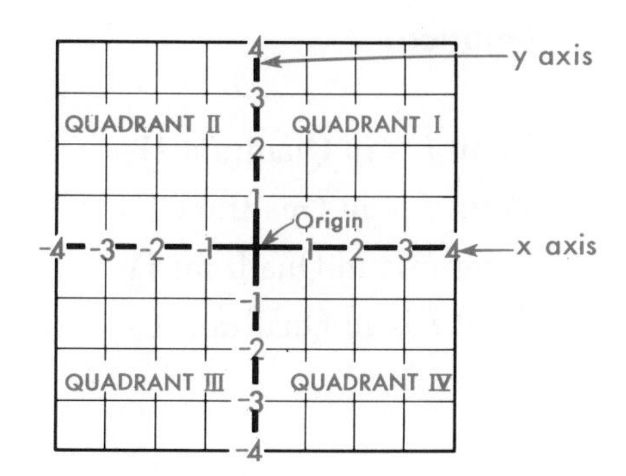

Fig. 4-2. The four quadrants.

Notice that the axes divide the paper into four parts called *quadrants.* These are numbered I, II, III and IV, using Roman numerals.

Problem 3. Find the following lines:

a $x = -2$ **b** $x = -1$ **c** $x = 0$
d $x = 2.5$ **e** $x = -3\frac{1}{3}$

Solution: (See diagram, at left, below)

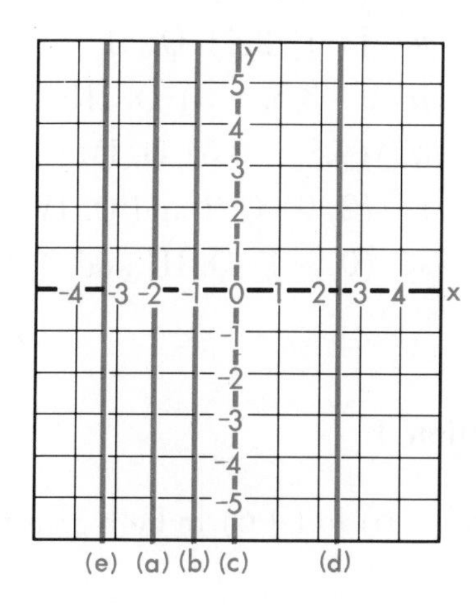

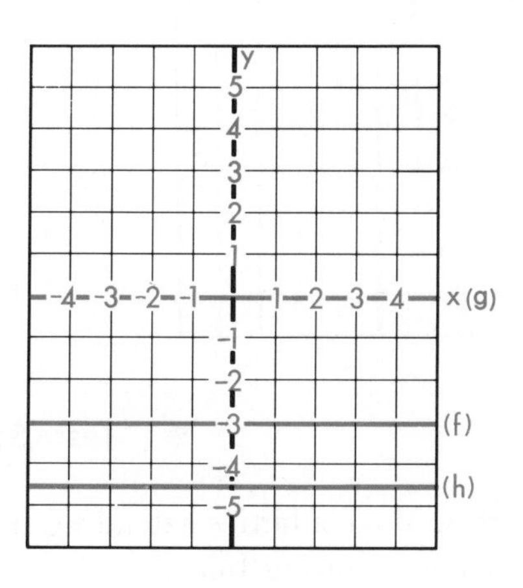

Problem 4. Find the following lines:

f $y = -3;$ **g** $y = 0;$ **h** $y = -4\frac{1}{2}$

Solution: (See diagram, at right, above)

Problem 5. Find the following points:

i $(-2, 3)$ **j** $(-4, -1)$ **k** $(2.5, -3)$ **l** $(3, 4)$

and name their quadrants.

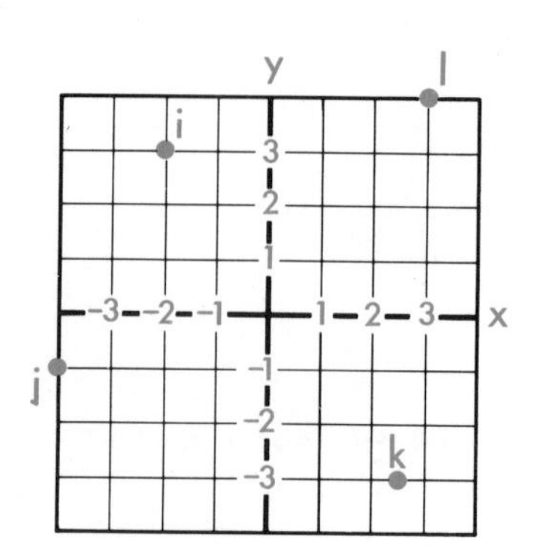

Solution:

Point i is in Quadrant II

Point j is in Quadrant III

Point k is in Quadrant IV

Point l is in Quadrant I

Problem 6. Find the coordinates of the points marked on the lattice in the figure and name the quadrants.

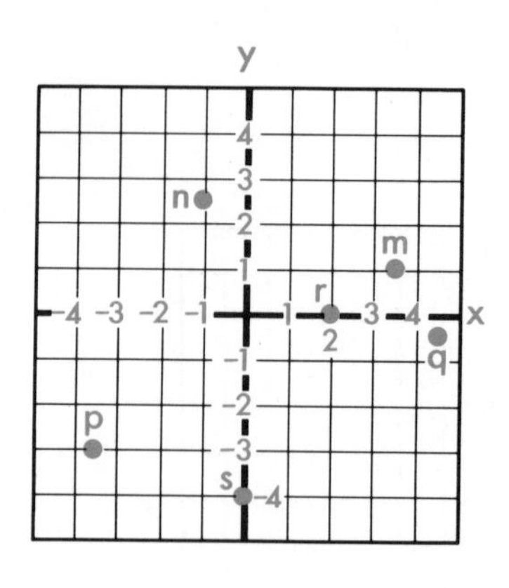

Solution:

m $(3.5, 1)$ Q. I

n $(-1, 2.5)$ Q. II

p $(-3.5, -3)$ Q. III

q $(4.5, -0.5)$ Q. IV

r $(2, 0)$ Q. I and Q. IV

s $(0, -4)$ Q. III and Q. IV

Test: Section 1

Part A. Make a lattice extending from (-6) to $(+6)$ in both directions, and draw the following lines:

1 $x = 3$ 2 $x = -2$ 3 $y = 5$

4 $y = -2$ 5 $x = 5.5$ 6 $x = -3.5$

7 $y = 4.5$ 8 $y = -1.5$ 9 $x = 0$

10 $y = 0$

Part B. Find the coordinates of each point in the following lattice, and name its quadrant.

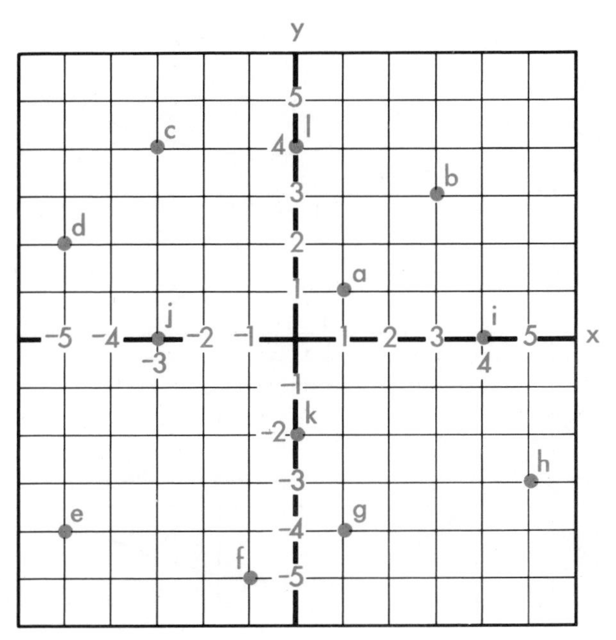

Part C. Make a lattice extending from (-6) to $(+6)$ in both directions, and find the following points. Name their quadrants.

1	$(2, 5)$	2	$(3, 4)$	3	$(-3, +5)$
4	$(-5, 6)$	5	$(4, 6)$	6	$(5, -5)$
7	$(-2, -3)$	8	$(-5, -6)$	9	$(-2, 0)$
10	$(0, -5)$	11	$(3.5, -4.5)$	12	$(-2.5, 5.5)$
13	$(-4.5, -2.5)$	14	$(-0.5, +0.5)$		

2 TABLES OF VALUES

Coordinates can be used to transmit information. In fact, you do this every day when you give an address. You may be surprised to learn that you can transmit a *picture* by means of coordinates! For example, Fig. 4-3 is a sketch of a fish. Suppose you wanted to "code" the sketch in number form. You could place a set of axes on it (Fig. 4-4) and read the coordinates of the most important points. Some of the points are $(-12, 0)$, $(-13, \pm 4)$, $(-8, 0)$, $(-5, \pm 2)$, and so on. $(-13, \pm 4)$ is the short way of writing two points: $(-13, +4)$, and $(-13, -4$.)

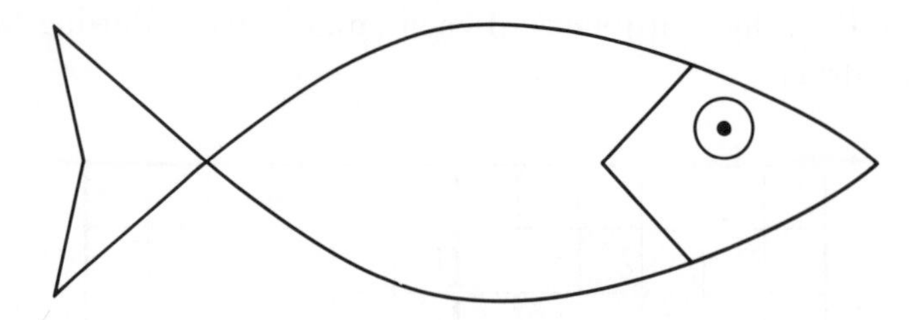

Fig. 4-3. A fish.

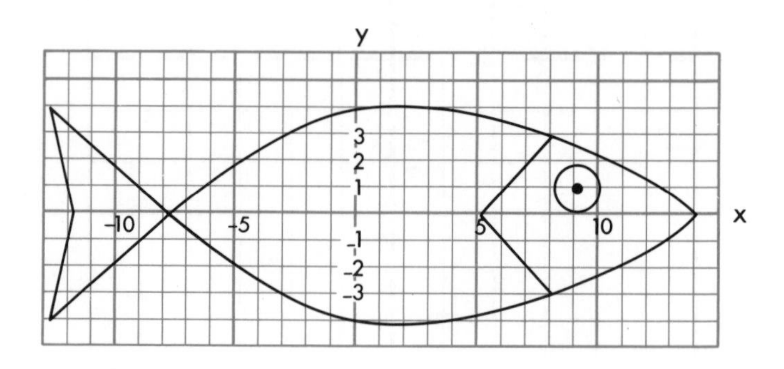

Fig. 4-4. Coding the fish.

A more convenient way to write these coordinates is in a table (see below) called a *table of values.*

x	-12	-13	-8	-5	-3	0	3	6	8	12.5	14
y	0	± 4	0	± 2	± 3	± 4	± 4	± 3.5	± 3	± 1	0

To complete the instructions, you would have to say, "Connect (8, 3) to (5, 0) and (5, 0) to (8, -3). Then draw a circle with radius 1, and center at (9, 1)."

In ordinary work, we use lattices with marks "one apart" as we have done so far. However, it is possible to change the distances provided all the distances agree on each *axis*. In Fig. 4-5, the marks have been "spread out" more on the *Y-axis*. This was done by letting *two* "boxes" equal one division. Notice how this distorts the picture.

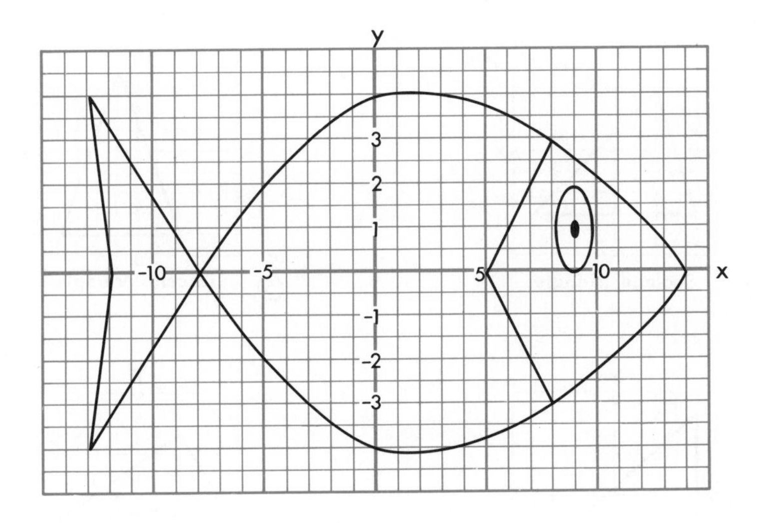

Fig. 4-5. A fat fish.

Test: Section 2

Part A. Write a table of values for each of the following sketches:

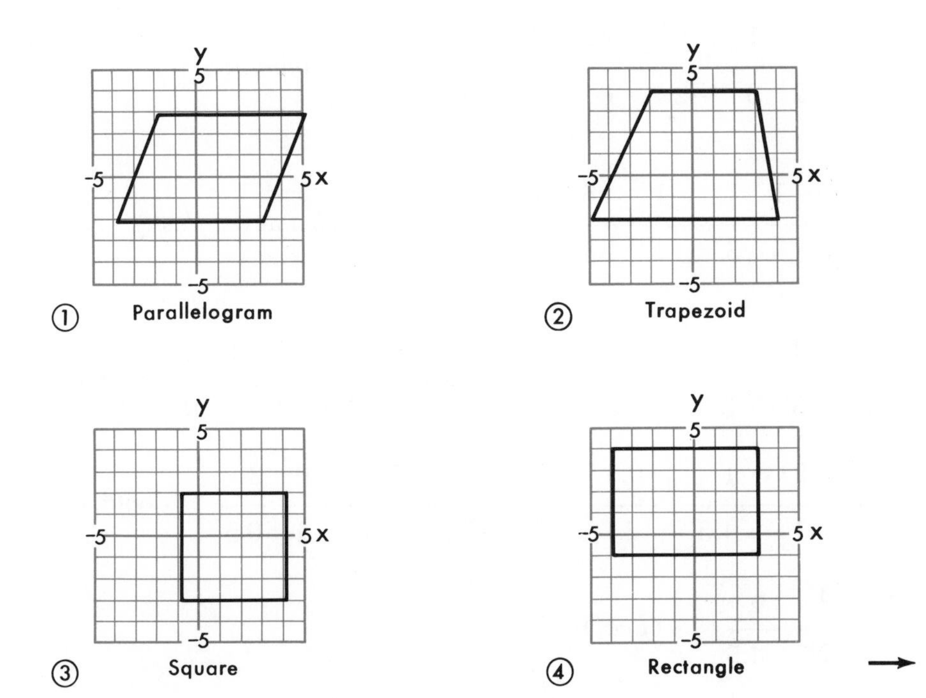

→

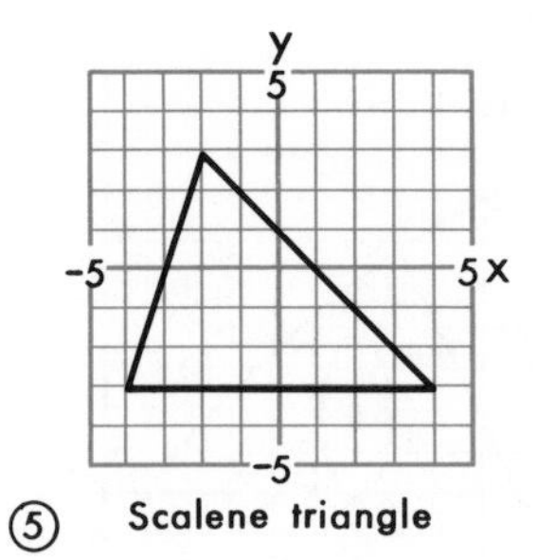

⑤ Scalene triangle

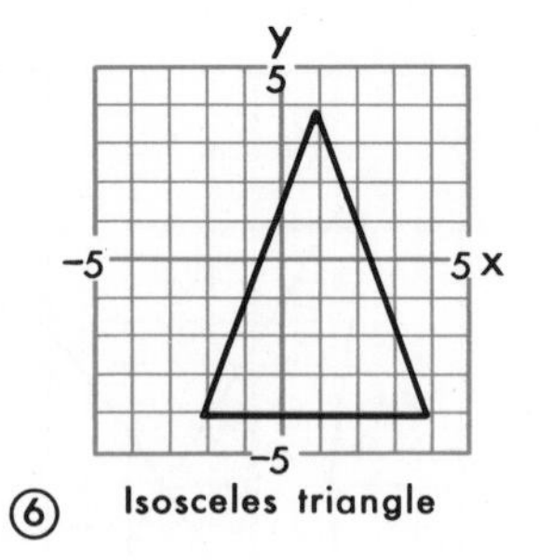

⑥ Isosceles triangle

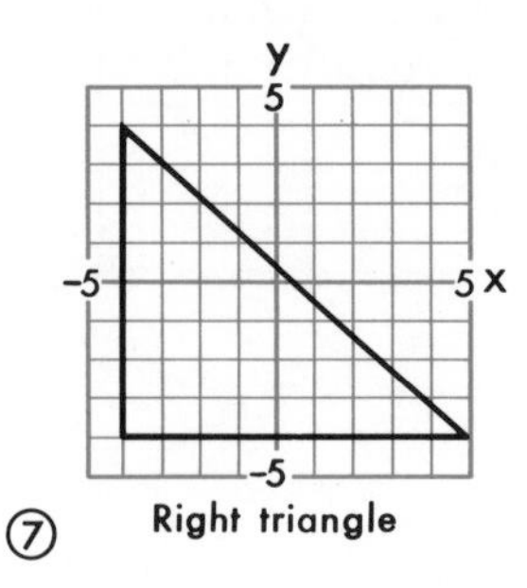

⑦ Right triangle

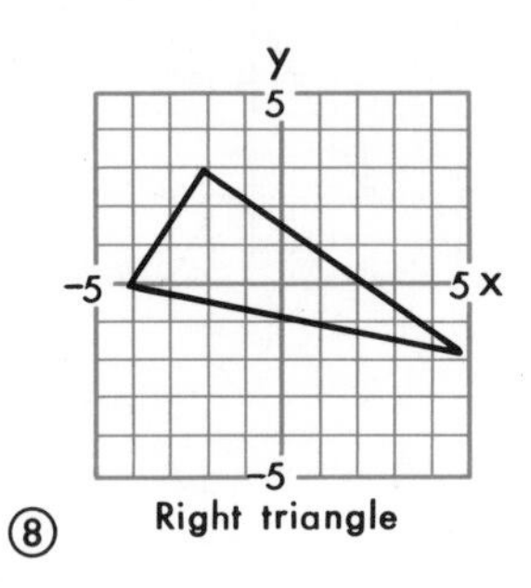

⑧ Right triangle

Part B. Using the following tables of values, sketch the figures.

1 (*Five-pointed star*)

x	-2	1	3	-2	$+3$	-2
y	-2	3	-2	1	1	-2

2 (*Erlenmeyer flask*)

x	0	1	1	-1	5	3	3	4
y	5	5	3	-4	-4	3	5	5

3

x	-4	-3	-2	-1	0	2	3	6	5	4	3
y	-5	-3.5	-2	0	1	2.5	3	4.5	3	1	0

(Contd.)

x	2	1	-0.5	-2	-4	-2	0	2
y	-1	-1.5	-2	-3	-5	-2.5	-1	0.5

(Contd.)

x	4	6
y	2.5	4.5

(*Leaf*)

4

x	-4.5	-4.5	1.5	1	1.5	4	5	4	2	3
y	-3.5	-4	-1	-0.5	-1	0	1	4	3	1

(Contd.)

x	2.5	2	1	-4.5
y	0.5	0	-0.5	-3.5

(Pipe)

Part C. Make a lattice extending from -10 to $+10$ on the X-axis and from -15 to $+15$ on the Y-axis. All the following tables are for a single picture of a girl's face.

1

x	-3	-4	$-5\frac{1}{4}$	$-5\frac{3}{4}$	-5	-2	0	2	3	4
y	-4	-3	0	6	$7\frac{1}{2}$	$8\frac{1}{2}$	$8\frac{1}{4}$	8	$7\frac{1}{2}$	5

(Contd.)

x	4	5	4	3	0	$-2\frac{1}{2}$	-3	$-5\frac{1}{2}$
y	2	1	-1	$-2\frac{1}{2}$	$-4\frac{1}{2}$	$-4\frac{1}{2}$	-4	-2

(Contd.)

x	-7	-8	$-6\frac{1}{2}$	-6	$-5\frac{1}{4}$	-4	0	3	5
y	0	$2\frac{1}{2}$	5	7	8	$10\frac{1}{2}$	12	$11\frac{1}{2}$	11

(Contd.)

x	$6\frac{1}{2}$	$6\frac{1}{2}$	9	8	8	6	$4\frac{1}{2}$	4
y	9	7	$2\frac{1}{2}$	0	$-1\frac{1}{2}$	-3	-3	-1

(Outline of face)

2

x	-5	$-4\frac{1}{2}$	-3
y	4	$4\frac{1}{2}$	4

(Right eyebrow)

3

x	0	$1\frac{1}{2}$	$3\frac{1}{2}$
y	$4\frac{1}{2}$	$4\frac{3}{4}$	$4\frac{1}{2}$

(Left eyebrow)

4

x	-5	-4	-3	$-2\frac{1}{2}$	$-3\frac{1}{2}$	$-4\frac{1}{2}$	-5
y	3	$3\frac{1}{2}$	$3\frac{1}{2}$	3	$2\frac{1}{2}$	$2\frac{1}{2}$	3

(Right eye)

5

x	$-\frac{1}{4}$	1	2	$2\frac{1}{2}$	1	$-\frac{1}{4}$
y	3	4	$3\frac{1}{2}$	3	$2\frac{3}{4}$	3

(Left eye)

6

x	$-3\frac{1}{2}$	$-2\frac{3}{4}$	-2	$-\frac{1}{2}$	$\frac{1}{2}$	$-3\frac{1}{2}$	$-2\frac{1}{2}$
y	$-1\frac{1}{2}$	$-\frac{1}{2}$	-1	$-\frac{1}{2}$	$-1\frac{1}{2}$	$-1\frac{1}{2}$	-2

(Contd.)

x	$-1\frac{1}{2}$	$\frac{1}{2}$
y	-2	$-1\frac{1}{2}$

(*Mouth*)

3 COMPARISON GRAPHS

You have seen that a picture can be described using pairs of numbers to locate points. Sometimes people want to make a picture of a *situation* instead of a thing. For example, the table of values in Table I, tells about a certain important situation:

Table I: Defense Expenditures of the Five Great Powers in 1956, in millions of U.S. Dollars

Country	*Millions of Dollars*
United States	39,968
British Commonwealth	6,435
France	3,723
West Germany	2,300
USSR	24,450

Let us try to make a picture of this situation. First, we "round off" the numbers so that the *largest* number has three significant figures. This is done in Table II.

Table II: Defense Expenditures (Rounded Off)

Country	*Millions of U.S. Dollars*
United States	40,000
British Commonwealth	6,400
France	3,700
West Germany	2,300
USSR	24,500

The second step is to plan our graph so that the vertical axis has 40 divisions (the first two significant figures of the largest number in the table). Then we make five divisions on the horizontal axis (Fig. 4-6).

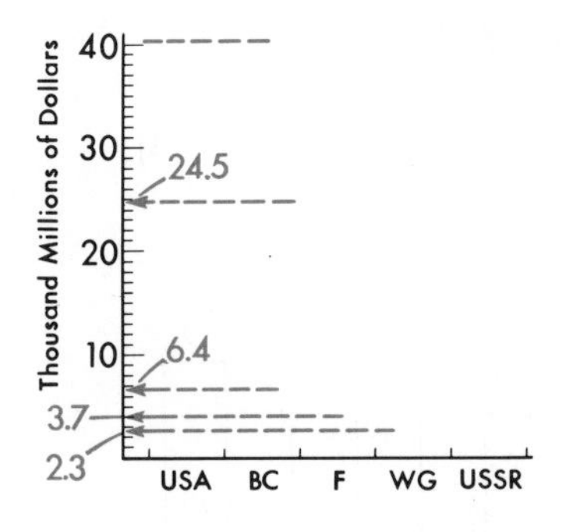

Fig. 4-6. Beginning the bar graph.

Fig. 4-7. The bar graph completed.

At 40,000 million, we now draw a horizontal line segment covering the United States. For the British Commonwealth, we need 6400 million. We find the 6000 million and the 7000 million marks on the vertical axis, and guess at the 6400 million mark. Then, over the space for the British Commonwealth, we draw a line segment. We do the same thing for the other countries. Lastly, we complete the *bars* by closing the "boxes" and filling in the spaces. The completed figure (Fig. 4-7) is called a *bar graph.*

Problem. Make a bar graph showing the life span of the animals as shown in the following table:

Bear:	20 years	*Hippopotamus*:	30 years
Dog:	12 years	*Lion*:	10 years
Chicken:	8 years	*Monkey*:	15 years
Elephant:	40 years	*Mouse*:	3 years

Solution:

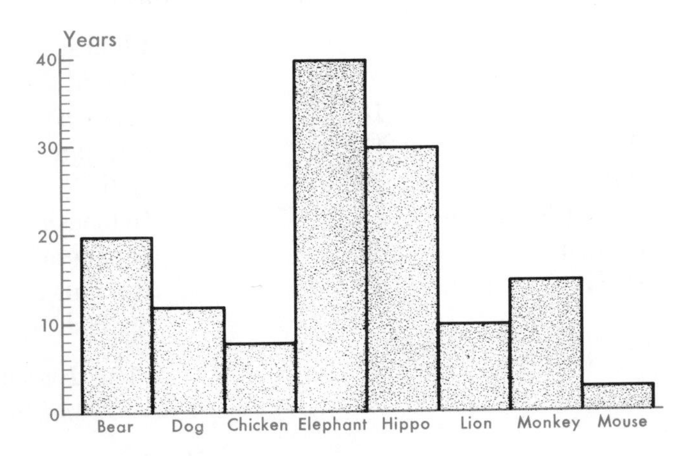

Test: Section 3

Part A. What story does each of the following bar graphs tell?

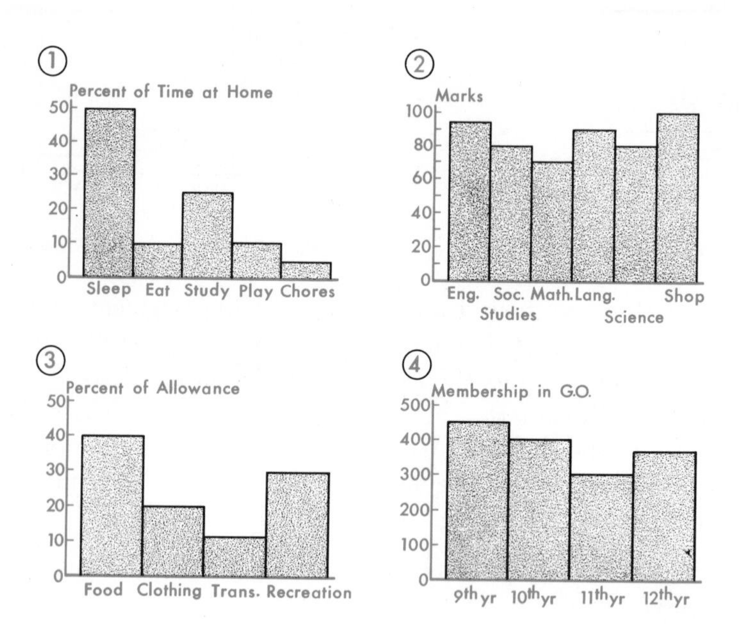

Part B. Make a bar graph of the information tabulated below.

1 The average number of minutes of working time required to make enough money to buy one quart of milk in various countries.

U.S.	7
France	18
West Germany	13
Italy	29
United Kingdom	15
Mexico	33
USSR	41

2 The number of people (in millions) who speak each of the following languages of the world.

Chinese	475
Dravidian	95
English	265
German	90
Indic	415
Indonesian	105
Japanese	90
Russian	200
Spanish	150

(*Use 1 vertical mark to = 20 million people.*)

Part C. In the following, (*a*) make a new table by rounding off the largest number to three significant figures; (*b*) make a bar graph.

1 Enrollment in Full-Time Day Schools in 1956

Elementary	26,256,943
Secondary	7,098,225
College	2,514,712

(*Use 1 million for each vertical mark.*)

2 Air Force Monthly Base Pay for Enlisted Personnel

Airman, Basic	$83.20
Airman, 3rd class	85.80
Airman, 2nd class	99.37
Airman, 1st class	122.30
Staff Sgt.	145.24
Tech. Sgt.	175.81
Master Sgt.	206.39

(*Use 10 dollars for each vertical mark.*)

3 Make a bar graph of the assumed six months circulation figures of the following magazines:

Boys' Life	1,466,041
Life	5,738,226
Mechanix Illustrated	1,040,989
Photoplay	1,435,551
Readers Digest	10,718,943
Seventeen	1,014,832
Sports Afield	928,356
TV Guide	4,218,832

(*Use 1 million for each vertical mark.*)

4 TIME-CHANGE GRAPHS

Instead of comparing *different* things, we may wish to see how a single item (such as stocks, or the weather) changes in a period of time. Sometimes this is of great value in prediction.

For example, the graph of Fig. 4-8 shows how Babe Ruth's home run record went up and down in the years from 1914 to 1935. You can see on the graph that in 1918 (horizontal axis), Babe Ruth hit 11 home runs. In 1928, he hit 54 home runs. More important, you can see from the shape of the graph that by 1919 or 1920 it was very clear that Babe Ruth was probably going to be a great hitter — and by 1933 it was very clear that his great hitting was behind him!

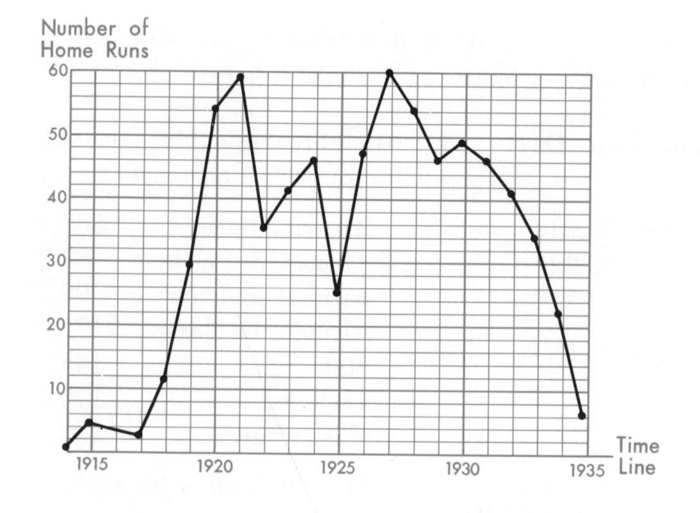

Fig. 4-8. Babe Ruth's major league home run record (regular season only).

Let us find out how to make these important graphs. The following table gives figures for the population of the USA in various years:

Year	*Population*
1650	51,700
1700	275,000
1750	1,207,000
1800	5,308,000
1850	23,192,000
1900	75,995,000
1950	151,132,000

To make a graph, we follow the usual first step of rounding off the numbers until the largest one has only three significant figures:

Year	*Population*
1650	–
1700	–
1750	1 million
1800	5 million
1850	23 million
1900	76 million
1950	151 million

The numbers for 1650 and 1700 are so small compared with the largest one (151 million) that they cannot be shown on the graph. They do not have enough significant figures.

Since the largest number is 151 million, we make each vertical division 10 million so that the height of the graph will be a little over 15 boxes. The

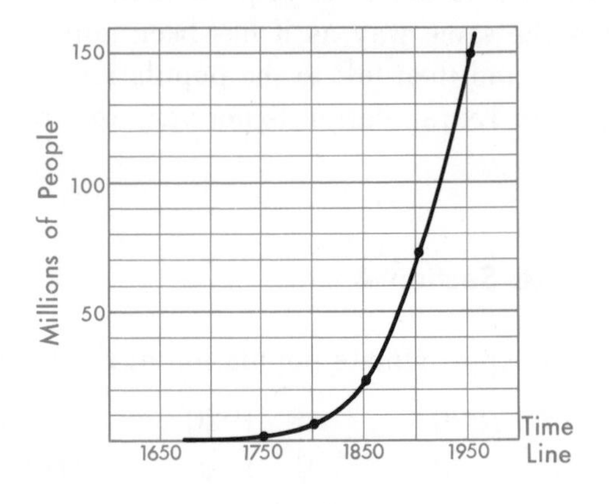

Fig. 4-9. The growth of population of the USA from 1650 to 1950.

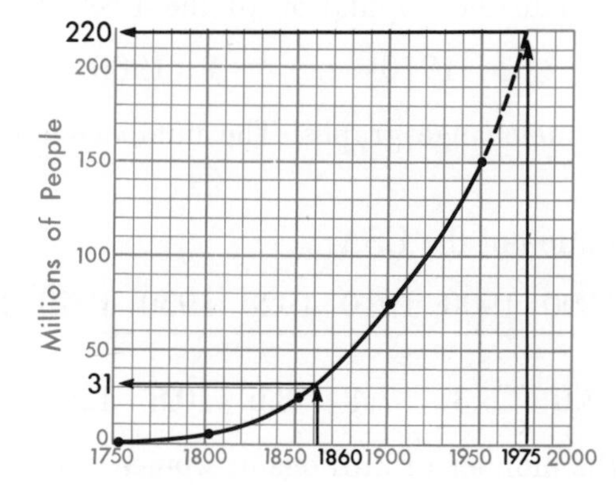

Fig. 4-10. Interpolation and extrapolation.

base line is marked off for years; this is the *time line*. Now the points (1750, 1), (1800, 5), are located as shown in previous sections on coordinates.

It is customary for mathematicians to make a "smooth" curve for "growth" graphs, instead of using straight-line segments as was done with the Babe Ruth figures. The result is shown in Fig. 4-9.

A curve like this is very useful for getting additional information. In Fig. 4-10, the curve has been drawn more carefully because it is going to be used to read information instead of just giving a general picture of the situation.

Suppose you wish to read from the graph the population in 1860. Then you find 1860 on the time line, "climb up" to the curve, then read across to the population line. The answer is about 31 million. (The actual census figure in 1860 was 31,443,321.) This process is called *interpolation* (ĭn·tûr′pô·lā′shŭn). Another question is, "What will the population be in 1975?" This process of prediction is called *extrapolation* (ĕks·trȧ·pôlā′shŭn) and is used by mathematicians known as *statisticians,* to help predict the need for housing, schools, and hospitals. To do this kind of prediction, *extend* the graph (Fig. 4-10) so that it goes the same way as it has been going. Now, reading from 1975 up to the curve, and then left to the population line, the answer comes out about 220 million. Extrapolation is not very reliable, but it is better than nothing.

Test: Section 4

Part A. Using Fig. 4-10, find the approximate population of the USA in:

1 1770 2 1820 3 1870 4 1920 5 1930
6 1790 7 1890 8 1940 9 1830 10 1910

Part B. Using Fig. 4-10, estimate the population of the USA in:

1 1960 2 1965 3 1970 4 1980

Part C. Make the following time-change graphs. The numbers have already been rounded off.

1 Women in the working population of the USA:

Time	1870	1880	1890	1900	1910	1920	1930	1940	1950
Millions of Women	1.9	2.6	4.0	5.3	7.4	8.6	10.8	12.8	16.5

2 From your graph, estimate the number of millions of women working in 1935.

3 From your graph, predict how many women will be working in 1970.

4 Number of TV sets in use in the USA since 1948:

Time	1948	1949	1950	1951	1952	1953	1955	1956
Millions of TV sets	1.0	4.0	10.5	15.8	22.2	28.0	39.4	43.9

5 From your graph, estimate the number of millions of TV sets in use in 1954.

6 From your graph, estimate the number of TV sets in use in 1960.

5 SHOWING DISTRIBUTION BY GRAPHS

So far, we have discussed four uses of graphs: locating points, reproducing a picture, comparing different items, and showing time changes. A fifth use is to show how often something happens. This is called a *frequency graph.*

For example, suppose a merchandise manager in a department store wishes to order mens' shoes ranging in size from 6 to 13, including half-sizes. One way of doing this might be to order an equal number of each size: 50 pairs of size 6, 50 pairs of size $6\frac{1}{2}$, 50 pairs of size 7, and so on, up to 50 pairs of size 13.

But this would be foolish! Very few men wear size 6 or size 13. Most men wear size 9 or 10. The store should "stock up" on these common sizes and just get a few pairs of the large and small sizes.

The merchandise manager now asks the buyer in the shoe department to check his sales records and let him know what percentage of the customers are buying each size. The buyer goes over the records of 7934 shoe sales and makes the following table for himself:

Size	*Pairs Sold*	*Percent of Total*
6	220	2.8
$6\frac{1}{2}$	260	3.3
7	300	3.8
$7\frac{1}{2}$	395	5.0
8	515	6.5
$8\frac{1}{2}$	721	9.1
9	982	12.4
$9\frac{1}{2}$	1127	14.2
10	986	12.4
$10\frac{1}{2}$	723	9.1
11	516	6.5
$11\frac{1}{2}$	398	5.0
12	303	3.8
$12\frac{1}{2}$	264	3.3
13	224	2.8
	7934	100.0

The "per cent" figures were arrived at by dividing. For example, 220 divided by 7934 = 2.8%.

The graph for a *frequency distribution* may be drawn either with straight-line segments (Fig. 4-11), or with a smooth curve (Fig. 4-12). The one drawn with straight-line segments is called a *frequency polygon.* That drawn

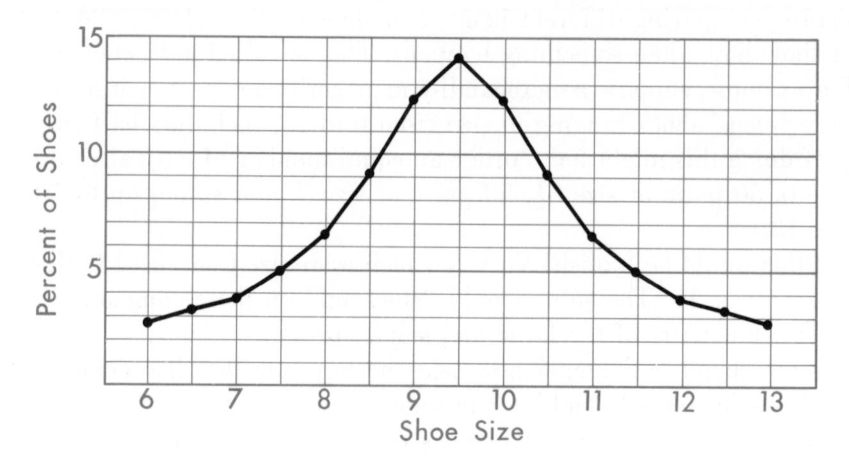

Fig. 4-11. A frequency polygon for shoe sizes.

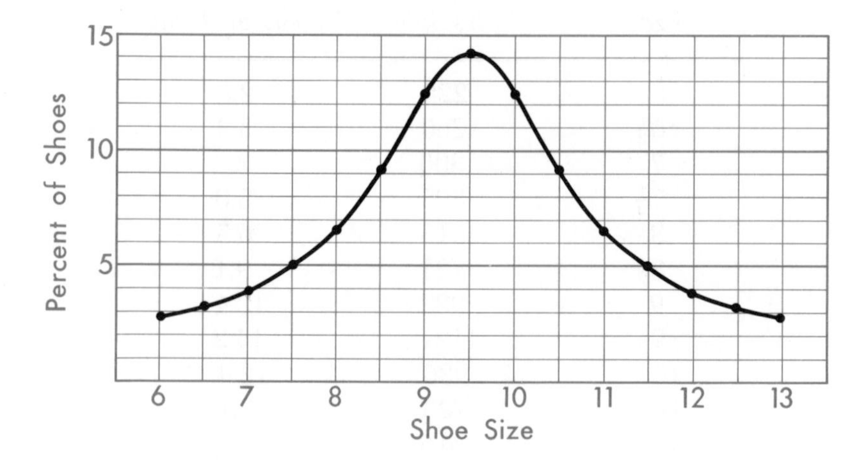

Fig. 4-12. A normal curve for shoe sizes.

with a smooth curve is called a *normal curve* if it is high in the middle and low at both ends. The number under the highest point is called the *mode.*

Using the table or the graph, the merchandise manager can now decide how many pairs of each size to order. For example, if he wishes to order 1000 pairs of shoes, he should order 28 pairs of size 6, 33 of size $6\frac{1}{2}$, and so on.

Problem 1. If the buyer wishes to order only 250 pairs of shoes, how many should be size $8\frac{1}{2}$?

Solution: $9.1\% = 0.091$

$250 \times 0.091 = 22.750$

Rounding off, he should order 23 pairs of size $8\frac{1}{2}$.

In some cases, the thing being measured has so many different values that this kind of table or graph is not very useful. In such a case, the measurements are *grouped* into *intervals*, as in the following problem.

Problem 2. After a class test, a teacher made a tally of the results and found the following to be true:

Interval	*Tally*	*Number*
40 to 49	//	2
50 to 59	///	3
60 to 69	~~////~~	5
70 to 79	~~////~~ ~~////~~	10
80 to 89	~~////~~ //	7
90 to 100	///	3

To graph this, she found the *middle* of each interval first. This is easy to do. The first interval begins at 40, and the next one begins at 50. The middle, or *midpoint*, is at 45. The new table looks like this:

Midpoints	45	55	65	75	85	95
Number	2	3	5	10	7	3

The frequency polygon for this table is shown in Fig. 4-13.

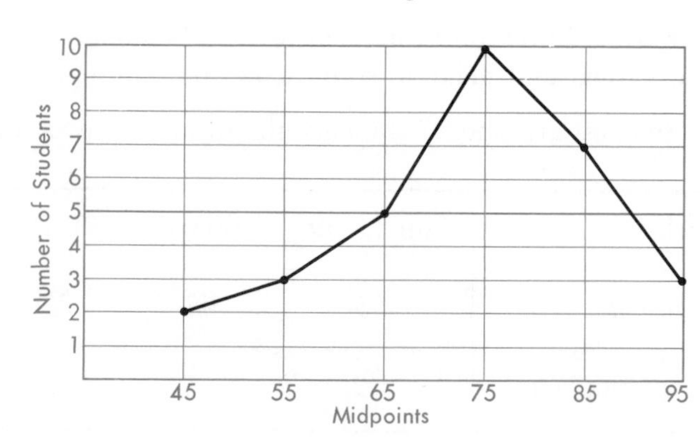

Fig. 4-13.

Frequency polygon using midpoints.

Test: Section 5

Part A. Using the table for shoe sizes, work out how many pairs of shoes in each of the sizes named below should be ordered for a total order of 175 pairs when 29 pairs have already been decided upon.

1 Size 7 2 Size 8 3 Size $8\frac{1}{2}$ 4 Size 9
5 Size $9\frac{1}{2}$ 6 Size 10 7 Size $10\frac{1}{2}$ 8 Size 11
9 Size $11\frac{1}{2}$ 10 Size 12

Part B. Using the tables given, make a graph for each of the following:

1 In a group of 1000 men, the heights in inches were distributed as follows:

Inches of height	61	63	65	67	69	71	73
Number of men	74	110	200	218	202	116	80

2 A person's intelligence is measured by a test, and the number used is called an *I.Q.* The following table shows the distribution of I.Q. scores in a certain school in the United States of America. Make a graph using the midpoints shown.

I.Q. Interval	65-74	75-84	85-94	95-104	105-114	115-124	125-134
Midpoint	*70*	*80*	*90*	*100*	*110*	*120*	*130*
Percent of Students	2	9	22	33	22	9	2

Part C. In the following, convert the "number" of students to "per cent" by dividing, and make a graph using the midpoints of the intervals.

1 In a test given to 27 students, the results were as follows:

Mark	up to 59	60-69	70-79	80-89	90-100
Midpoint	*55*	*65*	*75*	*85*	*95*
No. of Students	2	5	10	9	1

2 The following table gives the ages of the first 34 Presidents of the United States at their first inaugurations. Make a graph using the midpoint of the intervals, in percent form.

Age	41-45	46-50	51-55	56-60	61-65	66-70
Midpoint	$43\frac{1}{2}$					
No. of Presidents	1	7	11	9	5	1

6 DIRECT VARIATION

We have already noticed that when one thing changes (such as time) another thing (say number of home runs) may also change along with the first. Instead of mentioning "time" and "number of home runs," we might have mentioned "age" and "salary," or "height" and "weight." The situation where one thing appears to depend on another is so important that mathematicians have built a great deal of theory around it.

Let us think of one set of numbers, which we will call y numbers, which depends on some other set of numbers, which we will call x numbers. For example, here are two sets of numbers which are related:

Example

x	...	0	1	2	3	4	5	...	15	...	1257	...
y	...	0	2	4	6	8	10	...	30	...	2514	

In this example, you can see that the y number is always twice the x number. The mathematician writes this as a *rule* or *formula*:

$$y = 2x$$

Notice that this rule associates *pairs* of numbers: 0 with 0, 1 with 2, 2 with 4, 3 with 6, and so on. These can be written: (0, 0), (1, 2), (2, 4), (3, 6), and so on. If these are considered to be coordinates, they can be drawn on a graph (Fig. 4-14). The graph turns out to be a straight line. This straight line is called the *graph of the formula*: $y = 2x$.

We started with the idea that the value of the y number is double the value of the x number. Let us see how the graph can be used to find a y number if we know the x number. Suppose the x number is $1\frac{1}{2}$, or $x = 1\frac{1}{2}$. Find the

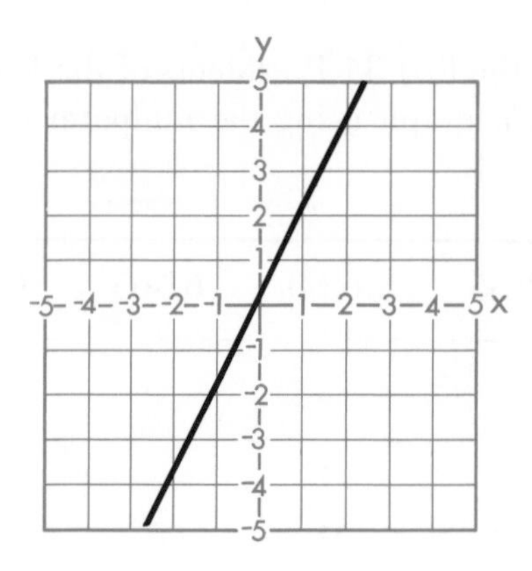

Fig. 4-14. $y = 2x$

Fig. 4-15. Finding a y number.

line for $x = 1\frac{1}{2}$ on the X-axis (Fig. 4-15), then read up to the graph of $y = 2x$ (Fig. 4-15), and across to the Y-axis. The correct y number is 3 for this x number.

Suppose we go *above* the graph (Fig. 4-16) to position A. Then the value for y will be 4. In other words, y will not be twice x at point A. It will be *greater* than $2x$. The mathematician writes this as

$$y > 2x \qquad (y \text{ is } \textit{greater} \text{ than } 2x)$$

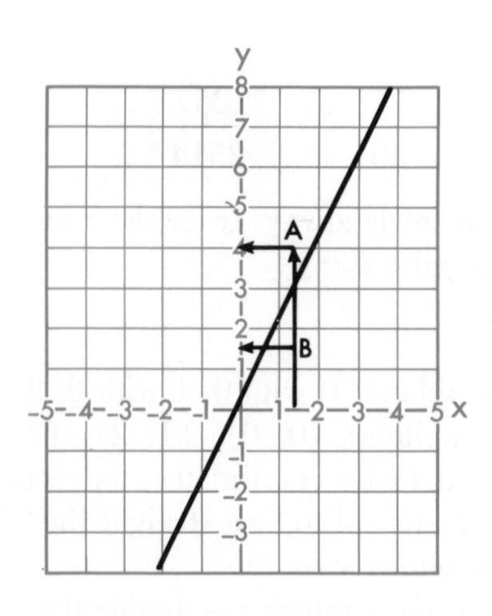

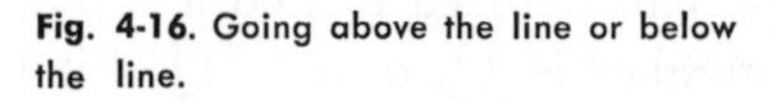
Fig. 4-16. Going above the line or below the line.

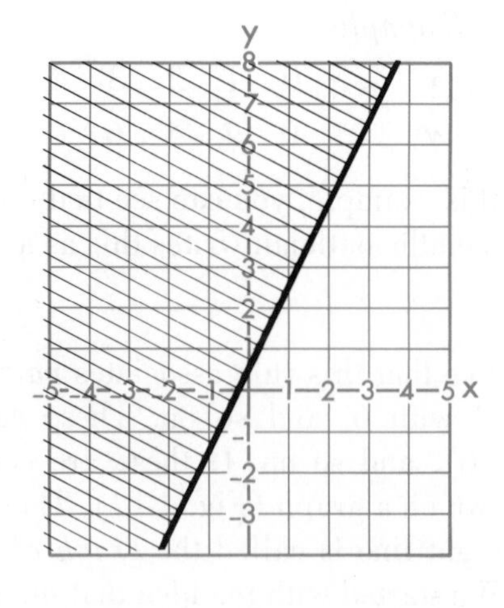

Fig. 4-17. The graph of $y > 2x$.

Figure 4-17 shows the region for which $y > 2x$ always holds. All the y numbers in the region marked are too great.

Going back to Fig. 4-16, what happens if we travel on the line for $x = 1\frac{1}{2}$,

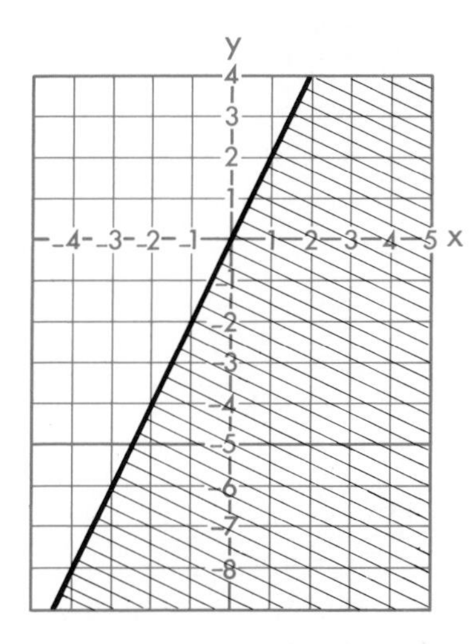

Fig. 4-18. The graph of $y < 2x$.

but do not get up to the line? If we stop at point B, this corresponds to a y number of $1\frac{1}{2}$ which is not double the x number. It is too small. In other words, if we are *under* the line,

$$y < 2x \qquad (y \text{ is less than } 2x)$$

The graph for this condition is shown in Fig. 4-18.

Problem 1. The following table shows how y varies with x:

x	0	1	2	3	4	5	etc.
y	−1	1	3	5	7	9	etc.

a What is the rule or formula?

b Make a graph for this rule.

c Using the graph, find y when $x = 3\frac{1}{2}$.

Solution: The y number is found by doubling the x number, then subtracting one. In mathematical language, this is written:

$$y = 2x - 1 \qquad (y \text{ is 1 less than twice } x)$$

Plotting the points given in the table, the straight line in the graph at the left [Fig. 4-19, part (a)] is obtained. This is the graph of $y = 2x - 1$.

To find the y number when the x number is $3\frac{1}{2}$, locate $3\frac{1}{2}$ on the X-axis, then read up to the line and across to the Y-axis. The correct y number is 6.

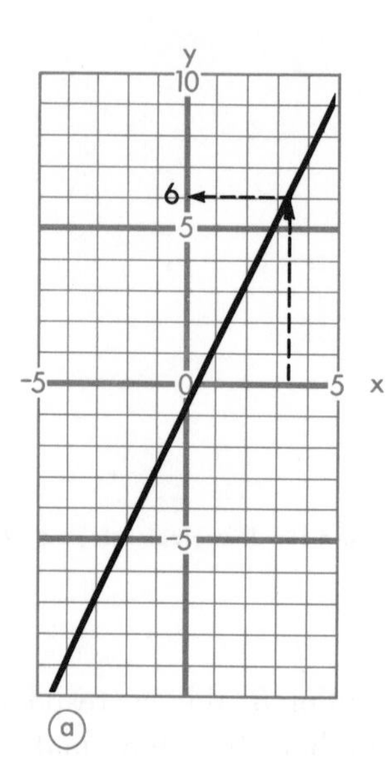

Fig. 4-19.

(a) $y = 2x - 1$

(b) $y > 2x - 1$.

(c) $y < 2x - 1$.

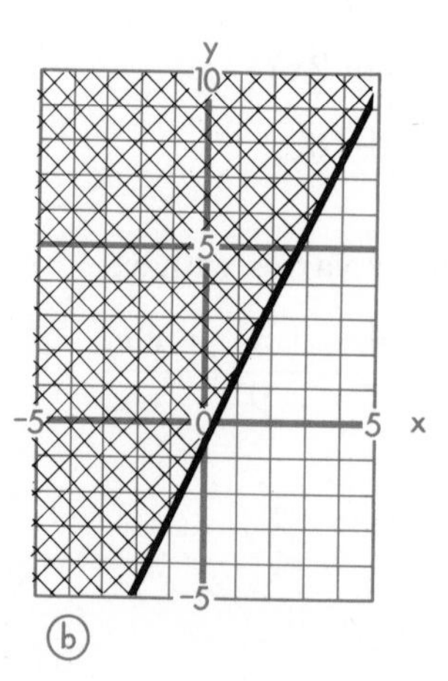

Problem 2. Draw the graphs for $y > 2x - 1$, and $y < 2x - 1$.

Solution: First draw the graph for $y = 2x - 1$ (as done in Problem 1). The part *above* the straight line is $y > 2x - 1$. The part *below* the straight line is $y < 2x - 1$.

Test: Section 6

Part A. In the following, (a) plot the graph, (b) identify the region where y is too great, and (c) identify the region where y is too small.

1 $y = x + 1$

x	0	1	2	3	4	5
y	1	2	3	4	5	6

2 $y = x - 1$

x	0	1	2	3	4	5
y	−1	0	1	2	3	4

3 $y = 2x + 3$

x	0	1	2	3	4	5
y	3	5	7	9	11	13

4 $y = 2x - 3$

x	0	1	2	3	4	5
y	−3	−1	1	3	5	7

5 $y = -x + 2$

x	−3	−2	−1	0	1	2	3
y	5	4	3	2	1	0	−1

6 $y = -x - 3$

x	−3	−2	−1	0	1	2	3
y	0	−1	−2	−3	−4	−5	−6

7 $y = -3x + 5$

x	0	1	2	3	4	5
y	5	2	−1	−4	−7	−10

8 $y = -3x - 2$

x	0	1	2	3	4	5
y	−2	−5	−8	−11	−14	−17

Part B. In the following: (a) discover the rule and (b) plot the graph.

1

x	-5	-3	-1	1	2	4
y	-5	-3	-1	1	2	4

2

x	-5	-3	-1	0	1	2	4
y	5	3	1	0	-1	-2	-4

3

x	-3	-2	-1	0	1	2	3
y	-6	-4	-2	0	2	4	6

4

x	-3	-2	-1	0	1	2	3
y	-9	-6	-3	0	3	6	9

5

x	-3	-2	-1	0	1	2	3
y	-7	-5	-3	-1	1	3	5

6

x	-3	-2	-1	0	1	2	3
y	-8	-5	-2	1	4	7	10

7 SUBSTITUTION

If a rule is given to you in words, as, "The y value is double the x value," it is easy to make a table of values. You just select some convenient x values, like -4, -2, 0, 2, 4, 6, . . . or any others you like, and double them to find the correct y values. This would correspond to using the formula, $y = 2x$.

Suppose the rule is, "Double the x value, then add three." This would correspond to the formula

$$y = 2x + 3$$

Let us see how a table of values can be made for this formula. First we select some convenient x values (any ones we like). Let us pick the x values: -5, -2, 0, and 4. These are as good as any others.

When the x number is (-5), we *replace* x by (-5). This replacement process is called *substitution*. The rule now reads:

$$y = 2(-5) + 3$$

But $2(-5)$ means two times negative five which is negative ten, so that we can continue:

$$y = (-10) + 3$$

But $(-10) + 3 = (-7)$, so that we come out with the answer:

$$\text{When } x = (-5),\ y = (-7)$$

Let us try another substitution. Suppose, in the same formula, we make the x *number* (4). Replacing x by (4) in the formula and continuing as before, we get:

$$y = 2x + 3$$
$$y = 2(4) + 3$$
$$y = (8) + 3$$
$$y = 11 \text{ when } x = 4$$

By continuing this process, we can build up a table as long as we wish. For $y = 2x + 3$, we would get:

x	−5	−4	−3	−2	−1	0	1	2	3	4	5
y	−7	−5	−3	−1	1	3	5	7	9	11	13

The following example shows how a scientist converts from the Fahrenheit thermometer scale used in the U.S., to the Centigrade thermometer scale used in Europe.

Problem. The rule for converting from Fahrenheit to Centigrade is: Subtract 32 from the Fahrenheit reading, then multiply by $\frac{5}{9}$.

a Write this as a formula.

b Make a table of values extending from 32°F to 212°F.

c Plot the graph.

d Using the graph, find out what 68°F corresponds to in the Centigrade scale.

Solution: (*a*) The formula is

$$C = \tfrac{5}{9}\,(F - 32)$$

The parentheses, ( ), around $F - 32$ means that the 32 is subtracted from the F number *before* multiplying by $\frac{5}{9}$.

(*b*) The table of values is as follows:

$x = F$	32	50	86	104	194	212
$y = C$	0	10	30	40	90	100

(*c*) The graph is shown in Fig. 4-20.

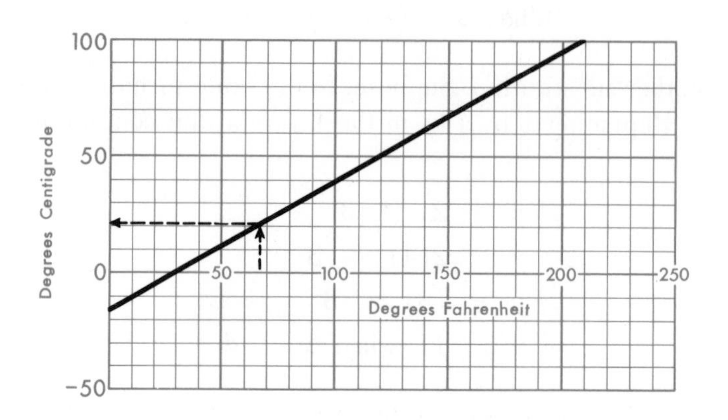

Fig. 4-20. Converting Fahrenheit to Centigrade.

(*d*) Find the $x = 68°$ line on the X-axis. Read up to the line and across to the Y-axis. The Centigrade reading is 20°.

Test: Section 7

Part A. Make a table of values for each of the following formulas. Use $x = -3, -2, -1, 0, 1, 2, 3$. Then draw the graph.

1 $y = 5x$ **2** $y = -3x$ **3** $y = -2x$

4 $y = 4x$ **5** $y = 5x - 1$ **6** $y = -3x + 2$

7 $y = -2x - 1$ **8** $y = 4x + 2$ **9** $y = 2(x + 1)$

10 $y = -3(x - 1)$

Part B. (*a*) Translate the following into a "rule" in mathematical language. (*b*) Using $x = -3, -2, -1, 0, 1, 2, 3$, make a table of values. (*c*) Draw the graph.

1 The y value is three times the x value.

2 The y value is twice the x value.

3 The y value is the negative of four times the x value.

4 The y value is the negative of three times the x value.
5 To find the y value, double the x value, then add 2.
6 To find the y value, double the x value, then subtract 1.
7 To find the y value, add 2 to the x value, then double the result.
8 To find the y value, take 1 from the x value, then triple the result.

8 SAYING THE SAME THING IN DIFFERENT WAYS

You already know that a rule can be given in words, as, "The y value is three more than the x value." In mathematical language, this could be written

$$y = x + 3$$

and the table of values for a graph would be:

x	-3	-2	-1	0	1	2	3
y	0	1	2	3	4	5	6

The graph of this formula would be the one shown in Fig. 4-21.

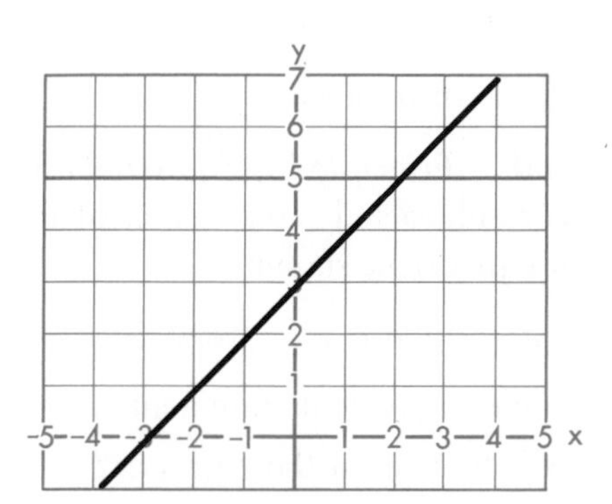

Fig. 4-21. $y = x + 3$.

Now, think of the rule, "If you take three away from the y value, you get the x value." In mathematical language, this is:

$$y - 3 = x$$

The table of values for this is:

x	-3	-2	-1	0	1	2	3
y	0	1	2	3	4	5	6

Compare this with the table of values for $y = x + 3$. You see that it is exactly the same.

This means that $y = x + 3$ and $y - 3 = x$ have exactly the same graphs, or the same sets of number-pairs! There is a special name for formulas which give the same pairs of numbers:

Definition. Formulas which give the same pairs of numbers are called *equivalent statements.* Equivalent statements, in other words, have the same graphs.

Now, examine the two equivalent statements: $y = x + 3$, and $y - 3 = x$. Notice that you can get the second one from the first one by subtracting three from each *member* (from each side) as follows:

$$\begin{aligned} \text{Starting with} \quad y \qquad &= x + 3 \\ \text{then} \quad y - 3 &= x + 3 - 3 \\ y - 3 &= x \end{aligned}$$

You can get the first equivalent statement from the second by *adding* three to each member, as follows:

$$\begin{aligned} \text{Starting with} \quad y - 3 \qquad &= x \\ \text{then} \quad y - 3 + 3 &= x + 3 \\ y \qquad &= x + 3 \end{aligned}$$

This illustrates an important principle:

The + and − Principle for Equivalent Statements. If the same number is added to (or subtracted from) each of the two members of a formula, the result is an equivalent statement.

Problem 1. Suppose $y = 2x + 5$.

a Write some equivalent statements.

b What will be true of their graphs?

Solution: (*a*) Add 3 to each member $\quad y + 3 = 2x + 8$

Take 2 from each member $\quad y - 2 = 2x + 3$

Add 1 to each member $\quad y + 1 = 2x + 6$

Take 5 from each member $\quad y - 5 = 2x$

(*b*) They will all have the same graphs.

Now let us see what happens if we try multiplication and division. Start with $y = 2x$. The table of values is:

x	−3	−2	−1	0	1	2	3
y	−6	−4	−2	0	2	4	6

and the graph is shown in Fig. 4-22. Let us multiply both members by 2. Then we get:

$$2y = 4x$$

The table of values proves to be exactly the same as that for $y = 2x$, which

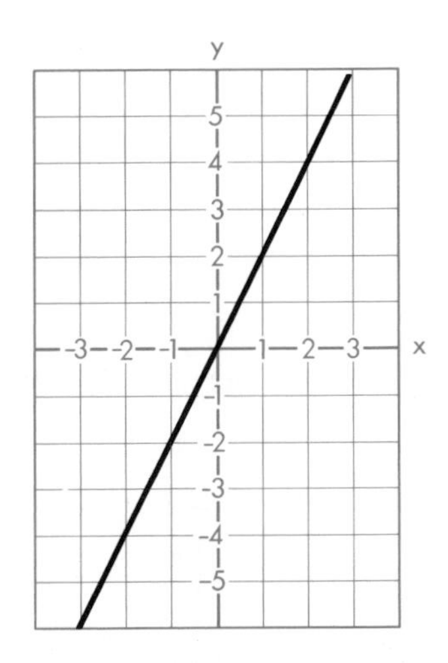

Fig. 4-22. $y = 2x$.

means that they have the same pairs of numbers and the same graph!

If we divide both members of $y = 2x$ by 2, we get

$$\tfrac{1}{2}y = x$$

which still gives the same set of numbers for the table of values. This illustrates the second very important principle.

The × and ÷ Principle for Equivalent Statements. If each member of a formula is multiplied or divided by the same number, the result is an equivalent statement.

Problem 2. Suppose $6y = 12x$.

a Write some equivalent statements.

b How will their graphs compare?

Solution: (*a*) Multiply both members by 3 $\quad 18y = 36x$

Divide both members by 6 $\quad y = 2x$

Multiply both members by 5 $\quad 30y = 60x$

Divide both members by 12 $\quad \tfrac{1}{2}y = x$

(*b*) They will all have the same graphs.

Sometimes, mathematicians use both rules in succession, as in the following problems. This is called *solving a formula.* It is done to make graphing easier. It is always easier to graph a solved formula.

Problem 3. $2y + 6 = 4x$. Solve for y.

Solution

$$2y + 6 = 4x$$
$$2y + 6 - 6 = 4x - 6 \quad \text{(Subtracting 6 from both members)}$$
$$2y = 4x - 6$$
$$y = 2x - 3 \quad \text{(Dividing both members by 2)}$$

Problem 4. $2y + 6 = 4x$. Solve for x.

Solution:

$$2y + 6 = 4x$$
$$4x = 2y + 6 \quad \text{(Reversing sides)}$$
$$x = \tfrac{1}{2}y + \tfrac{3}{2} \quad \text{(Dividing by 4)}$$

Problem 5. $3y + 7 = 9x - 11$. Solve for y.

Solution:

$$3y + 7 = 9x - 11$$
$$3y + 7 - 7 = 9x - 11 - 7 \quad \text{(Subtracting 7)}$$
$$3y = 9x - 18$$
$$y = 3x - 6 \quad \text{(Dividing by 3)}$$

Notice that in these examples, the + and − principle is used *before* the × and ÷ principle. This is usually the most convenient way to solve a formula.

Test: Section 8

Part A. (a) Using the + and − principle with 1, 3, and 5, find equivalent statements for the following. (b) Using the × and ÷ principle with 2, 4, and 6, find equivalent statements for the following.

1 $12y = 24x$ 2 $12y = 36x$ 3 $24y = 36x$

4 $24y = 48x$ 5 $6y = 12x$ 6 $6y = 24x$

7 $y = 10x$ 8 $y = 15x$ 9 $2y = -3x$

10 $3y = -5x$

Part B. Using either the + and − principle or the × and ÷ principle, solve for y in each of the following:

1 $y = x - 5$ 2 $y = x - 7$ 3 $y = x + 2$
4 $y = x + 8$ 5 $y - 3 = x + 2$ 6 $y - 5 = x + 1$
7 $2y = 12x$ 8 $3y = 15x$ 9 $-5y = 5x$
10 $15y = -5x$

Part C. Using both rules, (a) solve for y, (b) graph the result.

1 $2y + 5 = 4x - 3$ 2 $3y - 7 = 9x + 2$
3 $4y - 11 = 12x + 5$ 4 $5y + 7 = 25x - 8$
5 $6y - 5 = 18x + 1$ 6 $7y + 4 = 21x - 3$
7 $-6y + 5 = -18x - 1$ 8 $-7y - 4 = -21x + 3$
9 $2y + 1 = 8x - 5$ 10 $3y + 3 = 3x + 3$

9 ANOTHER KIND OF VARIATION

It was discovered a long time ago that when a ball rolls down a hill, it goes faster and faster as time goes on. If we regard x, as time in seconds, and y, as distance traveled in feet, the following table of values may be found in a certain case:

x = seconds	0	1	2	3	4	5
y = feet	0	1	4	9	16	25

Here, you can see that you get the y number by multiplying the x number by itself. This is written:

$$y = x^2 \qquad (y = x \text{ square})$$

The small raised 2, is called an *exponent* (ĕks·pō′nent), is placed there to show that you really mean x times x. When the graph is drawn for this table of values, it looks like Fig. 4-23.

Many of the facts discovered for straight-line graphs hold for curved-line graphs as well. For example, as shown in Fig. 4-24, the region above the curve shows where $y > x^2$ (the y number is greater than the square of the x number), and the region below the curve shows where $y < x^2$ (the y number is less than the square of the x number).

Also, the principles for equivalent statements holds. For example, $y = x^2$ has the same graph as $y + 5 = x^2 + 5$, or $2y = 2x^2$, or $2y - 7 = 2x^2 - 7$.

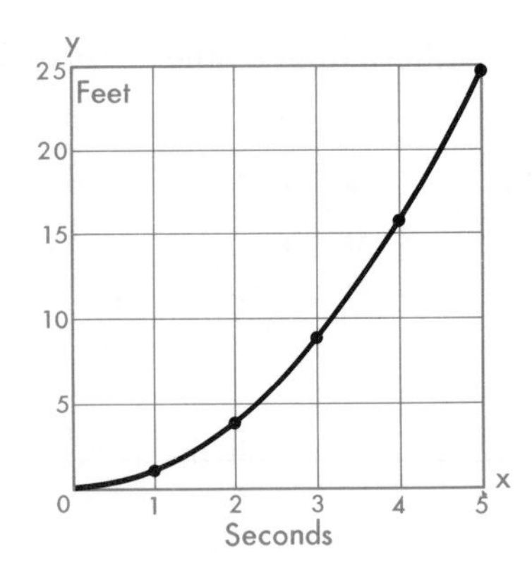

Fig. 4-23. Feet traveled by a rolling ball.

Fig. 4-24. $y > x^2$ and $y < x^2$.

Problem 1. **a** Solve $2y = 6x^2$ for y. **b** Graph the result.

Solution: (a) Dividing both members by 2, $y = 3x^2$. (b) To graph this, make a table of values. If $x = (-2)$, then x^2 is (-2) times (-2), which is $(+4)$. Then $3x^2$ is $3(+4) = 12$. Doing the same thing for other values of x, we get:

x	-2	-1	0	1	2
y	12	3	0	3	12

The graph is shown in Fig. 4-25.

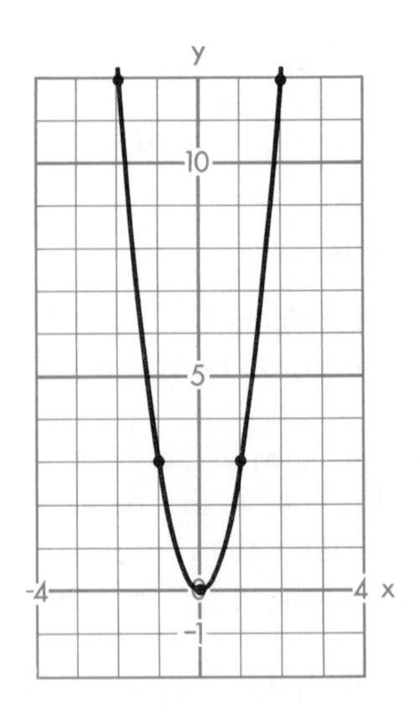

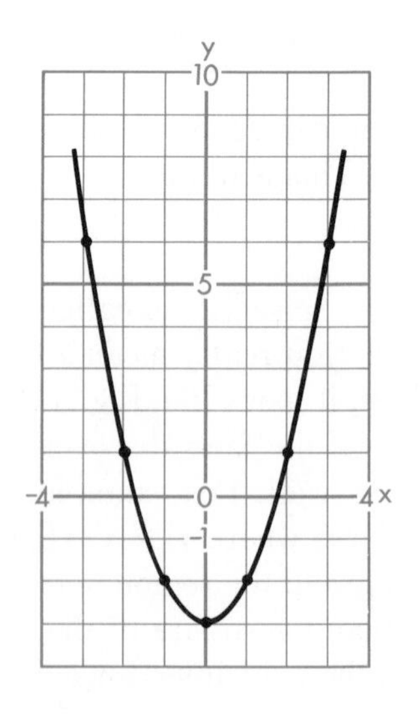

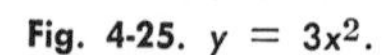

Fig. 4-25. $y = 3x^2$.

Fig. 4-26. $y = x^2 - 3$.

Problem 2. Make a table of values, using $x = -3, -2, -1, 0, 1, 2, 3$ for $y = x^2 - 3$, and graph the result.

Solution: The table of values is:

x	-3	-2	-1	0	1	2	3
y	6	1	-2	-3	-2	1	6

and the graph is shown in Fig. 4-26.

Test: Section 9

Part A. Write the formula, and graph the following:

1

x	-2	-1	0	1	2
y	4	1	0	1	4

2

x	-2	-1	0	1	2
y	8	2	0	2	8

3

x	-2	-1	0	1	2
y	12	3	0	3	12

4

x	-2	-1	0	1	2
y	16	4	0	4	16

Part B. Write tables of values using $x = -3, -2, -1, 0, 1, 2, 3$, and graph the following:

1 $y = x^2 - 1$

2 $y = x^2 + 1$

3 $y = 2x^2 - 3$

4 $y = 2x^2 + 3$

Part C. Solve for y, make a table of values, and graph the following:

1 $y + 1 = x^2$

2 $y - 1 = x^2$

3 $2y = 4x^2 - 6$

4 $2y + 4 = 2x^2 - 6$

10 SIMULTANEOUS SYSTEMS

Figure 4-27 shows two graphs: one for $y = 2x$, and one for $y = x + 3$. On the graph for $y = 2x$, each point stands for a pair of numbers such that the y number is double the x number. For example, the point $(1, 2)$ is on this line.

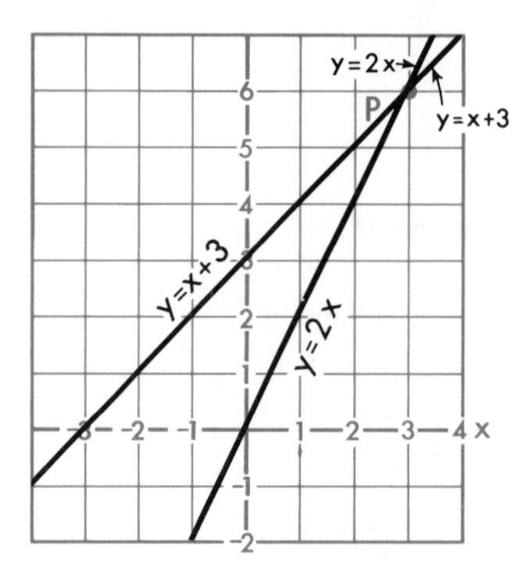

Fig. 4-27. $\begin{cases} y = 2x \\ y = x + 3. \end{cases}$

On the $y = x + 3$ line, each point stands for a pair of numbers such that the y number is three more than the x number. For example, the point $(1, 4)$ is on this line.

At point P, we find the coordinates $(3, 6)$. *This point satisfies both conditions.* In other words, when $x = 3$ and $y = 6$, it is true that (a) y is twice x, and (b) y is three more than x. This pair of numbers is called the *solution* of the *simultaneous equations*:

$$\begin{cases} y = 2x \\ y = x + 3 \end{cases}$$

Problem 1. Solve the system:

$$\begin{cases} y = x^2 - 3 \\ y = 2x \end{cases}$$

Solution: First we make tables of values (not shown) and plot the two graphs (Fig. 4-28). Looking at the graphs, we see that both conditions are met when

$$\begin{cases} x = 3 \\ y = 6 \end{cases} \text{ or when } \begin{cases} x = -1 \\ y = -2 \end{cases}$$

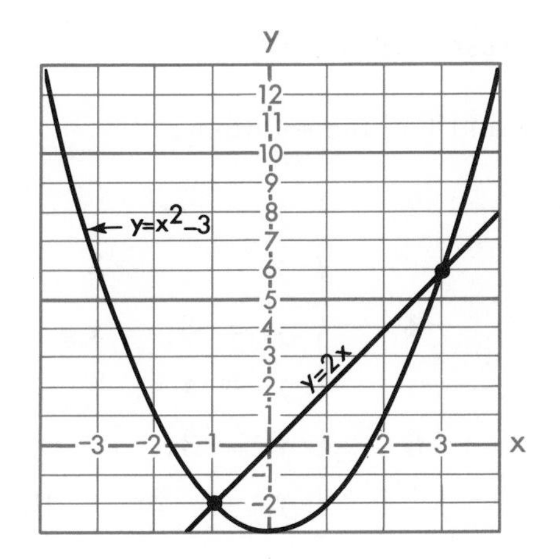

Fig. 4-28.

$$\begin{cases} y = x^2 - 3 \\ y = 2x. \end{cases}$$

Problem 2. Find the smallest positive whole numbers which satisfy the system:

$$\begin{cases} y > x \\ y < 2x \end{cases}$$

Solution: In Fig. 4-29, the graphs of $y = 2x$, and $y = x$, have been drawn.

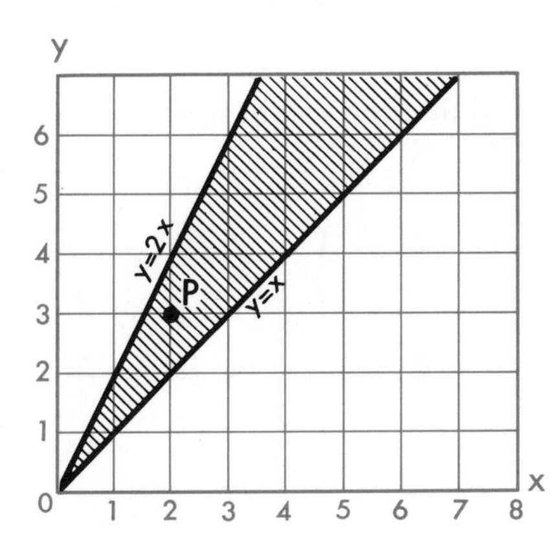

Fig. 4-29.

$$\begin{cases} y > x \\ y < 2x. \end{cases}$$

All the space *above* $y = x$ satisfies the first condition, that $y > x$. All the space *below* $y = 2x$ satisfies the second condition, that $y < 2x$. The space between the two lines gives all the points which satisfy *both* conditions. Looking at the graph, the smallest positive whole numbers are:

$$\begin{cases} x = 2 \\ y = 3 \end{cases}$$

Another solution is $x = 3$, $y = 4$, but this is not the *smallest* pair.

Test: Section 10

Part A. Graph the following and find the solutions:

1 $\begin{cases} y = x \\ y = 4 - x \end{cases}$ 2 $\begin{cases} y = 2x \\ y = x + 3 \end{cases}$

3 $\begin{cases} y = x + 5 \\ y = 2x + 1 \end{cases}$ 4 $\begin{cases} y = 3 - x \\ y = x + 5 \end{cases}$

5 $\begin{cases} y = 2 - 3x \\ y = x - 8 \end{cases}$ 6 $\begin{cases} y = 3x \\ y = -2x + 10 \end{cases}$

Part B. Graph the following and find the solutions:

1 $\begin{cases} y = x^2 \\ y = x + 6 \end{cases}$ 2 $\begin{cases} y = x^2 \\ y = 4x - 3 \end{cases}$

3 $\begin{cases} y = 2x^2 \\ y = 3x + 5 \end{cases}$ 4 $\begin{cases} y = 2x^2 \\ y = 5x + 3 \end{cases}$

Part C. Graph the following and find the smallest positive whole numbers which satisfy *both* conditions.

1 $\begin{cases} y > x \\ y < 4 - x \end{cases}$ 2 $\begin{cases} y > 2x \\ y < x + 3 \end{cases}$

3 $\begin{cases} y < x + 5 \\ y > 2x + 1 \end{cases}$ 4 $\begin{cases} y < x + 5 \\ y > 3 - x \end{cases}$

5

NUMBER PUZZLES

"Say, Joe," said Pete.

"What?"

"Here's a puzzle I saw in the newspaper. It says that there's a set of numbers that goes like this: 1, 5, 9, 13, 17, 21, and so on. It says that if you pick three of them next to each other, they'll add up to 99. They want to know which ones they are. How would you do it?"

"Oh," said Joe, "That's easy. Just add until you get to the right ones."

"That doesn't sound like a very good way to me," Pete said. "There must be an easier way."

There certainly *is* an easier way. In this chapter, we are going to explore different kinds of number puzzles and show you how to do them.

We will let you into a secret. We don't really care about puzzles, but the same methods that solve number puzzles also solve the problems of our times and civilization. If you can do one, you can do the other!

1 TRIAL AND ERROR METHODS

A person who does not know much about mathematics may sometimes be able to get the correct answer to a puzzle by trial and error. We are going to do some very easy puzzles this way first, because this is the way the mathematicians originally figured them out. Besides, we can learn a lot from this simple method.

Problem 1. I am thinking about a number. First, I double it; then I take away 11; my answer is 1. What number did I start with?

Solution: Let us try some numbers and see what happens. In the first line of the following table, we will try some numbers from 1 through 6. (In the trial and error method, if the number is not a small one — or if it is a fraction — you may run into trouble. We have chosen the problems so that they will "work out.")

Suppose the number is:	1	2	3	4	5	6
Double this:	2	4	6	8	10	12
Take away 11:	−9	−7	−5	−3	−1	(1)

From the table, the original number must have been *6*.

Problem 2. I am thinking about a certain number. Double it; take away 6; now take the original number and triple it; now take away 11. The two results are exactly the same. What number did I start with?

Solution: Again, we will try some numbers and see what happens.

Suppose the original number was:	1	2	3	4	5	6
Double it:	2	4	6	8	10	12
Take away 6:	−4	−2	0	2	(4)	6
Now triple the original number:	3	6	9	12	15	18
Take away 11:	−8	−5	−2	1	(4)	7

Compare the third line with the fifth line. Where were they exactly the same? Right! The answer is 5.

Test: Section 1

For each of the following, make a table and try numbers until you get one that "fits" the conditions.

Part A.

1 I am thinking of a number. When I add 2, the result is 5. What is the number?

2 I am thinking of a number. When I add 3 to it, the result is 7. What is the number?

3 Two less than a certain number is 3. What is the number?

4 Four less than a certain number is 1. What is the number?

5 One more than a certain number is 7. Find the number.

6 Two more than a certain number is 9. Find the number.

Part B.

1 I am thinking of a number. If I multiply it by 3 and then subtract 1, the result will be 8. What number am I thinking of?

2 I am thinking of a number. If I multiply it by 5 and then subtract 3, the result will be 12. What number am I thinking of?

3 I just thought of a number. I am multiplying it by 4; now I will add 7. The answer is 15. What number did I think of?

4 I just thought of a number. I am multiplying it by 7; now I will add 3. The answer is 38. What number did I think of?

Part C.

1 I think of a number. I double it and add three, and write down the answer. Now I take the original number, triple it, and take away 4. The answer is the same as I had before. What is the original number?

2 I have a number. I triple it, add 1, and write it down. Now I take the original number again, multiply it by 4 and take away 6. The answer is the same as I had before. What is the original number?

3 Twice a certain number, minus 5, is the same as five times the number, minus 8. What is the number?

4 Three times a certain number, plus 8, is the same as seven times the number, minus 8. What is the number?

2 THE LANGUAGE OF ALGEBRA

To be able to solve puzzles the way a mathematician does, you must learn the language that a mathematician uses. You must learn to translate from English to mathematics and back again!

For example, when you read the sentences: "I am thinking of a number. Add 4 to it." you may think of a specific number, but that is not what the mathematician does. He thinks of all the numbers in the world and then picks out the one that fits. This is not nearly as difficult as it sounds. Let us show you how it is done.

First, imagine the entire number line written down with all its fractions and decimals. Here, only a few numbers of this line are shown:

The number may be:	....	-5	-4	-3	-2	-1	0	1	2	3	4	5....
Now you add:	....	4	4	4	4	4	4	4	4	4	4	4....
The number *plus 4 is*:	...	-1	0	1	2	3	4	5	6	7	8	9....

As far as we know, the original number may be anywhere on the number line. It might be positive, zero, or negative. It might be a whole number, or it might be a decimal. No matter what it is, let us call the whole first line, x. This is called a *variable*, because it may stand for any number in the first line.

Definition. Any line of a table of numbers is a variable.

The second line of numbers is also a *variable*, but it always has the same value, in this case, 4.

Definition. A variable with only one value is called a *constant*.

The third line is the same as the first line except that in each case four has been added. If we call the first line of numbers x, then we must call the third line of numbers $x + 4$, which means that four has been added to every number in the first line.

English is called a "rich language" because there are so many ways of saying the same thing. Mathematicians, however, like to be exact, not have different things mean the same thing because it may lead to confusion. So let us agree on certain translations from English into mathematics. The table we give on the opposite page is like a dictionary.

Problem 1. Translate into mathematical language:

a a number increased by 7 **b** 8 less than a certain number

c 6 times a number **d** three fifths of a number

Solution: (a) $x + 7$ (b) $x - 8$ (c) $6x$ (d) either $\frac{3x}{5}$ or $\frac{3}{5}x$

ENGLISH	ALGEBRA
A number	x
A number plus 4 A number increased by 4 A number augmented by 4 A number added to 4 *4 more than a number	$x + 4$
A number minus 4 A number decreased by 4 A number diminished by 4 A number less 4 *4 less than a number *Take 4 from a number *Subtract 4 from a number	$x - 4$
4 times a number *a number multiplied by 4 4 times as large as a number The product of 4 and the number	$4x$
*A number divided by 4 One fourth of the number A fourth as large as the number *The quotient of the number and 4 *The ratio of the number and 4	$\frac{1}{4}x$ or $\frac{x}{4}$

*In these cases, notice that we say it backwards in English!

The word "is" usually becomes "equals" (=) in mathematics. When the = sign is used, the result is called an *equation* (ê·kwā′zh*u*n).

Definition. An equation is a mathematical statement in which one variable called the *left member* is equal to another variable called the *right member*.

Problem 2. Write equations for the following:

a A number diminished by 8 is 3.

b Twice a number increased by 5 is the same as 5 less than the number.

c One fourth of a number, diminished by 3, is 5 more than twice the number.

Solution:

a. A number diminished by 8 is 3

$$\underbrace{\text{A number diminished by 8}}_{x - 8} \quad \underbrace{\text{is}}_{=} \quad \underbrace{3}_{3}$$

In this equation, $x - 8$ is the left member, and 3 is the right member.

b. Twice a number increased by 5 is the same as 5 less than the number

$$\underbrace{\text{Twice a number increased by 5}}_{2x + 5} \quad \underbrace{\text{is the same as}}_{=}$$

$$\underbrace{\text{5 less than the number}}_{x - 5}$$

c. One fourth of a number, diminished by 3 is 5 more than twice the number

$$\underbrace{\text{One fourth of a number, diminished by 3}}_{\frac{1}{4}x - 3} \quad \underbrace{\text{is}}_{=}$$

$$\underbrace{\text{5 more than twice the number}}_{2x + 5}$$

• Test: Section 2

Part A. Write in algebraic language:

1. The number increased by 17
2. The number added to 5
3. Eight more than the number
4. Nine more than the number
5. A number decreased by 11
6. A number less 10
7. Six less than the number
8. Subtract 7 from the number
9. Eight times as large as the number
10. The product of 75 and the number
11. Two thirds of a number
12. The ratio of a number and 10

Part B. Write an equation for each of the following sentences:

1 Seven more than a certain number equals nine.
2 Two more than a certain number equals three.
3 Twice a certain number is 5 less than the number.
4 Five times a certain number is 8 less than the number.
5 Three times a certain number, increased by 4, is 16.
6 Five times a certain number, added to 7, is 17.
7 Five more than double a certain number is the same as 2 less than triple the number.
8 Seven more than triple a certain number is the same as 5 less than double the number.

Part C. Translate into English sentences:

1 $x + 3 = 5$
2 $x + 7 = 10$
3 $3x = x - 8$
4 $5x = x - 6$
5 $2x + 3 = 9$
6 $6x + 1 = -11$
7 $5x + 7 = 4x - 5$
8 $3x + 8 = 2x - 10$

3 SOLVING EQUATIONS WITH + AND −

If you pick a certain number and add 6, the answer will be 9. What is the number?

Of course, this is easy to guess, but — because most puzzles are much harder — let us try to develop a definite rule for solving these puzzles. Take another look at this very simple puzzle:

x	....	1	2	3	4	5	....
add 6							
$x + 6$	....	7	8	(9)	10	11	....

You can see from the table that

$$\text{if } x + 6 = 9$$
$$\text{then } x = 3$$

Let us try to work backwards, starting with $x + 6$. You will see something very interesting:

$x + 6$	....	7	8	(9)	10	11	....
subtract 6				↓			
x	....	1	2	3	4	5	....

Notice that in working backwards, we actually took each value of $x + 6$ and *subtracted* to get the correct value of x. If we write the same thing in mathematical language:

we started with:	$x + 6 = 9$
we subtracted 6 from each member:	$x + 6 - 6 = 9 - 6$
this is the same as:	$x + 0 = 3$
and so:	$x = 3$ *is the answer!*

This leads to the following rule:

Rule for Solving Equations With +. If a quantity is added to x in an equation, the value of x can be found by subtracting this quantity from both the left and the right members.

Problem 1. I am thinking of a certain number. If I add 3, the result is 8. What is the number?

Solution: Let $x =$ the number.

$$x + 3 = 8$$
$$x + 3 - 3 = 8 - 3$$
$$x + 0 = 5$$
$$x = 5$$

Answer: The number is 5

Problem 2. I am thinking of a certain number. When I add $\frac{5}{6}$ to it, the result is $\frac{7}{8}$. What is the number?

Solution: Let $x =$ the number.

$$x + \frac{5}{6} = \frac{7}{8}$$
$$x + \frac{5}{6} - \frac{5}{6} = \frac{7}{8} - \frac{5}{6}$$
$$x + 0 = \frac{1}{24}$$

Answer: The number is $\frac{1}{24}$

This is not so easy to see, so let us check the answer. From the words of the problem, $\frac{1}{24} + \frac{5}{6}$ should equal $\frac{7}{8}$. It does; so our answer is right. (Here's one that you couldn't do by trial and error!)

Let us try another one.

I am thinking of a number. When I subtract 2, the result is 3. What is the original number?

The table looks like this:

x	....	1	2	3	4	5	6	....
subtract 2								
$x - 2$	....	−1	0	1	2	(3)	4	....

You can see from the table that:

$$\text{if } x - 2 = 3$$
$$\text{then } x = 5$$

Let us work this one backwards, too. Starting with $x - 2$, we get the following:

$x - 2$	....	−1	0	1	2	(3)	4	....
add 2								
x	....	1	2	3	4	5	6	....

We took each value of $x - 2$ and added 2 to get the correct value of x. In mathematical language:

we started with: $x - 2 = 3$

we added 2 to each member: $x - 2 + 2 = 3 + 2$

this is the same as: $x + 0 = 5$

and so: $x = 5$

is the correct value of x.

This leads to the following rule:

Rule for Solving Equations With −. If a quantity is subtracted from x

in an equation, the value of x can be found by adding this quantity to both the left and right members of the equation.

Problem 3. I am thinking of a certain number. If you subtract 7 from it, the answer is 3. What is the number?

Solution: Let x = the number.

$$x - 7 = 3$$
$$x - 7 + 7 = 3 + 7$$
$$x + 0 = 10$$
$$x = 10$$

Answer: The number is 10

This is easily checked. (You should check all problems!)

Problem 4. I am thinking of a number. If I subtract $3\frac{1}{2}$ from it, the answer is $7\frac{2}{3}$. What is the number?

Solution: Let x = the number.

$$x - 3\tfrac{1}{2} = 7\tfrac{2}{3}$$
$$x - 3\tfrac{1}{2} + 3\tfrac{1}{2} = 7\tfrac{2}{3} + 3\tfrac{1}{2}$$
$$x + 0 = 11\tfrac{1}{6}$$
$$x = 11\tfrac{1}{6}$$

Answer: The number is $11\frac{1}{6}$

To check, take $3\frac{1}{2}$ from $11\frac{1}{6}$ and see whether you actually get $7\frac{2}{3}$.

• Test: Section 3

Part A. In the following, you are given tables of values. Solve the equations and check with the tables.

1

x	1	2	3	4	5
Add 3					
$x + 3$	4	5	6	7	8

If $x + 3 = 7$, what does x equal?

2

x	1	2	3	4	5
Add 5					
$x + 5$	6	7	8	9	10

If $x + 5 = 6$, what does x equal?

3

x	1	2	3	4	5
Subtract 8					
$x - 8$	-7	-6	-5	-4	-3

If $x - 8 = -5$, what does x equal?

4

x	1	2	3	4	5
Subtract 5					
$x - 5$	-4	-3	-2	-1	0

If $x - 5 = 0$, what does x equal?

Part B. Solve the following by writing an equation, then solving it.

1. Eight more than a certain number is 12. Find the number.
2. Seven more than a certain number is 10. Find the number.
3. A certain number increased by 2 is 7. What is the number?
4. A certain number increased by 3 is 3. What is the number?
5. A number minus 8 is negative 2. What is the number?
6. A number minus 1 is negative 4. What is the number?
7. Five less than a number is negative 8. Find the number.
8. Seven less than a number is negative 3. Find the number.

Part C. Solve the following equations:

1. $x + \frac{2}{3} = \frac{5}{3}$
2. $x + \frac{1}{5} = \frac{3}{5}$
3. $x - \frac{3}{8} = \frac{7}{8}$
4. $x - \frac{1}{4} = \frac{3}{4}$
5. $x + 1\frac{2}{3} = \frac{2}{3}$
6. $x + 2\frac{5}{7} = 3\frac{6}{7}$
7. $x + \frac{2}{5} = \frac{3}{4}$
8. $x + \frac{3}{4} = \frac{8}{9}$
9. $x - 3\frac{1}{3} = \frac{2}{5}$
10. $x - 5\frac{1}{7} = 3\frac{1}{8}$
11. $x - 1\frac{1}{2} = -3\frac{1}{2}$
12. $x - \frac{2}{3} = -4\frac{1}{3}$

4 SOLVING EQUATIONS WITH MULTIPLICATION

If you pick a certain number and multiply by 3, the answer is 12. What is the number?

To get a rule for this kind of problem, let us examine a table and work backwards, just as we did in the + and − type.

x	....	1	2	3	4	5	6	....
multiply by 3					↑			
$3x$	....	3	6	9	(12)	15	18	....

If $3x = 12$, then $x = 4$ is the correct value.

Working backwards:

$3x$	....	3	6	9	(12)	15	18	....
divide by 3					↓			
x	....	1	2	3	4	5	6	....

and, in mathematical language:

we started with: $3x = 12$

we divided each member by 3: $\frac{1}{3} \cdot 3x = \frac{1}{3} \cdot 12$

this is the same as: $1x = 4$

and so: $x = 4$

For a reason that you will see (in the next section), we will call this the *first* rule for equations for multiplication. There is another one, more general, which we shall use later.

First Rule for Equations With Multiplication. If a quantity multiplies x in an equation, the value of x can be found by dividing both members by this quantity.

Problem 1. Five times a certain number is 15. What is the number?

Solution: Let x = the number.

$$5x = 15$$
$$\frac{1}{5} \cdot 5x = \frac{1}{5} \cdot 15$$
$$1x = 3$$
$$x = 3$$

Answer: The number is 3

You can check this answer easily, in the original problem.

Problem 2. If a certain number is multiplied by negative 2, the result is negative 8. What is the number?

Solution: Let x = the number.

$$-2x = -8$$
$$(-\tfrac{1}{2})\ (-2x) = (-\tfrac{1}{2})\ (-8)$$
$$1x = 4$$
$$x = 4$$

Answer: The number is 4

Checking, you see that $(-2)\ (4)$ is -8, so the answer is correct.

Problem 3. Three times a certain number is $\frac{2}{5}$. What is the number?

Solution: Let x = the number.

$$3x = \tfrac{2}{5}$$
$$\tfrac{1}{3} \cdot 3x = \tfrac{1}{3} \cdot \tfrac{2}{5}$$
$$1x = \tfrac{2}{15}$$
$$x = \tfrac{2}{15}$$

Answer: The number is $\frac{2}{15}$

Checking, three times $\frac{2}{15}$ is $\frac{2}{5}$, so the answer is correct.

Test: Section 4

Part A. In the following, you are given tables of values and a question to answer. Use the rule for equations with multiplication, and check by the tables.

1

x	1	2	3	4	5
$2x$	2	4	6	8	10

If $2x = 10$, what does x equal?

2

x	1	2	3	4	5
$5x$	5	10	15	20	25

If $5x = 20$, what does x equal?

3

x	1	2	3	4	5
$-x$	-1	-2	-3	-4	-5

If $-x = -3$, what does x equal?

4

x	1	2	3	4	5
$-2x$	-2	-4	-6	-8	-10

If $-2x = -8$, what does x equal?

Part B. Solve the following problems by writing an equation, then solving it. Check each answer by testing to see whether it satisfies the original problem.

1 Twice a certain number is 12. Find the number.

2 Three times a certain number is 18. Find the number.

3 If I take a number and multiply it by 5, the result is 25. What is the number?

4 If I take a number and multiply it by 7, the result is 84. What is the number?

Part C. Solve the following equations by the rule. Check each one.

1 $2x = \frac{4}{7}$ 2 $3x = \frac{6}{5}$ 3 $2x = 1\frac{1}{2}$

4 $3x = 2\frac{3}{4}$ 5 $5x = \frac{1}{2}$ 6 $4x = \frac{1}{3}$

5 SOLVING EQUATIONS WITH DIVISION

A rule for division is easy and you can probably guess how such a rule would read. However, it turns out to be much more convenient to think of division as a form of multiplication. For example, dividing 8 by 2 is the same as multiplying 8 by $\frac{1}{2}$. Dividing 15 by $\frac{3}{2}$ is the same as multiplying 15 by $\frac{2}{3}$.

You may remember (from Chapter 2) that the pairs of numbers: 2 and $\frac{1}{2}$, $\frac{2}{3}$ and $\frac{3}{2}$, -7 and $-\frac{1}{7}$, are called *reciprocals*. When you multiply two reciprocals, the result is always *1*.

Problem 1. Find the reciprocals of:

a 3 **b** $\frac{5}{7}$ **c** $-\frac{2}{3}$ **d** -1 **e** 0

Solution:

a. The reciprocal of 3 is $\frac{1}{3}$. *Check*: $3 \times \frac{1}{3} = 1$

b. The reciprocal of $\frac{5}{7}$ is $\frac{7}{5}$. *Check*: $\frac{5}{7} \times \frac{7}{5} = 1$

c. The reciprocal of $-\frac{2}{3}$ is $-\frac{3}{2}$. *Check*: $-\frac{2}{3} \times -\frac{3}{2} = 1$

d. The reciprocal of -1 is -1. *Check*: $-1 \times -1 = 1$

e. Zero has no reciprocal. (If you forgot this, reread pp. 55–56.)

Now we are ready to deal with a problem such as: I am thinking of a number. Two-thirds of this number is 2. What is the number?

First, let us make a table.

x	....	1	2	3	4	5	6	....
multiply by $\frac{2}{3}$								
$\frac{2}{3}x$	....	$\frac{2}{3}$	$1\frac{1}{3}$	2	$2\frac{2}{3}$	$3\frac{1}{3}$	4	....

If $\frac{2}{3}x = 2$, then x must equal 3

Working backwards:

$\frac{2}{3}x$	....	$\frac{2}{3}$	$1\frac{1}{3}$	2	$2\frac{2}{3}$	$3\frac{1}{3}$	4	....
multiply by $\frac{3}{2}$								
x	....	1	2	3	4	5	6	....

In mathematical language, here is what we did:

we started with: $\frac{2}{3}x = 2$

we multiplied both members by $\frac{3}{2}$: $\frac{3}{2} \cdot \frac{2}{3}x = \frac{3}{2} \cdot 2$

this is the same as: $1x = 3$

and so: $x = 3$

Answer: The number is 3

This leads to the *second* rule for equations with either multiplication or division.

Second Rule for Equations With Multiplication or Division. In an equation, if x is multiplied by a fraction, the value of x can be found by multiplying both members by the reciprocal of the fraction.

Problem 2. Half of a certain number is 16. What is the number?

Solution: Let x = the number.

$$\frac{1}{2}x = 16$$
$$2 \cdot \frac{1}{2}x = 2 \cdot 16$$
$$1x = 32$$
$$x = 32$$

Answer: The number is 32. This is easily checked.

Problem 3. If a certain number is divided by 6, the result is $2\frac{1}{2}$. What is the number?

Solution: Let x = the number.

$$\frac{1}{6}x = 2\frac{1}{2}$$
$$6 \cdot \frac{1}{6}x = 6 \cdot \frac{5}{2}$$
$$1x = 15$$
$$x = 15$$

Answer: The number is 15

Checking: One sixth of 15 is $2\frac{1}{2}$, so the answer checks.

Problem 4. Two thirds of a certain number is $\frac{5}{6}$. What is the number?

Solution: Let x = the number.

$$\frac{2}{3}x = \frac{5}{6}$$
$$\frac{3}{2} \cdot \frac{2}{3}x = \frac{3}{2} \cdot \frac{5}{6}$$
$$1x = \frac{5}{4}$$
$$x = 1\frac{1}{4}$$

Answer: The number is $1\frac{1}{4}$

Checking: $\frac{2}{3} \times 1\frac{1}{4} = \frac{2}{3} \times \frac{5}{4} = \frac{5}{6}$, so the answer is correct.

Problem 5. One and one half times a certain number is $1\frac{1}{5}$. What is the number?

Solution: Let x = the number.

$$1\frac{1}{2}x = 1\frac{1}{5}$$

It is more convenient to rewrite this in the following form:

$$\frac{3}{2}x = \frac{6}{5}$$
$$\frac{2}{3} \cdot \frac{3}{2}x = \frac{2}{3} \cdot \frac{6}{5}$$
$$1x = \frac{4}{5}$$
$$x = \frac{4}{5}$$

Answer: The number is $\frac{4}{5}$

Checking: $1\frac{1}{2} \times \frac{4}{5} = \frac{3}{2} \times \frac{4}{5} = \frac{6}{5} = 1\frac{1}{5}$, so the answer is correct.

Test: Section 5

Part A. Find the reciprocals for each of the following:

1 5 2 7 3 $\frac{2}{3}$ 4 $\frac{3}{4}$ 5 $2\frac{1}{2}$

6 $3\frac{1}{2}$ 7 $2\frac{5}{6}$ 8 $3\frac{3}{7}$ 9 $-2\frac{1}{2}$ 10 $-3\frac{1}{2}$

Part B.

1

x	....	1	2	3	4	5	....
$\frac{2}{3}x$	....	$\frac{2}{3}$	$1\frac{1}{3}$	2	$2\frac{2}{3}$	$3\frac{1}{3}$	....

If $\frac{2}{3}x = 1\frac{1}{3}$, what does x equal?

2

x	....	1	2	3	4	5	....
$1\frac{1}{2}x$	....	$1\frac{1}{2}$	3	$4\frac{1}{2}$	6	$7\frac{1}{2}$	....

If $1\frac{1}{2}x = 4\frac{1}{2}$, what does x equal?

3 Half a certain number is 3. What is the number?

4 One quarter of a certain number is 5. What is the number?

5 One third of a certain number is 6. What is the number?

6 One fifth of a certain number is 2. What is the number?

Part C. Solve the following equations by rule. Check each one.

1 $\frac{2}{3}x = 6$ 2 $\frac{3}{4}x = 6$ 3 $\frac{2}{5}x = 4$ 4 $\frac{3}{4}x = 12$

5 $1\frac{1}{2}x = 1\frac{5}{7}$ 6 $1\frac{1}{2}x = 3\frac{1}{2}$ 7 $2\frac{2}{3}x = 5\frac{1}{3}$ 8 $3\frac{3}{5}x = 1\frac{4}{5}$

6 EQUATIONS WITH FOUR OPERATIONS

So far, the puzzles that we used for practice were very easy to do mentally. You may even have been wondering why we bothered to make rules for solving such easy problems. Well, now we are going to do some that are not so easy to do mentally, but which are just as easy to do by mathematical rules.

Let us start with a really easy one. I am thinking of a number; first I double it; then I add 3. My answer is 11. What is the number?

If we make a table for this problem, it looks like this:

x	....	1	2	3	4	5	6	....
multiply by 2								
$2x$	....	2	4	6	8	10	12	....
add 3								
$2x + 3$	....	5	7	9	(11)	13	15	....

If $2x + 3 = 11$, then $x = 4$

Going backwards, our method for digging x out seems to be:

$2x + 3$	5	7	9	11	13	15
subtract 3, get $2x$	2	4	6	8	10	12
multiply by $\frac{1}{2}$ to get x	1	2	3	4	5	6

In mathematical language:

we started with: $2x + 3 = 11$

we subtracted 3 from both members: $2x + 3 - 3 = 11 - 3$

which is the same as: $2x = 8$

we multiplied both members by $\frac{1}{2}$: $\frac{1}{2} \cdot 2x = \frac{1}{2} \cdot 8$

which is the same as: $x = 4$

Procedure for Equations With Addition, Subtraction, Multiplication, and Division. First use the rule for + and −, then the rule for ×.

Problem 1. A number is multiplied by 3. Then it is increased by 5. The result is 17. What is the number?

Solution: Let x = the number.

$$3x + 5 = 17$$
$$3x + 5 - 5 = 17 - 5$$
$$3x = 12$$
$$\frac{1}{3} \cdot 3x = \frac{1}{3} \cdot 12$$
$$x = 4$$

Answer: The number is 4

Check: Multiply by 3; this gives you 12; increase this by 5; this gives you 17. So our answer is correct.

Problem 2. A number is multiplied by 5. The result is diminished by 2. The result is 13. What is the number?

Solution: Let x = the number.

$$5x - 2 = 13$$
$$5x - 2 + 2 = 13 + 2$$
$$5x = 15$$
$$\frac{1}{5} \cdot 5x = \frac{1}{5} \cdot 15$$
$$x = 3$$

Answer: The number is 3

Check: Multiply by 5; this gives you 15; diminish this by 2; the result is 13. So our answer is correct.

Problem 3. Two less than three times a certain number is -1. What is the number?

Solution: Let x = the number.

$$3x - 2 = -1$$
$$3x - 2 + 2 = -1 + 2$$
$$3x = 1$$
$$\frac{1}{3} \cdot 3x = \frac{1}{3} \cdot 1$$
$$x = \frac{1}{3}$$

Answer: The number is $\frac{1}{3}$

Check: Three times the number is 1; two less is -1. So the answer is correct.

Problem 4. Seven and a half more than 5 times a certain number is $3\frac{3}{4}$. What is the number?

Solution: Let x = the number.

$$5x + 7\frac{1}{2} = 3\frac{3}{4}$$
$$5x + 7\frac{1}{2} - 7\frac{1}{2} = 3\frac{3}{4} - 7\frac{1}{2}$$
$$5x = -3\frac{3}{4}$$

This is more conveniently rewritten as

$$5x = -\frac{15}{4}$$
$$\frac{1}{5} \cdot 5x = \frac{1}{5} \cdot \left(-\frac{15}{4}\right)$$
$$x = -\frac{3}{4}$$

Answer: The number is negative $\frac{3}{4}$

Check: Five times negative $\frac{3}{4}$ is negative $\frac{15}{4}$ or negative $3\frac{3}{4}$. Add to this $7\frac{1}{2}$ and you get $3\frac{3}{4}$, so our answer is correct.

Problem 5. Take two thirds of a number. Add five sixths. The answer is $3\frac{1}{2}$. What is the number?

Solution: Let x = the number.

$$\frac{2}{3}x + \frac{5}{6} = 3\frac{1}{2}$$
$$\frac{2}{3}x + \frac{5}{6} - \frac{5}{6} = 3\frac{1}{2} - \frac{5}{6}$$
$$\frac{2}{3}x = 2\frac{2}{3}$$

or

$$\frac{2}{3}x = \frac{8}{3}$$
$$\frac{3}{2} \cdot \frac{2}{3}x = \frac{3}{2} \cdot \frac{8}{3}$$
$$x = 4$$

Answer: The number is 4

Check: Take $\frac{2}{3}$ of the number. This is $\frac{2}{3} \times 4 = \frac{8}{3} = 2\frac{2}{3}$. Add $\frac{5}{6}$. This means $2\frac{2}{3} + \frac{5}{6}$ which is $3\frac{1}{2}$. The answer is correct.

Test: Section 6

Part A. In the following, you are given tables of values to help you check your solutions of the equations below.

1

x	....	1	2	3	4	5	6	....
$5x$	....	5	10	15	20	25	30	....
$5x - 6$	....	-1	4	9	14	19	24	....

If $5x - 6 = 4$, what does x equal?

2

x	....	1	2	3	4	5	....
$4x$	....	4	8	12	16	20	....
$4x - 3$	....	1	5	9	13	17	....

If $4x - 3 = 5$, what does x equal?

3

x	....	1	2	3	4	5	....
$\frac{1}{2}x$	....	$\frac{1}{2}$	1	$1\frac{1}{2}$	2	$2\frac{1}{2}$	....
$\frac{1}{2}x - 3$	....	$-2\frac{1}{2}$	-2	$-1\frac{1}{2}$	-1	$-\frac{1}{2}$	....

If $\frac{1}{2}x - 3 = -1\frac{1}{2}$, what does x equal?

4

x	....	1	2	3	4	5	....
$\frac{2}{3}x$	....	$\frac{2}{3}$	$1\frac{1}{3}$	2	$2\frac{2}{3}$	$3\frac{1}{3}$	....
$\frac{2}{3}x - 1$	....	$-\frac{1}{3}$	$\frac{1}{3}$	1	$1\frac{2}{3}$	$2\frac{1}{3}$	....

If $\frac{2}{3}x - 1 = 1\frac{2}{3}$, what does x equal?

5

x	....	1	2	3	4	5	....
$2x$	....	2	4	6	8	10	....
$2x - 3$	....	-1	1	3	5	7	....

If $2x - 3 = 1$, what does x equal?

6

x	....	1	2	3	4	5	....
$\frac{1}{2}x$	....	$\frac{1}{2}$	1	$1\frac{1}{2}$	2	$2\frac{1}{2}$	....
$\frac{1}{2}x + \frac{2}{3}$	....	$1\frac{1}{6}$	$1\frac{2}{3}$	$2\frac{1}{6}$	$2\frac{2}{3}$	$3\frac{1}{6}$	....

If $\frac{1}{2}x + \frac{2}{3} = 2\frac{1}{6}$, what does x equal?

Part B.

1. Four less than 5 times a certain number is 11. What is the number?
2. Three less than 6 times a certain number is 9. What is the number?
3. One more than 8 times a certain number is 41. Find the number.
4. Seven more than 9 times a certain number is 52. Find the number.
5. What number multiplied by 4, then added to 3, gives you 5?
6. What number multiplied by 12, then added to 3, gives you 7?

Part C. Solve the following by rule:

1 $2x + 8 = 9$	2 $5x + 3 = 5$	3 $4x - \frac{1}{3} = 2$
4 $5x - 1\frac{1}{2} = 6$	5 $3x + 5\frac{1}{3} = 7$	6 $2x + 7\frac{1}{2} = 10$
7 $\frac{2}{3}x - 1 = 1\frac{1}{3}$	8 $\frac{3}{4}x - \frac{1}{4} = 1\frac{5}{8}$	

7 COMPLICATED PUZZLES

When we speak of the *sum* of 8 and 5, we mean the number 13. Twice the sum of 8 and 5 is twice 13, or 26. We could write this $2(8 + 5)$, if we liked, since $(8 + 5)$ is just another way of writing 13.

In the same way, when we speak of the *sum* of x and 4, we mean that x stands for a line of a table and 4 has already been added to every number in that line. We show this by writing it as $(x + 4)$. In other words, the sum of x and 4 is always written $(x + 4)$. Twice the sum of x and 4 is written:

$$2(x + 4)$$

From our discussion in Chapter 2 we know that

$$2(x + 4) \text{ is the same as } 2x + 8$$

because of the *distributive law.* (If you've forgotten this, look back at pp. 57–58.)

Now let us talk about the *difference* between two numbers. What is the difference between 8 and 5? Let us agree that when we ask this question we mean $(8 - 5)$, or 3. This also means that the difference between 5 and 8 is $(5 - 8)$, or negative 3. In general, we will understand that when we speak of the difference between x and 4, it means that x is the number line in a table and 4 has already been subtracted from every number in that line. We show this, again, by using the parentheses. In other words, the difference of x and 4 is always written $(x - 4)$. Three times the difference between x and 4 is written:

$$3(x - 4)$$

Using the distributive law again, we know that

$$3(x - 4) \text{ is the same as } 3x - 12$$

Many complicated puzzles are built on these words. In this section, we will just learn to write the equations for the puzzles. In the next section, we will show you how to solve them.

Problem. Write equations for the following sentences:

a The sum of a number and 4 is twice their difference.

b Three times the sum of a number and 4 is 8 less than twice their difference.

c Three more than twice the difference between 3 times a number and 4, is 20 less than 3 times the sum of 4 times the number and 5.

Solution: *a.* $(x + 4) = 2(x - 4)$

b. $3(x + 4) = 2(x - 4) - 8$

c. $2(3x - 4) + 3 = 3(4x + 5) - 20$

Test: Section 7

Write equations for the following sentences. Do not try to solve them yet.

Part A.

1 Twice the sum of a number and 1 is 6.

2 Three times the sum of a number and 2 is 12.

3 Eight times the difference between a number and 4 is 56.

4 Six times the difference between a number and 5 is 6.

5 Three times the sum of a number and 2 is 21.

6 Five times the sum of a number and 7 is 40.

7 Four times the difference between a number and 3 is 16.

8 Twice the difference between a number and 2 is 6.

Part B.

1 Three times the sum of a number and 5 is the same as 5 times the difference between the number and 3.

2 Four times the sum of a number and 3 is the same as 5 times the difference between the number and 2.

3 Eight times the difference between a number and 3 is the same as 5 times the sum of the number and 6.

4 Seven times the difference between a number and 5 is the same as twice the sum of the number and 10.

5 Twice the sum of three times the number and 1 is the same as 8 times the difference of the number and 4.

6 Three times the sum of twice the number and 1 is the same as 9 times the difference of the number and 7.

7 Five times the difference between three times the number and 1 is the same as four times the sum of twice the number and 4.

8 Seven times the difference between twice the number and 1 is the same as three times the sum of triple the number and 1.

Part C.

1 Four more than 3 times the sum of a number and 1 is the same as 23 less than 5 times the difference of twice the number and 1.

2 Nine more than twice the sum of a number and 1 is the same as 10 less than 3 times the difference between twice the number and 1.

3 Twice the sum of twice a number and 1, less 1, equals 3 times the difference of 3 times the number and 1, less 16.

4 Twice the difference of 4 times a number and 1, added to 6, is the same as 4 times the sum of triple the number and 1, with 8 subtracted.

8 SOLVING COMPLICATED PUZZLES

In the last section, you learned how to write a very complicated sentence as a mathematical equation. For example, look at:

Three times the sum of a certain number and 5 is 22 more than twice the difference between the number and 2. Find the number. This is written:

$$3(x + 5) = 2(x - 2) + 22$$

Now, how do we solve this?

First, we will take advantage of the distributive law to "clean up" or shorten, a bit.

$$3x + 15 = 2x - 4 + 22$$

Now, notice (in the right member) that $-4 + 22$ is the same as 18, so we may clean up still more. This process of *shortening* an equation by using the distributive law and adding or subtracting wherever possible is called *simplifying*. Mathematicians always try to simplify an equation as much as possible before doing anything about solving it. Now we have:

$$3x + 15 = 2x + 18$$

This is the first time we have met an equation with x on both sides.

Before solving this, let us review what we did in solving simple equations before this came up.

1 In $x + 8 = 12$, we subtracted 8 from both members and got $x = 4$.
2 In $x - 5 = 7$, we added 5 to both members and got $x = 12$.
3 In $3x = 15$, we divided both members by 3 and got $x = 5$.
4 In $\frac{1}{2}x = 5$, we multiplied both members by 2 and got $x = 10$.

In other words, it is perfectly all right to add, subtract, multiply, or divide, provided we do it to *both* members. Mathematicians say that the equation was originally *balanced*, and we keep it balanced by using the same operations on both members.

Now watch what we do with the equation we wish to solve. We start with:

$$3x + 15 = 2x + 18$$

First, we will take $2x$ away from each member:

$$3x - 2x + 15 = 2x - 2x + 18$$
$$x + 15 = 18$$

Now, we will take 15 from each member:

$$x + 15 - 15 = 18 - 15$$
$$x = 3$$

This tells us that the number is 3. If you try this number in the original puzzle, you will find that it checks.

The trick is to look ahead and to guess what to subtract or add so that x will be alone on one side and no x on the other.

Problem: Solve for x: $5(2x - 3) = 2(x + 7) + 35$.

Solution:

$$
\begin{aligned}
5(2x - 3) &= 2(x + 7) + 35 \\
10x - 15 &= 2x + 14 + 35 \\
10x - 15 &= 2x + 49 \\
10x - 2x - 15 &= 2x - 2x + 49 \\
8x - 15 &= 49 \\
8x - 15 + 15 &= 49 + 15 \\
8x &= 64 \\
\tfrac{1}{8} \cdot 8x &= \tfrac{1}{8} \cdot 64 \\
x &= 8
\end{aligned}
$$

Answer: The number is 8

Check: $5(2x - 3) = 5(16 - 3) = 5(13) = 65$
$2(x + 7) + 35 = 2(15) + 35 = 30 + 35 = 65$

Test: Section 8

Part A. Solve the equations in Test: Section 7, Part A.

Part B. Solve the equations in Test: Section 7, Part B.

Part C. Solve the following equations and check.

1. $3(x + 1) + 4 = 5(2x - 1) - 23$
2. $2(x + 1) + 9 = 3(2x - 1) - 10$
3. $2(2x + 1) - 1 = 3(3x - 1) - 16$
4. $2(4x - 1) + 6 = 4(3x + 1) - 8$

9 PUZZLES ABOUT TWO NUMBERS

So far, we have done puzzles about a *single* number. Many puzzles have to do with *pairs* of numbers. For example, suppose you are told that there are two numbers; one of them is twice the other, and the sum of the two numbers is 12.

Let us try this by the trial and error method:

the smaller number might be:	1	2	3	4	5	6
then the larger would be:	2	4	6	8	10	12
the sum would be:	3	6	9	(12)	15	18

You can see from the table that the numbers are 4 and 8.

Now, let us try to do this by mathematics. The first line of numbers is x. Then the second line must be $2x$. And the sum, $(x + 2x)$ is 12!

Here is how it looks:

Problem 1. I am thinking of two numbers. One of them is twice the other. Their sum is 12. What are the numbers?

Solution: Let x = the smaller number.
Then $2x$ = the larger number

$$(x + 2x) = 12$$
$$3x = 12$$
$$\frac{1}{3} \cdot 3x = \frac{1}{3} \cdot 12$$
$$x = 4$$

Answer: The two numbers are 4 and 8

Here is another situation. There are two numbers. One is 3 more than the other. Their sum is 13. Find the numbers. The trial-and-error table looks like this:

the smaller number might be:	1	2	3	4	5	6
then the larger one would be:	4	5	6	7	8	9
the sum would be:	5	7	9	11	(13)	15

From the table, the two numbers are 5 and 8.

The same problem is done mathematically as follows:

Problem 2. I am thinking of two numbers. One of them is 3 more than the other. Their sum is 13. Find the numbers.

Solution: Let x = the smaller number.
Then $x + 3$ = the larger number.

$$
\begin{aligned}
(x + x + 3) &= 13 \\
2x + 3 &= 13 \\
2x + 3 - 3 &= 13 - 3 \\
2x &= 10 \\
\tfrac{1}{2} \cdot 2x &= \tfrac{1}{2} \cdot 10 \\
x &= 5
\end{aligned}
$$

Answer: The two numbers are 5 and 8

Problem 3. I am thinking of two numbers. The second is 3 more than the first. Twice the first, added to the second, is 18. Find the numbers.

Solution: Let x = the first number.
Then $x + 3$ = the second number.

$$
\begin{aligned}
(2x + x + 3) &= 18 \\
3x + 3 &= 18 \\
3x + 3 - 3 &= 18 - 3 \\
3x &= 15 \\
\tfrac{1}{3} \cdot 3x &= \tfrac{1}{3} \cdot 15 \\
x &= 5
\end{aligned}
$$

Answer: The numbers are 5 and 8

Problem 4. I am thinking about two numbers. The second is 4 less than the first. Twice the first added to 3 times the second is 28. What are the numbers?

Solution: Let x = the first number.
Then $x - 4$ = the second number.

$$
\begin{aligned}
2x + 3(x - 4) &= 28 \\
2x + 3x - 12 &= 28 \\
5x - 12 &= 28 \\
5x - 12 + 12 &= 28 + 12 \\
5x &= 40 \\
\tfrac{1}{5} \cdot 5x &= \tfrac{1}{5} \cdot 40 \\
x &= 8
\end{aligned}
$$

Answer: The numbers are 8 and 4

Test: Section 9

In each of the following, write an equation and solve the puzzle.

Part A.

1 One number is twice another. Their sum is 15. What are the numbers?

2 One number is twice another. Their sum is 18. What are the numbers?

3 One number is 3 times another. Their sum is 16. What are the numbers?

4 One number is 3 times another. Their sum is 12. What are the numbers?

5 One number is 3 more than another. Their sum is 7. What are the numbers?

6 One number is 4 more than another. Their sum is 10. What are the numbers?

7 One number is 6 more than another. Their sum is 26. What are the numbers?

8 One number is 12 more than another. Their sum is 26. What are the numbers?

9 One number is 6 more than another. Their sum is 10. What are the numbers?

10 One number is 4 more than another. Their sum is 42. What are the numbers?

Part B.

1 One number is 2 more than another. Twice the first, added to the second, is 11.

2 One number is 3 more than another. Twice the first, added to the second, is 18.

3 One number is 6 more than another. Three times the first, added to the second, is 26.

4 One number is 9 more than another. Three times the first, added to the second, is 33.

Part C.

1 One number is 5 more than another. Twice the first, added to 3 times the second, is 25.

2 One number is 1 more than another. Twice the first, added to 5 times the second, is 61.

3 One number is 3 less than another. Three times the first, added to 4 times the second, is 65.

4 One number is 5 less than another. Three times the first, added to 8 times the second, is 70.

10 PUZZLES WITH LOTS OF NUMBERS

The word *consecutive* (kŏn•sĕk′*u*•tĭv) is used to tell you that two or more things follow each other. For example, 5 and 6 are two *consecutive numbers*, 4 and 6 are two *consecutive even numbers*, and 11, 13, and 15 are three *consecutive odd numbers*. Sometimes, these words are used in number puzzles.

Notice that if x stands for a number, $x + 1$ is the next (consecutive) number, and $x + 2$ is the next (consecutive) number after that. For example, 8, $(8 + 1)$, and $(8 + 2)$ are consecutive numbers.

If x stands for an *even* number, the next even number is $x + 2$, and $x + 4$ is the one after that, because the even numbers are two apart. *Example*: 12, 14, 16.

If x stands for an *odd* number, $x + 2$ is the next odd number, and $x + 4$ is the one after that, because the odd numbers are also two apart. *Example*: 23, 25, 27.

Problem 1. The sum of three consecutive numbers is 18. Find the three numbers.

Solution: Let x = the first number.
Then $x + 1$ = the second number
and $x + 2$ = the third number.

$$(x + x + 1 + x + 2) = 18$$
$$3x + 3 = 18$$
$$3x + 3 - 3 = 18 - 3$$
$$3x = 15$$
$$\tfrac{1}{3} \cdot 3x = \tfrac{1}{3} \cdot 15$$
$$x = 5$$

Answer: The three numbers are 5, 6, and 7. (Check this!)

Problem 2. The sum of three consecutive *even* numbers is 48. Find the three even numbers.

Solution: Let x = the first even number.
Then $x + 2$ = the second even number
and $x + 4$ = the third even number.

$$(x + x + 2 + x + 4) = 48$$
$$3x + 6 = 48$$
$$3x + 6 - 6 = 48 - 6$$
$$3x = 42$$
$$\tfrac{1}{3} \cdot 3x = \tfrac{1}{3} \cdot 42$$
$$x = 14$$

Answer: The even numbers are 14, 16, and 18. (Check this!)

Problem 3. The sum of four consecutive *odd* numbers is 136. Find the four numbers.

Solution: Let x = the first odd number.
Then $x + 2$ = the second odd number
and $x + 4$ = the third odd number
and $x + 6$ = the fourth odd number.

$$(x + x + 2 + x + 4 + x + 6) = 136$$
$$4x + 12 = 136$$
$$4x + 12 - 12 = 136 - 12$$
$$4x = 124$$
$$\tfrac{1}{4} \cdot 4x = \tfrac{1}{4} \cdot 124$$
$$x = 31$$

Answer: The four odd numbers are 31, 33, 35, and 37. (Check this!)

Problem 4. The sum of two consecutive *even* numbers is 12. Find the two even numbers.

Solution: Let x = the first even number.
Then $x + 2$ = the second even number.

$$(x + x + 2) = 12$$
$$2x + 2 = 12$$
$$2x + 2 - 2 = 12 - 2$$
$$2x = 10$$
$$\tfrac{1}{2} \cdot 2x = \tfrac{1}{2} \cdot 10$$
$$x = 5$$

Answer: The numbers are 5, and 7 — but they are not even! There is no *correct* answer.

In this problem, the answers seem to be right but they are actually wrong. The correct answer is: *There are no such numbers.* You must always check your answers to see that they satisfy the original puzzle. If they do not, then you might have made an error, or, as in this case, the problem may have no answer!

The following puzzle is just a bit different.

Problem 5. In the set of numbers 1, 5, 9, 13, 17, and so on, there are three in a row that add up to 99. Which three are they?

Solution: Let x = the smallest of the three numbers.
Then $x + 4$ = the next one
and $x + 8$ = the last one.

$$(x + x + 4 + x + 8) = 99$$
$$3x + 12 = 99$$
$$3x + 12 - 12 = 99 - 12$$
$$3x = 87$$
$$\tfrac{1}{3} \cdot 3x = \tfrac{1}{3} \cdot 87$$
$$x = 29$$

Answer: The three numbers are 29, 33, and 37. If you check, you will see that they add up to 99.

Test: Section 10

Write the equations for the following puzzles and solve them. Be sure to check.

Part A.

1 The sum of two consecutive numbers is 11.
2 The sum of two consecutive numbers is 17.
3 The sum of three consecutive numbers is 33.
4 The sum of three consecutive numbers is 48.
5 The sum of four consecutive numbers is 50.
6 The sum of five consecutive numbers is 265.

Part B.

1 The sum of two consecutive even numbers is 38.
2 The sum of two consecutive even numbers is 54.
3 The sum of two consecutive odd numbers is 64.
4 The sum of two consecutive odd numbers is 164.

5 The sum of four consecutive even numbers is 92.

6 The sum of four consecutive even numbers is 268.

7 The sum of four consecutive odd numbers is 64.

8 The sum of four consecutive odd numbers is 288.

9 The sum of five consecutive even numbers is 45.

10 The sum of five consecutive odd numbers is 30.

Part C.

1 In the set of numbers 1, 5, 9, 13, and so on, find three consecutive numbers that add up to 279.

2 In the set of numbers 3, 6, 9, 12, and so on, find three consecutive numbers that add up to 207.

3 In the set of numbers 3, 9, 15, 21, and so on, find three consecutive numbers that add up to 1827.

4 In the set of numbers 4, 9, 14, 19, and so on, find three consecutive numbers that add up to 1512.

6

FORMULA PROBLEMS

"You know," said Tim, as he entered the math class, "we always use formulas to do problems. My uncle is an engineer and he says that most of his work is done by formulas. Where do the formulas come from?"

"That's a good question," replied the teacher. "Most people never wonder how scientists make formulas. Let's spend a few days finding out more about them."

1 THE ARITHMETIC OF FORMULAS

Suppose that someone kept a tally, each hour, of the number of men and women who went into a theater. It might look something like this:

m (number of men)	10	9	15	17	18
w (number of women)	12	13	9	12	16
p (number of people)	22	22	24	29	34

In this case, the variables m, w, and p, refer to the lines of a table, and you can see that the third line, p, is the result of adding the first and second lines. In other words, it is true for every number in the table that

$$p = m + w$$

The lines of a table can be added, subtracted, multiplied, and divided to make a formula. If the admission charge for adults is 50¢, the receipts would be as follows:

p (number of people)	22	22	24	29	34
\$0.50 (admission)	.50	.50	.50	.50	.50
r (number of dollars)	11.00	11.00	12.00	14.50	17.00

and you can see that $r = 0.50p$, where 0.50 is a constant. (A constant is a special kind of variable: a variable with only one value.)

Now, suppose that we start with a line of a table which we shall call n. Let us add $n + 5$ and $n - 3$ and see what we get:

n	1	2	3	4	5	6
$n + 5$	6	7	8	9	10	11
$n - 3$	-2	-1	0	1	2	3
$(n+5) + (n-3)$	4	6	8	10	12	14

Compare this with $2n + 2$

n	1	2	3	4	5	6
$2n$	2	4	6	8	10	12
$2n + 2$	4	6	8	10	12	14

As you can see, $(n + 5) + (n - 3) = 2n + 2$. In general, mathematicians try to *simplify* as much as possible by adding or subtracting what they call *like terms*. In the example, n and n are *like terms* and -3 and 5 are also like terms. Other *like terms* would be $3p$ and $7p$ because they have the same letters, but $3p$ and $7q$ would not be like terms. Notice that n is the same as $1n$, and in the following, m is the same as $1m$.

Problem 1. Add $(m + 3)$ and $(2m + 1)$.

Solution:

$$\begin{array}{r} m + 3 \\ 2m + 1 \\ \hline 3m + 4 \end{array}$$

Problem 2. Add $m + 3$ and $n - 5$.

Solution:

$$\begin{array}{llr} m & & + 3 \\ & n & - 5 \\ \hline m & + n & - 2 \end{array}$$

Notice that *like terms* are placed in columns under each other.

Problem 3. Add $(2m + 5n + 6)$ and $(3m - 7n + 4)$.

Solution:

$$\begin{array}{r} 2m + 5n + 6 \\ 3m - 7n + 4 \\ \hline 5m - 2n + 10 \end{array}$$

Problem 4. Add $p = 3m$ and $q = 5m$.

Solution:

$$\begin{array}{rcl} p & = & 3m \\ q & = & 5m \\ \hline p + q & = & 8m \end{array}$$

Problem 5. Subtract $5m$ from $8m$.

Solution: As explained in Chapter 2 (p. 52), "subtract $5m$" means "add the negative of $5m$." The negative of $5m$ is $-5m$, so the problem becomes:

$$\begin{array}{r} 8m \\ -5m \\ \hline 3m \end{array}$$

Problem 6. Subtract $(5m + 4)$ from $(8m - 2)$.

Solution: The negative of $(5m + 4)$ is $(-5m - 4)$.

$$\begin{array}{r} 8m - 2 \\ -5m - 4 \\ \hline 3m - 6 \end{array}$$

Problem 7. Subtract $(2x - y)$ from $(3x + 7y)$.

Solution:

$$\begin{array}{r} 3x + 7y \\ -2x + y \\ \hline x + 8y \end{array}$$

Problem 8. Subtract $(2a + b)$ from $(3a - c)$.

Solution:

$$\begin{array}{rrr} 3a & & -c \\ -2a & -b & \\ \hline a & -b & -c \end{array}$$

Problem 9. Subtract $y = 2x - 5$ from $y = 3x - 7$.

Solution: The negative of $(y = 2x - 5)$ is $(-y = -2x + 5)$.

$$\begin{array}{rcrcr} y & = & 3x & - & 7 \\ -y & = & -2x & + & 5 \\ \hline 0 & = & x & - & 2 \end{array}$$

Problem 10. Find $\frac{1}{2}(2n + 4)$.

Solution: Let us investigate a table, first.

n	1	2	3	4	5	6
$2n$	2	4	6	8	10	12
$2n + 4$	6	8	10	12	14	16
$\frac{1}{2}(2n + 4)$	3	4	5	6	7	8

Notice that

$$\tfrac{1}{2}(2n + 4) = n + 2$$

In other words, $\frac{1}{2}(2n + 4) = \frac{1}{2} \cdot 2n + \frac{1}{2} \cdot 4 = n + 2$. This is an application of the distributive law which we studied in Chapter 2 (p. 58).

Test: Section 1

Part A. In each of the following, complete the table on a separate sheet of paper. If you want to, copy this whole table, but *DO NOT WRITE IN THIS BOOK.*

1

m	1	2	3	4	5	6
n	3	5	7	9	12	15
$m + n$			?			
$m - n$						

2

p	3	7	9	10	15
q	1	5	3	4	6
$p + q$			?		
$p - q$					

→

3

a	-1	2	3	4	5
b	-2	5	-4	7	-8
$a + b$			?		
$a - b$					

4

c	-3	-2	0	4	6
d	-8	0	4	5	7
$c + d$			?		
$c - d$					

5

f	1	2	3	4	5
g	-2	8	4	5	5
$2f$					
$3g$			?		
$2f + 3g$					
$2f - 3g$					

6

h	1	2	3	4	5
r	-3	-2	-1	2	8
$3h$					
$5r$			?		
$3h + 5r$					
$3h - 5r$					

Part B.

1 Add $(x + 3y)$ and $(2x - 4y)$
2 Add $(2a + b)$ and $(7a - 2b)$
3 Add $(p - 8r)$ and $(2p + 7r)$
4 Add $(s - 9t)$ and $(3s + 10t)$
5 Add $(5x + 8y)$ and $(2x - 10y)$
6 Add $(7t + 4u)$ and $(3t - 9u)$
7 Take $(2a + x)$ from $(3a + 5x)$
8 Take $(3b + 2y)$ from $(7b + 9y)$
9 Take $(5h - \mathrm{k})$ from $(9h - k)$

→

10 Take $(4m - c)$ from $(5m - 2c)$
11 Take $(n - 3p)$ from $(-8n + p)$
12 Take $(q - 7r)$ from $(-3q + 2r)$
13 Add $(y = 2x + 3)$ and $(z = 3x - 5)$
14 Add $(y = 3x + 5)$ and $(z = x + 7)$
15 Add $(p = 3m + 8)$ and $(p = -m + 10)$
16 Add $(p = 7m + 6)$ and $(p = -4m - 3)$
17 Take $(y = 5x + 6)$ from $(y = x - 8)$
18 Take $(y = 3x + 7)$ from $(y = 2x - 5)$
19 Take $(q = 4r - 5)$ from $(q = r + 7)$
20 Take $(q = -2r + 1)$ from $(q = 3r + 9)$

Part C. Complete the following tables.

1

n	1	2	3	4	5
$3n$					
$\frac{1}{3}(3n)$			?		

What is your conclusion?

2

n	1	2	3	4	5
$5n$					
$\frac{1}{5}(5n)$			?		

What is your conclusion?

3

n	1	2	3	4	5
$2n$					
$2n + 6$			?		
$\frac{1}{2}(2n + 6)$					

What is your conclusion?

4

n	1	2	3	4	5
$3n$					
$3n + 12$			?		
$\frac{1}{3}(3n + 12)$					

What is your conclusion?

2 WRITING FORMULAS FROM TABLES

You already know how to write a formula for simple tables. For example, if the table is

p	1	2	3	4	5
c	3	6	9	12	15

then you can see that $c = 3p$. This means that a number on the c line is always *three times as large* as the corresponding number on the p line.

Now look at this one:

p	1	2	3	4	5
r	2	5	8	11	14

You might think, at first glance, that $r = 2p$ but this is not true. For example, while $p = 5$, r does not equal 10. By comparing this table with the first table, notice that r is always one less than $3p$. In other words, $r = 3p - 1$.

If you do not have another table to compare, you may have to try several formulas before getting the one that really works.

Here is another one:

s	1	2	3	4	5
A	1	4	9	16	25

You probably see that $A = ss$, or, in our shorthand, $A = s^2$ (s square). But what about this?

s	1	2	3	4	5
B	−2	1	6	13	22

If you compare this with the previous table, you can see that $B = s^2 - 3$. This is not so easy!

Most formulas used by engineers and technicians have more than two variables.

Problem 1. Find a formula for the following table:

r	1	3	7	8
s	2	6	4	11
t	3	9	11	19

Solution: $t = r + s$.

Problem 2. Find a formula for the following table:

d	1	2	3	4
e	5	3	6	8
f	7	7	12	16

Solution: $f = 2d + e.$

Problem 3. Find a formula for the following table:

g	1	2	3	4
h	5	8	17	18
m	4	6	14	14

Solution $m = h - g.$

Test: Section 2

Part A. Write a formula for each of the tables below. In each case, you may assume that the rule that holds for this portion of the table holds for all numbers.

1

m	2	4	6	8
p	1	2	3	4

2

r	1	2	3	4
t	2	4	6	8

3

s	2	3	4	5
p	1	2	3	4

4

a	1	2	3	4
c	2	3	4	5

5

t	1	2	3	4
b	1	3	5	7

6

n	1	2	3	4
d	3	5	7	9

Part B. Write a formula for each of the following.

1

p	1	2	3	4
r	1	8	27	64

2

p	1	2	3	4
s	0	7	26	63

3

b	1	2	3	4
a	2	9	28	65

4

b	1	2	3	4
d	3	10	29	66

5

t	1	2	3	4
w	2	5	10	17

6

t	1	2	3	4
z	0	3	8	15

Part C. See whether you can find a formula for each of the following.

1

a	1	2	3	4
b	1	1	3	3
c	2	3	6	7

2

a	1	2	3	4
b	5	7	9	15
c	4	5	6	11

3

m	1	2	3	4
n	3	5	7	3
p	3	10	21	12

4

m	1	2	3	4
n	3	7	5	6
r	3	$3\frac{1}{2}$	$1\frac{2}{3}$	$1\frac{1}{2}$

3 WRITING SCIENTIFIC FORMULAS

In the preceding section, you were given an idea as to how formulas are arrived at. Unfortunately, scientists are seldom lucky enough to get such easy numbers. A scientist who is working with two variables, r and p, may get the following readings from his instruments:

r	0.8	2.1	3.5	4.5	6.5	8.6
p	0.6	2.5	3.3	4.8	6.4	8.9

Here is what he does. First, he plots the points (Fig. 6-1) and studies them very closely.

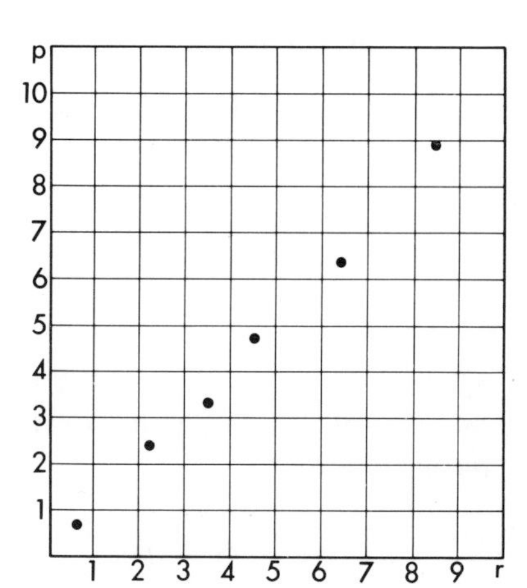

Fig. 6-1. Plotting the points.

They *seem* to run along a straight line. There is a special technique for finding the *line of best fit*, but it requires a knowledge of higher mathematics.

However, even a good guess will show that the line is something like the one shown in Fig. 6-2.

Now, let us read some points from the line.

The new table becomes:

r'	1	2	3	4	5	6	7
p'	1	2	3	4	5	6	7

where r' (r prime) and p' (p prime) are the points read from the graph. Using this table, we get the formula, $p = r$, which is very close to the actual condition.

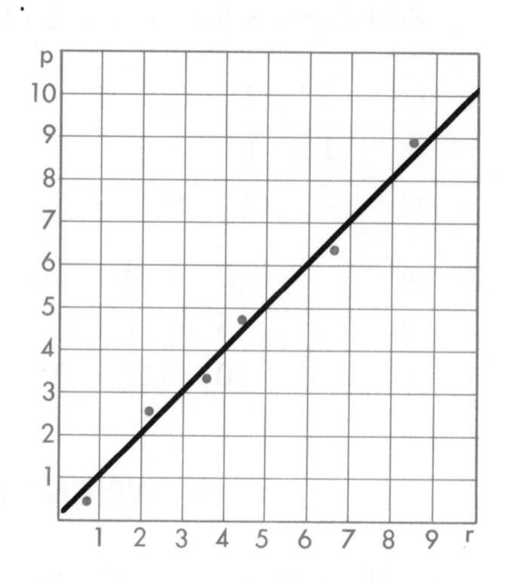

Fig. 6-2. Guessing a line for r and p.

Problem 1. Find a formula for

q	3.4	4.2	5.8	6.7
t	1.2	2.4	3.6	5.0

Solution: (Fig. 6-3.) Using the points, they appear to lie on a straight line. Draw the best line you can. Now, reading points, we get:

q'	3	4	5	6
t'	1	2	3	4

so that our best scientific guess is that $t = q - 2$.

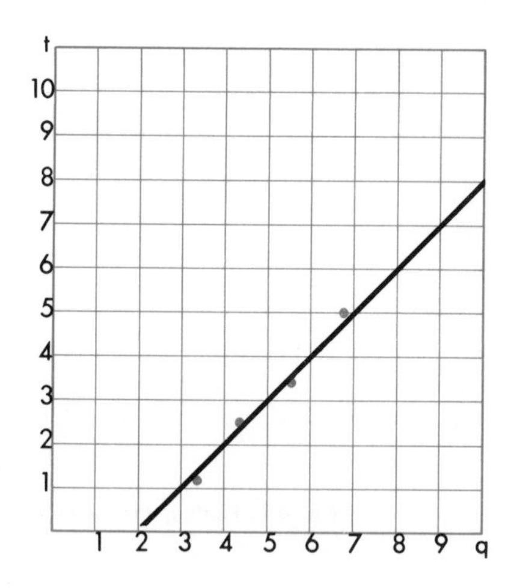

Fig. 6-3. Guessing a line for q and t.

Problem 2. Find a formula for the table:

b	0.9	2.2	3.1	4.4
u	4.0	3.1	1.6	0.8

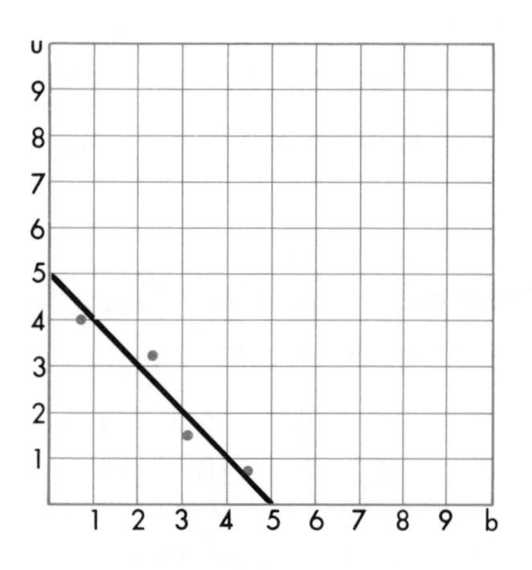

Fig. 6-4. Guessing a line for b and u.

Solution: (Fig. 6-4). Plotting the points, they appear to lie on a straight line. Draw the best line you can. Now, reading points from the line, we have

b'	1	2	3	4
u'	4	3	2	1

from which our best scientific guess is that $b + u = 5$.

Problem 3. Find a formula for the table:

a	0.2	0.6	1.8	2.6	3.7	4.5
d	0.1	1.9	2.5	6.1	14.0	22.0

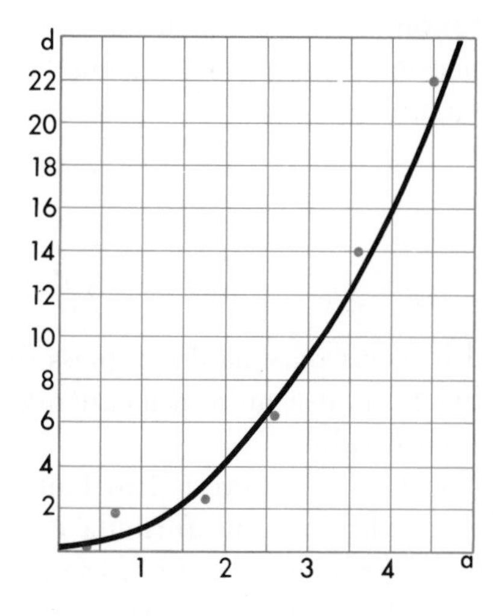

Fig. 6-5. Guessing a line for a and d.

Solution: (Fig. 6-5.) This is definitely not a straight line. Draw the smoothest curve you can. Read points.

a'	1	2	3	4	5
d'	1	4	9	16	25

From this, our best guess is that $d = a^2$.

Problem 4. Find a formula for the table:

b	0.1	0.6	1.8	2.0	2.6	3.7	4.5
d	0.4	2.0	3.5	5.9	7.1	15.0	23.0

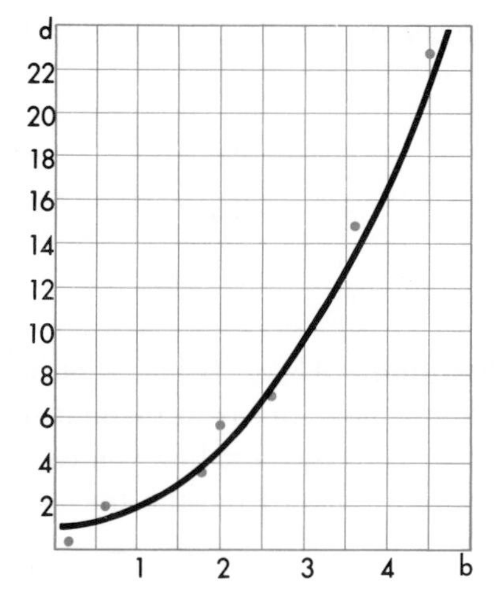

Fig. 6-6. Guessing a line for *b* and *d*.

Solution: (Fig. 6-6.) From the figure, we get the values:

b'	1	2	3	4	5
d'	2	5	10	17	26

for which the formula is $d = b^2 + 1$.

Problem 5. Find a formula for the table:

g	0.9	2.2	3.9	5.3	7.9
h	2.2	4.1	2.1	7.6	0.9
k	3.2	5.9	5.8	13.2	9.2

Solution: This is much more difficult because it is hard to make a three-dimensional graph to get smoothed values. Sometimes it helps to round-off the figures:

g'	1	2	4	5	8
h'	2	4	2	8	1
k'	3	6	6	13	9

and it seems reasonable to guess that $k = g + h$.

Scientists use more difficult methods and computing machines to get the smoothed values.

You may be interested to look at a three-dimensional graph (Fig. 6-7.) This graph shows the formula $E = IR$, a very important law in electricity, called *Ohm's law*. In this formula, E stands for the number of volts in an electrical circuit, I stands for the current (number of amperes), and R stands for the resistance (number of ohms). On the graph, point M is at $E = 4$ volts, $I = 1$ ampere, and $R = 4$ ohms. (Read down to the bottom

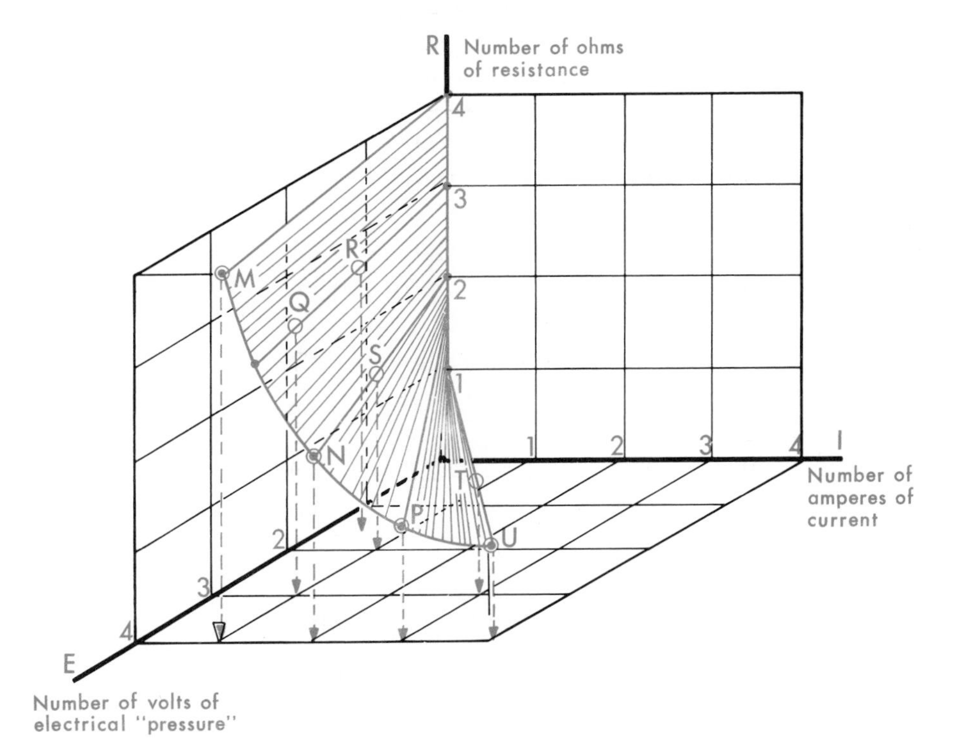

Fig. 6-7. A three-dimensional graph.

and across to find out how much E and I are.) Point Q is at $E = 3$ volts, $I = 1$ ampere, and $R = 3$ ohms.

Test: Section 3

Part A. In each of the following, plot the points, make a graph, read points from the graph, and guess a formula.

1	m	1.0	1.9	3.1	4.0	2	q	0.1	0.6	1.0	2.0
	p	0.9	2.1	2.9	3.9		r	0.3	1.0	2.3	3.8
3	s	0.3	1.2	2.1	3.1	4	u	1.5	2.3	3.2	4.1
	t	1.2	2.2	2.9	3.9		v	0.6	1.2	2.3	3.0
5	w	0.3	0.7	1.3	1.8	6	a	0.2	1.2	1.5	2.6
	z	1.8	1.1	0.7	0.2		s	2.6	1.9	1.3	1.3

Part B. In each of the following, plot the points, make a graph, read points from the graph, and guess a formula.

1	b	0.6	1.3	2.3	3.0	3.7
	t	0.1	2.0	4.6	10.0	14.5
2	c	0.5	1.1	1.8	2.8	3.4
	u	0.5	1.0	3.8	7.9	13.0
3	d	0.6	1.3	2.3	3.0	3.7
	w	1.1	3.0	5.6	11.0	15.5
4	e	0.5	1.1	1.8	2.8	3.4
	z	−0.5	0.0	2.8	6.9	12.0

Part C. Try to guess formulas for the following.

1	m	0.9	3.2	6.8	8.3	10.6
	n	2.1	4.6	5.1	1.9	3.3
	p	3.0	7.9	11.8	10.1	14.5
2	r	5.2	5.6	8.3	8.7	13.4
	s	5.9	3.5	3.6	3.4	0.7
	t	11.2	9.1	12.2	11.9	14.0
3	a	0.8	2.2	3.9	4.3	6.2
	b	1.9	3.1	5.1	2.7	1.8
	c	2.1	6.3	15.0	11.9	12.8
4	f	3.2	4.9	6.3	7.8	10.4
	n	4.8	2.3	2.7	5.4	2.6
	r	14.6	9.8	17.7	42.0	31.1

Read the graph in Fig. 6-7 and find the three values at each of the following points:

5 R **6** S **7** N **8** P **9** T **10** U

4 SOLVING FORMULA PROBLEMS BY SUBSTITUTION

The *perimeter* of a triangle is found by adding the lengths of the three

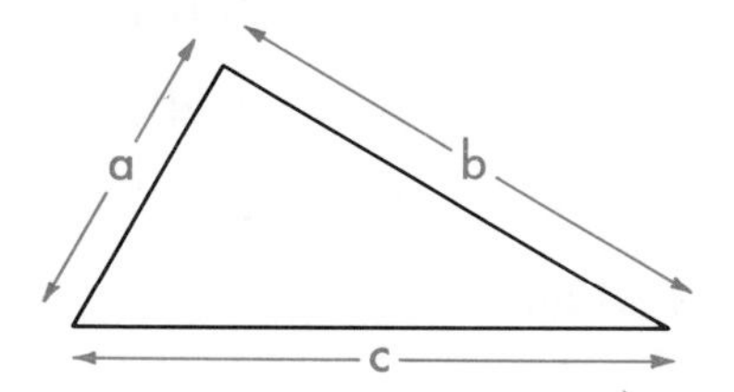

sides. In the following table, p stands for the number of inches of perimeter, and a, b, and c stand for the number of inches of each of the sides.

a	2	5	9	10
b	3	7	2	12
c	3	6	8	13
p	8	18	19	?

In the table, one value of p has been omitted. How can we find it?

Problem 1. The formula for the perimeter of a triangle is $p = a + b + c$, where p is the perimeter, and a, b, and c are the lengths of the sides. If $a =$ 10 in., $b = 12$ in., and $c = 13$ in., find the perimeter.

Solution:

Formula	$p = a + b + c$
	$\downarrow \quad \downarrow \quad \downarrow \quad \downarrow$
Substitution	$p = 10 + 12 + 13$
Numerical solution	$p = 35$

Answer: The perimeter is 35 in.

Problem 2. The formula for the perimeter of a rectangle is $p = 2b + 2h$, where b is the length of one side and h is the length of an adjacent side. Adjacent (ad·ja′cent) means "next to." If $b = 10$ in., and $h = 4$ in., find the perimeter.

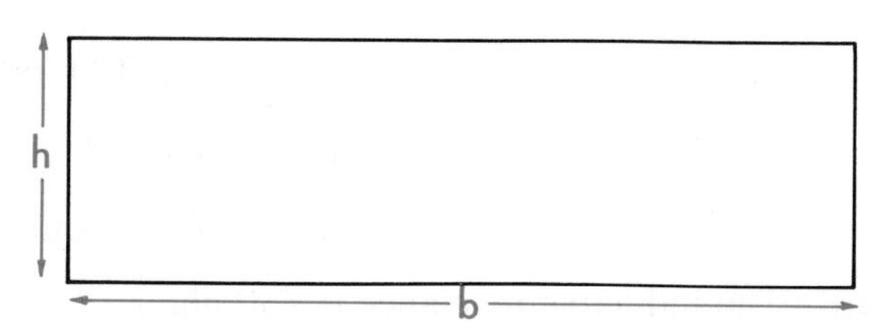

Solution:

Formula $p = 2b + 2h$

Substitution $p = 2(10) + 2(4)$

$p = 20 + 8$

Numerical solution $p = 28$

Answer: The perimeter is 28 in.

Problem 3. The formula for the power of an electric appliance is $P = EI$, where P is the number of watts, E is the number of volts, and I is the number of amperes. Find the wattage of an air conditioner using 110 volts and 12.0 amperes.

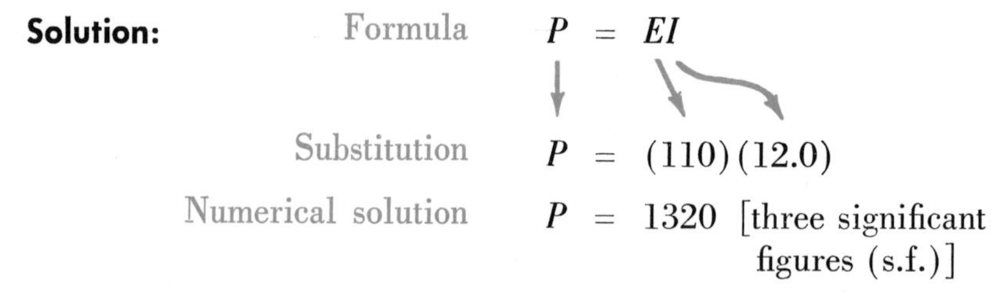

Solution:

Formula $P = EI$

Substitution $P = (110)(12.0)$

Numerical solution $P = 1320$ [three significant figures (s.f.)]

Answer: The power is 1320 watts.

Electric companies use *kilowatts* to measure power. One kilowatt is 1000 watts, so this answer may be written as 1.32 kw.

Problem 4. The formula for the inductive reactance of a radio circuit is $X_L = 2\pi fL$ where X_L (X sub L) is the number of ohms, π is a constant (about 3.14), f (frequency) is the number of cycles per second, and L (inductance of a radio coil) is measured as the number of henries. What is the inductive reactance of a circuit where the frequency is 60 cycles per second and the inductance is 2.0 henries?

Solution:

Formula $X_L = 2\ \pi\ f\ L$

Substitution $X_L = 2(3.14)(60)(2.0)$

$X_L = 753.60$

Numerical solution $X_L = 750$ (rounded to two s.f.)

Answer: The inductive reactance is 750 ohms.

Problem 5. The formula for the capacitive reactance of a radio circuit is $X_C = \dfrac{1}{2\pi fC}$, where X_C (X sub C) is the number of ohms due to the capacitors in the radio, π is a constant (about 3.14), f (frequency) the number of cycles per second, and C. (capacitance) is measured as the number of farads. What is the capacitive reactance of a circuit where the frequency is 60 cycles per second, and the capacitance is 0.50 farads?

Solution:

Formula $$X_C = \frac{1}{2\pi fC}$$

Substitution $$X_C = \frac{1}{2(3.14)(60)(0.50)}$$

$$X_C = \frac{1}{188.40}$$

$$X_C = 0.00531$$

Numerical solution $X_C = 0.0053$ (rounded to two s.f.)

Answer: The capacitive reactance is 0.0053 ohms.

Problem 6. When a steel bar is stretched, its elongation in inches is given by the formula:

$$e = \frac{Pl}{AE}$$

where e is the number of inches of elongation, P is the number of pounds of force applied, l is the length of the bar in inches, A is its cross-section area in sq. in., and E is a constant which in this case, is 29 million. If there is a force of 1 million pounds on a 10-ft. bar of steel with a cross-section of 25 sq. in., how much will it stretch?

Solution:

Formula $$e = \frac{Pl}{AE}$$

Substitution $$e = \frac{(1{,}000{,}000)(120)}{(25)(29{,}000{,}000)}$$

(Notice that 10 ft. was changed to 120 in. to fit the formula, but this still has only two significant figures.)

$$e = \frac{120{,}000{,}000}{725{,}000{,}000}$$

$$e = 0.166$$

Numerical solution $\quad e = 0.17$ (rounded to two s.f.)

Answer: The bar will stretch 0.17 in., or about $\frac{11}{64}$ in.

• Test: Section 4

Part A. Solve for the unknown quantities, using the formulas given.

(1) (2) When two conductors of electricity are connected end-to-end, their total resistance, R_T (R sub T), is given by the formula $R_T = R_1 + R_2$ (R sub 1 plus R sub 2), where R_1 is the resistance of one of the conductors, and R_2 is the resistance of the other.

1 If $R_1 = 7.6$ ohms and $R_2 = 8.7$ ohms, find the total resistance.

2 If $R_1 = 3.9$ ohms and $R_2 = 4.2$ ohms, find the total resistance.

(3) (4) The perimeter of an isosceles triangle (a triangle with two sides equal) is given by the formula $P = 2l + b$, where l is the length of one of the *equal* sides, and b is the length of the third side.

3 If $l = 7.1$ in., and $b = 5.3$ in., find P.

4 If $l = 6.5$ in., and $b = 3.2$ in., find P.

(5) (6) To drill the correct size hole for a screw, a machinist or carpenter calculates the *root diameter*. This is the size of the hole that must be made to allow the screw to enter without splitting the work. The formula used is:

$$R = T - 2P$$

where R is the root diameter, T is the *outside diameter* of the screw, and P is the *depth of the thread* (see diagram).

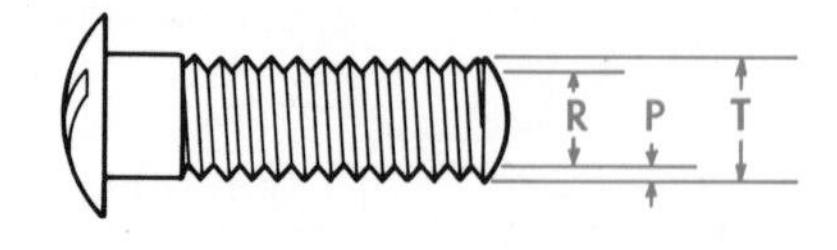

5 If the outside diameter is 1.7225 in., and the depth of thread is 0.3615 in., what is the root diameter?

6 If the outside diameter is 1.3500 in., and the depth of thread is 0.1445 in., what is the root diameter?

Part B. Solve for the unknown quantities, using the formulas given.

(1) (2) The area of a rectangle is: $A = lw$, where l is the length and w is the width. It does not matter which you call the length and which you call the width.

1 Find the area of a rectangle with sides 2.75 in., and 3.17 in.

2 Find the area of a rectangle with sides 3.12 in., and 4.76 in.

(3) (4) The area of a triangle is $A = \frac{1}{2} bh$ (see diagram).

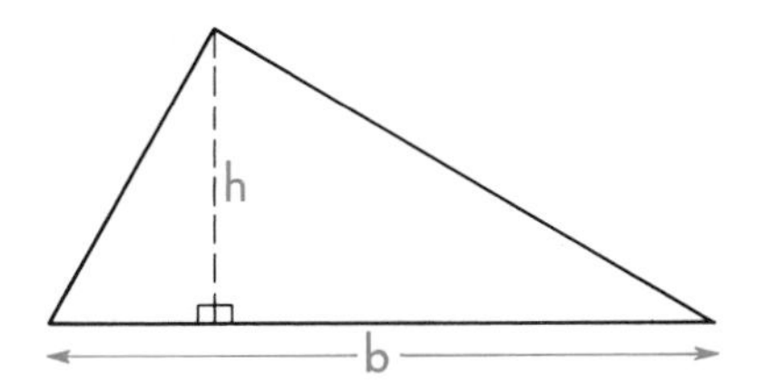

3 Find the area of a triangle if $b = 8.35$ in., and $h = 4.18$ in.

4 Find the area of a triangle if $b = 6.18$ in., and $h = 5.40$ in.

(5) (6) If anything is moving at a fixed rate of speed, the distance traveled is given by the formula $d = rt$. If d is the distance in miles, then r can be in miles per hour and t in hours.

5 Find the distance traveled if $r = 40$ mph. and $t = 3\frac{3}{4}$ hours.

6 Find the distance traveled if $r = 60$ mph. and $t = 2\frac{1}{2}$ hours.

(7) (8) The basic law of electricity is *Ohm's law* which tells the electrician how much current (amperes) he can expect for a given voltage. This depends upon the number of components receiving electricity, and the amount of *resistance* each component has. This resistance is measured in *ohms* (named after the man credited with the general principle). The form of Ohm's law which holds for all kinds of current is: $E = IZ$, where E is the number of volts, I is the number of amperes, and Z is the number of ohms. When alternating current is used, the number of ohms is called the *impedance.*

7 Find the number of volts in a circuit having 5.0 amperes of current, and an impedance of 6.3 ohms.

8 Find the number of volts in a circuit having 7.0 amperes of current, and an impedance of 3.7 ohms.

(9) (10) *Simple interest* is no longer used. It was used, many years ago, and by ancient civilizations. It is calculated by the formula: $I = prt$, where I is the number of dollars of interest, p is the number of dollars of principal (the amount originally put in the bank), r is the rate of interest, usually per year, and t is the time, usually in years.

9 Find the simple interest on $2500 at 2.5% for 3 years.

10 Find the simple interest on $1700 at 2.5% for 5 years.

Part C. Solve for the unknown quantity using the formulas given.

(1) (2) The efficiency of an engine is measured by engineers using the formula $E = \frac{U}{I}$, where U is the *useful output* and I is the *input*. In other words, if an engine takes 100 foot-pounds of energy to do 5 foot-pounds of useful work it is $\frac{5}{100}$, or 5% efficient. Most engines are very inefficient. We allow it, because while the *input* may be something seemingly useless (like steam), the *output* may be something very useful (like driving a locomotive).

1 Find the efficiency of an engine if the useful output is 7.9 foot-pounds, and the input is 56 foot-pounds.

2 Find the efficiency of an engine if the useful output is 12.7 foot-pounds, and the input is 101 foot-pounds.

(3) (4) Carpenters calculate the *pitch* of a roof (see diagram) by the formula: $P = 2S/N$ where S, the *rise* of the roof, shows how high it goes above

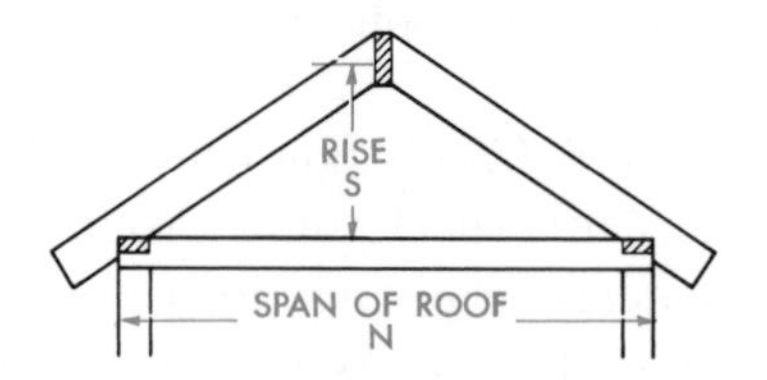

its lowest point, and N, is the *span* or the width of the roof. A roof must be pitched to allow rain and snow to run off.

3 Find the pitch of a roof if the rise is 6.37 ft., and the span is 5.18 ft.

4 Find the pitch of a roof if the rise is 8.12 ft., and the span is $6\frac{1}{2}$ ft.

(5) (6) Lumber yards sell wood by *board feet.* This is calculated by the formula, $B = \frac{twl}{12}$, where t is the thickness in *inches*, w is the width in *inches*, and l is the length in *feet*.

5 Find the number of board feet in a piece of lumber $2'' \times 5'' \times 10'$.

6 Find the number of board feet in a piece of lumber $3'' \times 6'' \times 14'$.

(7) (8) In a machine shop, the speed at which machines cut metal depends upon the type of metal being cut. Each metal has a "best" speed and the machines are adjustable. The cutting speed, C, in *inches per minute*, is given by the formula, $C = \frac{\pi RD}{12}$, where π is a constant (about 3.14), R is the turning speed of the machine in rpm (revolutions, or how many times it turns around, per minute), and D is the diameter in inches.

7 Find the cutting speed if $R = 80$ rpm, and $D = 6.0$ in.

8 Find the cutting speed if $R = 150$ rpm, and $D = 3.50$ in.

5 MORE COMPLICATED FORMULA PROBLEMS

Many formulas involve combinations of different arithmetic operations. The following are samples.

Problem 1. If you have a camera with an expensive lens, the lens will have on it a number called the *focal length*. A lens with a large focal length is called a *long-focus* lens. To find the focal length of a lens, an object is placed on one side of the lens and a mark is made on the other side where it focuses the image. The formula used is

$$f = \frac{d_o \cdot d_i}{d_o + d_i}$$

where f is the focal length in inches, d_o is the distance from the object to the

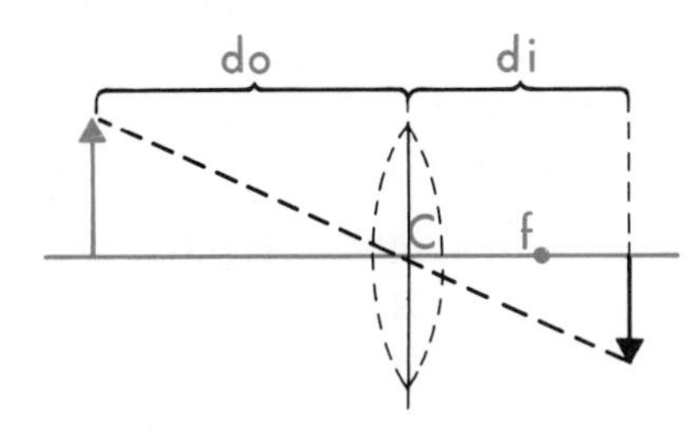

lens, and d_i is the distance from the image to the lens, both distances being measured in inches. If a lens focuses an object 3.0 in. away with an image 2.0 in. away, what is its focal length?

Solution:

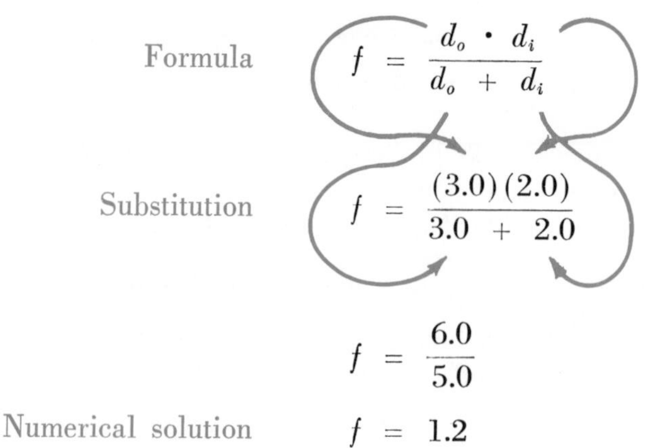

Formula $f = \dfrac{d_o \cdot d_i}{d_o + d_i}$

Substitution $f = \dfrac{(3.0)(2.0)}{3.0 + 2.0}$

$f = \dfrac{6.0}{5.0}$

Numerical solution $f = 1.2$

Answer: The focal length of the lens is 1.2 in.

Problem 2. Area of a trapezoid is given by the formula, $A = \frac{1}{2}h\ (B + b)$, where h, B, and b are the lengths shown in the diagram. What is the area of a trapezoid with $h = 5.6$ ft., $B = 7.2$ ft., and $b = 4.9$ ft?

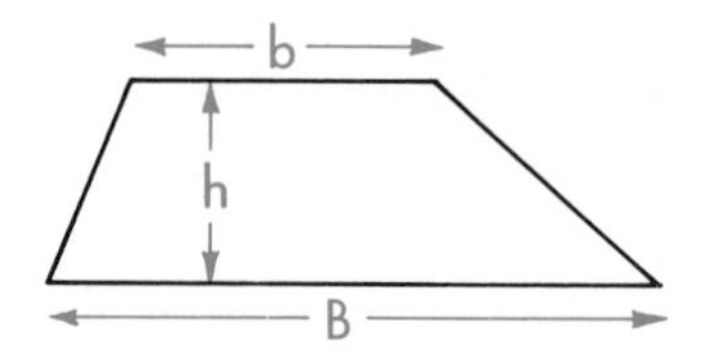

Solution:

Formula $A = \frac{1}{2}\ h\ (B + b)$

Substitution $A = \frac{1}{2}(5.6)\ (7.2 + 4.9)$

[At this point, we could, if we wished to, use the distributive law which allows us to multiply each of the two quantities inside the parentheses by the number in front, which is $\frac{1}{2}(5.6)$, or 2.8; however, it is more convenient not to do so in this case.]

$A = \frac{1}{2}(5.6)(12.1)$

$A = 33.88$

Numerical solution $A = 34$ (rounded to two s.f.)

Answer: The area is 34 sq. in.

Problem 3. The volume of a cone is given by the formula, $V = \frac{1}{3}\ \pi r^2 h$, where π is a constant (about 3.14), and r and h are the lengths shown on the diagram. What is the volume of a cone with $r = 2.7$ in., and $h = 4.1$ in.?

Solution: Formula $V = \frac{1}{3} \pi r^2 h$

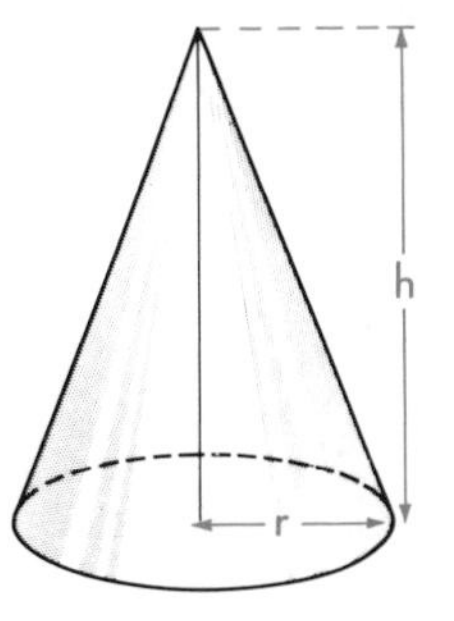

Substitution $V = \frac{1}{3}(3.14)(2.7)(2.7)(4.1)$

(Notice that r^2 means r times r.)

$V = 31.3$

Numerical solution $V = 31$ (rounded to two s.f.)

Answer: The volume is 31 cu. in.

Problem 4. Every material has a certain amount of *resistance* to an electric current. If the resistance is so high that almost no current will pass through it, the material is called an *insulator*. If the resistance is low, the material is called a *conductor*. Even insulators will take current, if there is enough force behind it. For example, the human body, which has a very high resistance, will accept and pass a bolt of lightning.

Engineers usually work with copper wire. A formula which predicts the resistance of copper wire is:

$$R = \frac{10.79l}{d^2}$$

where R is the resistance (in ohms), l is the length of the wire in feet, and d is the cross-section diameter in *mils*. A mil is one-thousandth of an inch, 0.001 in. What is the resistance of 100 ft. of copper wire with a cross-section of 12.5 mils?

Solution: Formula $R = \frac{10.79\,l}{d^2}$

Substitution $R = \frac{(10.79)(100)}{(12.5)(12.5)}$

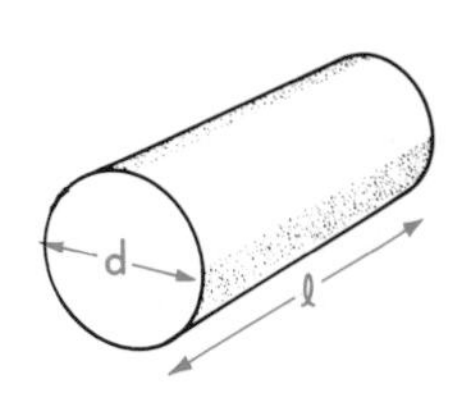

$$R = \frac{1079}{156.25}$$

$R = 6.906$

Numerical solution $R = 6.91$ (rounded to three s.f.)

Answer: The resistance is 6.91 ohms.

Problem 5. The length around an oval track is given by the formula, $C = \pi\sqrt{2(a^2 + b^2)}$, where C is the length in feet, and a and b are the lengths

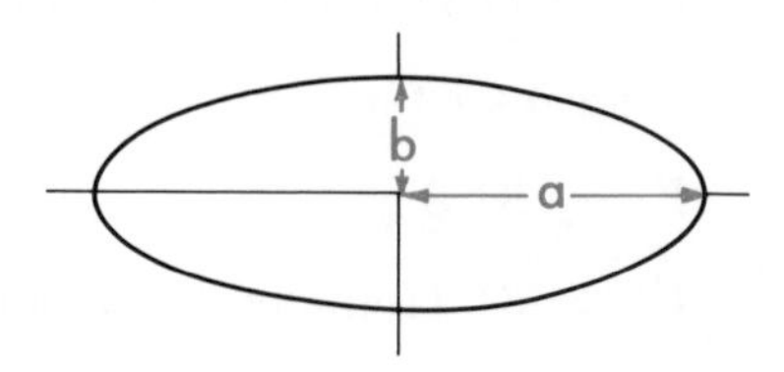

shown in the diagram. What is the distance around the track when $a = 35$ ft., and $b = 12$ ft.?

Solution:

Formula $C = \pi\sqrt{2(a^2 + b^2)}$

Substitution $C = 3.14\sqrt{2(35 \cdot 35 + 12 \cdot 12)}$

$C = 3.14\sqrt{2(1225 + 144)}$

$C = 3.14\sqrt{2(1369)}$

$C = 3.14\sqrt{2738}$

$C = (3.14)(52.3)$

$C = 164.2$

Numerical Solution $C = 160$ (rounded to two s.f.)

Answer: The distance around the track is 160 ft.

Problem 6. If the coils and capacitors in a radio or TV set are just right, they are said to be *in resonance* (rĕz′ō•năns). The *resonance frequency* in cycles per second is given by the formula:

$$f = \frac{1{,}000{,}000}{2\pi\sqrt{LC}}$$

where L is the inductance of the coil (in microhenries), and C is the capacitance of a capacitor (in microfarads). What is the resonant frequency of a set of coils and capacitors if the inductance is 15 microhenries and the capacitance is 0.25 microfarads?

Solution:

Formula $$f = \frac{1,000,000}{2\pi \sqrt{LC}}$$

Substitution $$f = \frac{1,000,000}{2(3.14) \sqrt{(15)(0.25)}}$$

$$f = \frac{1,000,000}{6.28 \sqrt{3.75}}$$

$$f = \frac{1,000,000}{(6.28)(1.94)}$$

$$f = \frac{1,000,000}{12.2}$$

$$f = 81,900$$

Numerical solution $f = 82,000$ (rounded to two s.f.)

Answer: The resonant frequency is 82,000 cycles per second. [A thousand cycles is called a *kilocycle* (kc), so this answer can be written: 82 kilocycles per second.]

Test: Section 5

Part A. In each of the following, find the unknown quantity.

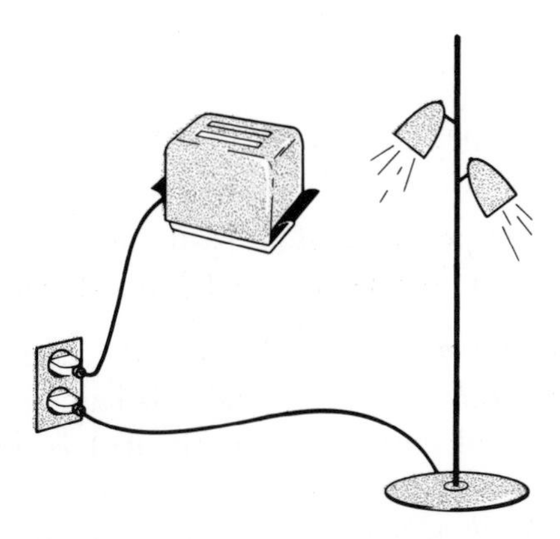

(1) (2) If two electrical appliances are plugged into the same outlet, they are said to be *in parallel*. The resistance of a pair of appliances in parallel

cannot be found by adding the individual resistances. Instead, the total resistance, R_T is found by the formula

$$R_T = \frac{R_1 \cdot R_2}{R_1 + R_2}$$

1 Find the total resistance of two electrical appliances plugged into the same outlet if the individual resistances are 500 ohms, and 750 ohms.

2 Find the total resistance of two electrical appliances plugged into the same outlet if the individual resistances are 1000 ohms, and 2000 ohms.

(3) (4) The rate of *taper* for an object like the leg of a chair is calculated by the formula

$$T = \frac{12(D - d)}{l}$$

where T is the taper in *inches per foot*, D and d are the diameters of the ends (in inches), and l is the length of the work (in inches).

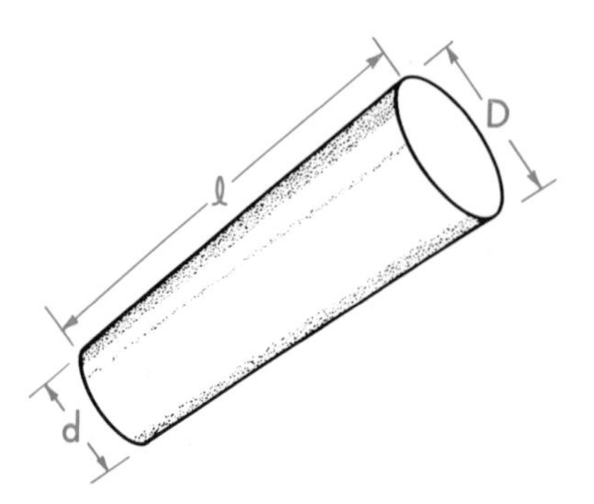

3 Find the taper per foot of a 2-ft. object (change to inches!) with a diameter of 5 in. at one end, and 3 in. at the other.

4 Find the taper per foot of a $1\frac{1}{2}$-ft. object (change to inches!) with a diameter of 3 in. at one end, and 1 in. at the other.

(5) (6) The *kinetic energy* of a body is the energy it has because *it is moving*. This energy, KE (in foot-pounds) is calculated by the formula, $KE = \frac{1}{2} mv^2$, where m is the *mass*, and v (velocity) is the speed in feet per second. The unit of mass is a little complicated, so we will simply call it *standard units*. You may *think* of mass as something related to *weight*. The only difference is that *weight* will change from place to place (as on the moon and the earth), but mass remains the same everywhere.

5 What is the kinetic energy of a 10-unit mass moving at 8.0 ft/sec?

6 What is the kinetic energy of a 15-unit mass moving at 12 feet per second?

Part B. In each of the following, find the unknown quantity.

(1) (2) The distance covered by a body falling from a height is calculated by the formula, $s = \frac{1}{2} gt^2$, where s is the distance fallen (in feet), t is the time (in seconds), and g is a number called the *acceleration of gravity.* It varies from place to place on the earth. We shall take it as 32.2 feet per second per second.

1 How far has a body fallen after 12 seconds?

2 How far has a body fallen after 18 seconds?

(3) (4) Everybody is interested in the horsepower of an automobile engine. The original "rule of thumb" formula used by the Society of Automotive Engineers (SAE) in determining this horsepower was $H = \frac{D^2N}{2.5}$, where D is the diameter of a cylinder in inches, and N is the number of cylinders. (This formula no longer holds good for modern cars.)

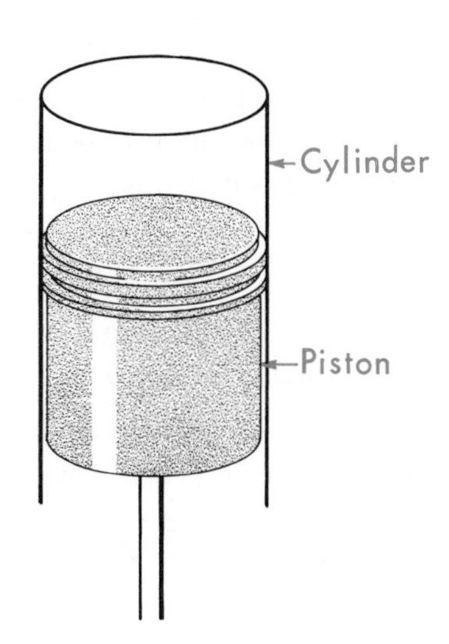

3 On the basis of the old formula, what would be the SAE horsepower of an 8-cylinder car with cylinders of 3.75-in. diameter?

4 What would be the SAE horsepower of a 6-cylinder car with cylinders of 3.25-in. diameter?

Part C. In each of the following, find the unknown quantity.

(1) (2) Side c of a right triangle can be found if the legs, a and b, are known. The formula for this is $c = \sqrt{a^2 + b^2}$.

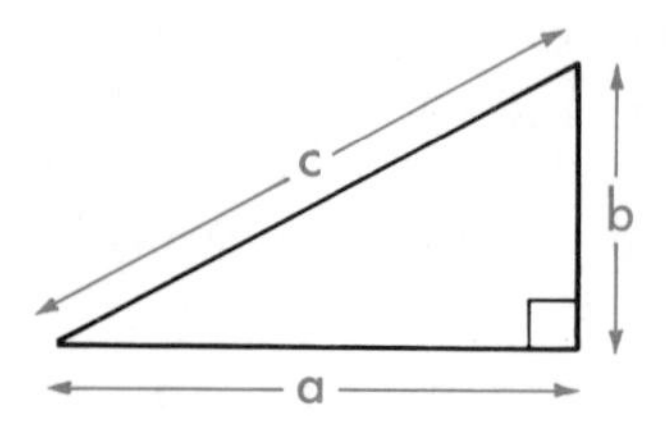

1 Find side c if $a = 6.0$, and $b = 8.0$.

2 Find side c if $a = 10$, and $b = 24$.

(3) (4) We have already mentioned that radios and TV sets have coils and capacitors. These coils and capacitors have a kind of resistance called *reactance,* for which we use the letter X. In addition, there is the usual resistance which we really call resistance. For this we use the letter R. The total result of both kinds of resistance is called *impedance,* and for this the letter Z is used. It is very important to know the impedance of a TV set because the antenna lead must have the same impedance as the set, or reception will be poor. The formula for impedance is

$$Z = \sqrt{X^2 + R^2}$$

3 What is the impedance of an electrical system where the reactance is 7.0 ohms, and the resistance is 9.0 ohms?

4 What is the impedance of an electrical system where the reactance is 8.0 ohms, and the resistance is 5.0 ohms?

(5) (6) The time, called the *period,* that it takes a pendulum to swing back and forth (one full swing) depends only upon the length of the pendulum, and the effect of gravity. This time, t (in seconds) is given by the formula

$$t = 2\pi \sqrt{\frac{l}{g}}$$

where l is the length of the pendulum in feet, and g is the acceleration of gravity, which we will take as 32 feet per second per second.

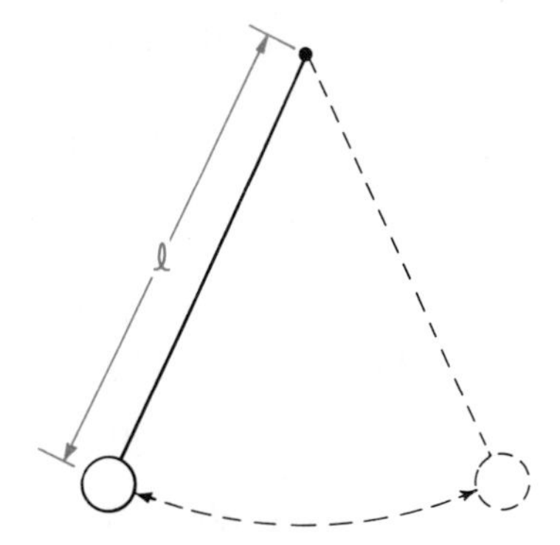

5 Find the time of the maximum (full) swing of a 64-ft. pendulum.

6 Find the time of the maximum (full) swing of a 96-ft. pendulum.

6 USING EQUATIONS TO SOLVE FORMULAS

Earlier in this chapter we learnt that the formula for the perimeter of a triangle is, $p = a + b + c$, where a, b, and c are the lengths of the sides. Suppose you want to make a triangle with a perimeter of 18 in., and you have two pieces of wood, one 3 in. long, and the other 8 in. long. How long must the third side be?

Substituting in the formula in the usual way we get:

Formula $\quad p = a + b + c$

$\downarrow \quad \downarrow \quad \downarrow \quad \downarrow$

Substitution $\quad 18 = 3 + 8 + c$

Simplifying this, we get

$$18 = 11 + c$$

(By now you will recognize this as an equation where it is necessary to subtract 11 from both members.)

$$18 - 11 = 11 - 11 + c$$

Numerical solution $\quad 7 = c$

Answer: The third side must be 7 in. long.

You can see that the use of equations makes it possible to use formulas whenever all but one value is known, no matter where the missing value is, in the formula. The following examples show other cases.

Problem 1. The formula for the perimeter of a rectangle is $p = 2b + 2h$, where b is the length of one side, and h is the length of an adjacent side. If $p = 28$ in., and $h = 4$ in., find out how long b is.

Solution:

Formula $p = 2b + 2h$

Substitution $28 = 2b + (2)(4)$

$28 = 2b + 8$

$28 - 8 = 2b + 8 - 8$

$20 = 2b$

$\frac{1}{2} \cdot 20 = \frac{1}{2} \cdot 2b$

Numerical solution $10 = b$

Answer: Side b must be 10 in. long.

Problem 2. The formula for the power of an electric appliance is $P = EI$, where P is the number of watts, E is the number of volts, and I is the number of amperes. If a certain air conditioner uses 1320 watts on a 110-volt line, what size fuse (how many amperes) must it use?

Solution:

Formula $P = E\ I$

Substitution $1320 = 110\ I$

$$\frac{1}{110} \cdot 1320 = \frac{1}{110} \cdot 110\ I$$

Numerical solution $12 = I$

Answer: The fuse must carry at least 12 amperes.

The next solution depends upon a very simple fact: if two numbers are equal, then their reciprocals are equal. For example, $\frac{5}{10}$, and $\frac{1}{2}$, are equal. Their reciprocals are $\frac{10}{5}$, and $\frac{2}{1}$, which are also equal.

This means, as another example, that if $\frac{2}{x} = 7$, then their reciprocals are also equal. In other words, we can write immediately: $\frac{x}{2} = \frac{1}{7}$.

Problem 3. The formula for the capacitive reactance of a radio circuit is $X_C = \dfrac{1}{2\pi f C}$, where X_C (X sub C) is the number of ohms, π is a constant (about 3.14), f (frequency) is the number of cycles per second, and C

(capacitance) is the number of farads. What is the frequency of a radio circuit if the reactance is 3.50 ohms, and the capacitors are tuned to a capacitance of 0.0200 farads?

Solution:

Formula $$X_C = \frac{1}{2\pi f C}$$

Substitution $$3.50 = \frac{1}{2(3.14)f(0.0200)}$$

If these numbers are equal → $$3.50 = \frac{1}{0.126\ f}$$

. . . Their reciprocals must be equal → $$\frac{1}{3.50} = \frac{0.126\ f}{1}$$

$$0.286 = 0.126\ f$$

$$\frac{1}{0.126} \cdot 0.286 = \frac{1}{0.126} \cdot 0.126\ f$$

$$\frac{0.286}{0.126} = f$$

Numerical solution $$2.27 = f$$

Answer: The frequency is 2.27 cycles per second.

Problem 4. The area of a trapezoid is $A = \frac{1}{2}h\ (B + b)$ where h, B, and b

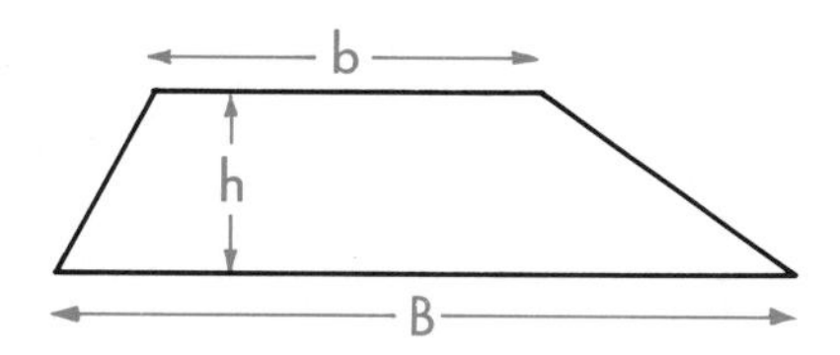

are the lengths shown in the diagram. If $A = 28$ sq. ft., $h = 7$ ft., and $B = 5$ ft., how long is b?

Solution:

Formula $$A = \frac{1}{2}h\ (B + b)$$

Substitution $$28 = \frac{1}{2}(7)(5 + b)$$

$$28 = \frac{7}{2}(5 + b)$$

To solve this equation, you must examine it very carefully to see what it tells you to do. *First,* you take the number, b, whatever it is, and *add five.* *Then,* you are supposed to *multiply by* $\frac{7}{2}$.

To get b "out," let us retrace these steps in reverse order. Instead of multiplying by $\frac{7}{2}$, we will multiply by the *reciprocal* of $\frac{7}{2}$. In other words, we will multiply by $\frac{2}{7}$. Then, instead of *adding* 5, we will *subtract* 5. This should get us back to b! Let us see if it does.

$$\frac{2}{7} \cdot 28 = \frac{2}{7} \cdot \frac{7}{2} (5 + b)$$

$$8 = 1 (5 + b)$$

$$8 = 5 + b$$

$$8 - 5 = 5 - 5 + b$$

Numerical solution $3 = b$

Answer: Side b should be 3 ft. long.

Test: Section 6

All the formulas given here have been explained in Sections 4 and 5 of this chapter. If you have forgotten what the letters stand for, look back at pp. 179–192. In each case, solve for the unknown value.

Part A.

1 $R_T = R_1 + R_2$. $R_T = 11.8$ ohms, $R_1 = 6.2$ ohms.
2 $R_T = R_1 + R_2$. $R_T = 159$ ohms, $R_2 = 70$ ohms.
3 $P = 2l + b$. $P = 27$ ft., $l = 5.0$ ft.
4 $P = 2l + b$. $P = 6.7$ in., $l = 1.2$ in.
5 $P = 2l + b$. $P = 175.0$ yd., $b = 70.0$ yd.
6 $P = 2l + b$. $P = 10.0$ cm., $b = 3.0$ cm.
7 $R = T - 2P$. $R = 1.5000$ in., $P = 0.2258$ in.
8 $R = T - 2P$. $R = 1.2500$ in., $P = 0.1176$ in.
9 $R = T - 2P$. $R = 2.5000$ in., $T = 3.5000$ in.
10 $R = T - 2P$. $R = 4.7500$ in., $T = 5.5000$ in.

Part B.

1 $d = rt$. $d = 120$ mi., $r = 40.0$ mph.
2 $d = rt$. $d = 250$ mi., $r = 50.0$ mph.

3 $d = rt$. $d = 250$ mi., $t = 3.5$ hr.
4 $d = rt$. $d = 425$ mi., $t = 4.20$ hr.
5 $A = lw$. $A = 309$ sq. in., $l = 23.4$ in.
6 $A = lw$. $A = 1288$ sq. ft., $w = 23.00$ ft.
7 $A = \frac{1}{2}bh$. $A = 1688$ sq. yd. $b = 75.00$ yd.
8 $A = \frac{1}{2}bh$. $A = 104$ sq. in., $h = 16.0$ in.
9 $I = prt$. $I = \$555$, $p = \$3700$, $r = 3\%$ $(3\% = 0.03)$.
10 $I = prt$. $I = \$364$, $p = \$2600$, $r = 2\%$ $(2\% = 0.02)$.
11 $I = prt$. $I = \$876$, $p = \$7300$, $t = 3$ yr.
12 $I = prt$. $I = \$312$, $p = \$2600$, $t = 2$ yr.

Part C.

1 $E = \frac{U}{I}$. $E = 70\%$ $(= 0.70)$, $U = 80.0$ foot-pounds.

2 $E = \frac{U}{I}$. $E = 15\%$ $(= 0.15)$, $U = 120$ foot-pounds.

3 $P = \frac{R}{S}$. $P = 1.3$, $R = 12$ ft.

4 $P = \frac{R}{S}$. $P = 1.2$, $R = 10$ ft.

5 $E = \frac{p}{e}$. $E = 65$, $p = 15$ lb. (Answer in inches.)

6 $E = \frac{p}{e}$. $E = 83$, $p = 17$ lb. (Answer in inches.)

7 SOLVING PROPORTIONS

In the previous section, you met an equation that looked like this:

$$\frac{2}{x} = \frac{5}{3}$$

and you learned that it could be solved by using the reciprocals of both numbers.

Equations which have one fraction in each member are so important that fast methods for solving them have been invented for the convenience of mathematicians, engineers, and scientists. These equations are called *proportions.*

Definition. A proportion is an equation in which the left member is a fraction, and the right member is a fraction.

Problem 1. Which of the following are proportions?

a $\frac{3}{5} = \frac{6}{10}$ **b** $\frac{8}{5} = 1\frac{3}{5}$ **c** $\frac{10}{5} = 2$
d $\frac{x}{2} = \frac{2}{4}$ **e** $\frac{2}{3} = \frac{3}{4}$

Solution:

a. Yes, this is a proportion.
b. No. The right member is really a sum: $1 + \frac{3}{5}$. If you change it to $\frac{8}{5} = \frac{8}{5}$, both members will be fractions and it will be a proportion.
c. No. But it can be made into one by writing the right member as $\frac{2}{1}$. The word *proportion* refers to the *form* of the equation, not its truth.
d. Yes. It is a *true* proportion when $x = 1$, as you can see.
e. Yes. Unfortunately, this one is never true.

A proportion has four parts. Two are called *middles* (or means), and two are called *ends* (or extremes). When you read it, the first and the last terms you read are the *ends.*

$$\begin{array}{rcl} \text{end} \rightarrow & \dfrac{2}{3} = \dfrac{4}{6} & \leftarrow \text{middle} \\ \text{middle} \rightarrow & & \leftarrow \text{end} \end{array}$$

Here, the 2 and the 6 are the *ends*, and the 3 and the 4 are the *middles.*

Problem 2. Identify the ends and middles in $\frac{5}{7} = \frac{1}{2}$.

Solution: The ends are 5, and 2. The middles are 7, and 1. This proportion, of course, is never true.

Now, look at the table opposite.

Notice that in the first three cases, which are *true*, the product of the middles equals the product of the ends. In the last two cases, which are *false*, the product of the middles does not equal the product of the ends. These are examples of an important law of mathematics.

The Law of Proportions. If a proportion is true, the product of the middles equals the product of the ends.

Problem 3. In each of the following, find the product of the middles, and the product of the ends. Is the proportion true, in each case?

a $\frac{2}{3} = \frac{10}{15}$ **b** $\frac{1\frac{1}{2}}{3} = \frac{3\frac{1}{4}}{6\frac{1}{2}}$ **c** $\frac{x}{5} = \frac{42}{30}$ **d** $\frac{2}{3} = \frac{5}{6}$

Solution:

a. The product of the middles is $2 \times 15 = 30$. The product of the ends is $3 \times 10 = 30$. This is a true proportion.
b. The product of the middles is $3 \times 3\frac{1}{4} = 9\frac{3}{4}$. The product of the ends is $1\frac{1}{2} \times 6\frac{1}{2} = 9\frac{3}{4}$. This is a true proportion.
c. The product of the middles is $5 \times 42 = 210$. The product of the ends is $30x$. This is sometimes true. As a matter of fact, it is true when $30x = 210$, or when $x = 7$.
d. The product of the middles is 15. The product of the ends is 12. This is a false proportion.

Using the *law of proportions,* we can easily solve any problem with proportions.

Proportion	*Is It True?*	*Middles*	*Product of Middles*	*Ends*	*Product of Ends*
$\frac{1}{2} = \frac{2}{4}$	Yes	2, 2	4	1, 4	4
$\frac{3}{6} = \frac{12}{24}$	Yes	6, 12	72	3, 24	72
$\frac{5}{7} = \frac{10}{14}$	Yes	7, 10	70	5, 14	70
$\frac{11}{12} = \frac{1}{2}$	No	12, 1	12	11, 2	22
$\frac{5}{6} = \frac{7}{8}$	No	6, 7	42	5, 8	40

Problem 4. Solve the following proportions.

a $\frac{x}{6} = \frac{8}{3}$ **b** $\frac{35}{x} = \frac{5}{4}$ **c** $\frac{7}{15} = \frac{x}{5}$ **d** $\frac{5}{2} = \frac{15}{x}$

Solutions:

a. $\frac{x}{6} = \frac{8}{3}$.

$$\text{Product of middles} \rightarrow (6)(8) = (x)(3) \leftarrow \text{Product of ends}$$
$$48 = 3x$$
$$\tfrac{1}{3} \cdot 48 = \tfrac{1}{3} \cdot 3x$$
$$16 = x$$

Check: $\frac{16}{6}$ is equal to $\frac{8}{3}$.

b. $\frac{35}{x} = \frac{5}{4}$.

$$\text{Product of middles} \rightarrow (x)(5) = (35)(4) \leftarrow \text{Product of ends}$$
$$5x = 140$$
$$\tfrac{1}{5} \cdot 5x = \tfrac{1}{5} \cdot 140$$
$$x = 28$$

Check: $\frac{35}{28}$ is equal to $\frac{5}{4}$.

c. $\frac{7}{15} = \frac{x}{5}$.

$$\text{Product of middles} \rightarrow (15)(x) = (7)(5) \leftarrow \text{Product of ends}$$
$$15x = 35$$
$$\tfrac{1}{15} \cdot 15x = \tfrac{1}{15} \cdot 35$$
$$x = 2\tfrac{1}{3}$$

Check: $\frac{2\frac{1}{3}}{5} = (2\tfrac{1}{3})(\tfrac{1}{5}) = \frac{7}{3} \cdot \frac{1}{5} = \frac{7}{15}$.

d. $\frac{5}{2} = \frac{15}{x}.$

$$\begin{aligned} \text{Product of middles} \rightarrow (2)(15) &= (5)(x) \leftarrow \text{Product of ends} \\ 30 &= 5x \\ \tfrac{1}{5} \cdot 30 &= \tfrac{1}{5} \cdot 5x \\ 6 &= x \end{aligned}$$

Check: $\frac{5}{2}$ equals $\frac{15}{6}$.

Test: Section 7

Part A. Which of the following are true proportions?

1 $\frac{2}{5} = \frac{4}{10}$ 2 $\frac{5}{6} = \frac{10}{12}$ 3 $\frac{8}{5} = \frac{17}{10}$

4 $\frac{3}{4} = \frac{7}{8}$ 5 $\frac{8}{7} = 1\frac{1}{7}$ 6 $\frac{3}{2} = 1\frac{1}{2}$

7 $\frac{19}{15} = \frac{2}{3} + \frac{3}{5}$ 8 $\frac{41}{24} = \frac{5}{6} + \frac{7}{8}$ 9 $\frac{15}{5} = 3$

10 $\frac{28}{4} = 7$

In each of the following: (a) identify the middles; (b) identify the ends; (c) find the product of the middles; (d) find the product of the ends.

11 $\frac{3}{8} = \frac{9}{24}$ 12 $\frac{5}{7} = \frac{25}{35}$ 13 $\frac{9}{11} = \frac{27}{33}$

14 $\frac{1}{8} = \frac{2\frac{3}{4}}{22}$

Part B. Solve the following proportions (or, in other words, find the value of x which makes the proportion true). Check your answers.

1 $\frac{x}{12} = \frac{3}{4}$ 2 $\frac{x}{35} = \frac{5}{7}$ 3 $\frac{12}{x} = \frac{6}{11}$ 4 $\frac{6}{x} = \frac{2}{3}$

5 $\frac{5}{8} = \frac{x}{24}$ 6 $\frac{7}{20} = \frac{x}{80}$ 7 $\frac{8}{9} = \frac{32}{x}$ 8 $\frac{10}{13} = \frac{80}{x}$

Part C. Solve the following proportions, and check your answers.

1 $\frac{x}{9} = \frac{5}{6}$ 2 $\frac{x}{15} = \frac{9}{10}$ 3 $\frac{12}{x} = \frac{9}{7}$ 4 $\frac{20}{x} = \frac{15}{16}$

5 $\frac{5}{4} = \frac{x}{10}$ 6 $\frac{3}{2} = \frac{x}{3}$ 7 $\frac{16}{15} = \frac{44}{x}$ 8 $\frac{18}{11} = \frac{48}{x}$

8 PROBLEMS INVOLVING PROPORTIONS

According to the American Automobile Association (AAA), a trip by car costs about $35 per day for a small family. If this is true, then an actual record of total cost by days would look something like this:

number of days	0	1	2	3	4
number of dollars	0	35	70	105	140

Notice that taking pairs of numbers from the table, we can write, $\frac{1}{2} = \frac{35}{70}$, $\frac{1}{3} = \frac{35}{105}$, and so on. Notice, also, that as the number of days goes up, the cost goes up *in proportion.* This is called a direct *proportion.*

Definition. If the numbers in a table all go up together (or down together) in proportion, we say that they are in *direct proportion.*

In other words, if you take any two columns of this kind of table:

number of days	. . . . . .	12	. .	15	. . .
number of dollars	. . . . . .	420	. .	525	. . .

you can write the proportion:

$$\frac{12}{15} = \frac{420}{525}$$

↑ ↑

days *dollars*

and this proportion will be true.

Problem 1. A 12-day trip cost Mr. Traveler $420. How much would a 30-day trip cost?

Solution: We will assume that the costs go up in proportion.

Let x = number of dollars for a 30-day trip.

$$\frac{12}{30} = \frac{420}{x}$$

$$\begin{array}{cc} \uparrow & \uparrow \\ \textit{days} & \textit{dollars} \end{array}$$

For convenience, reduce $\frac{12}{30}$:

$$\frac{2}{5} = \frac{420}{x}$$

$$(5)(420) = (2)(x)$$

$$2100 = 2x$$

$$\tfrac{1}{2} \cdot 2100 = \tfrac{1}{2} \cdot 2x$$

$$1050 = x$$

Answer: The trip should cost \$1050.

Problem 2. The Smith family is deciding how many days vacation to take. Last year, they spent \$350 in 13 days. This year they do not want to spend more than \$470. How many days can they take?

Solution: We will assume that the costs go up in direct proportion.

Let x = the number of days.

$$\textit{dollars} \longrightarrow \frac{350}{470} = \frac{13}{x} \longleftarrow \textit{days}$$

For convenience, reduce $\frac{350}{470}$ to $\frac{35}{47}$:

$$\frac{35}{47} = \frac{13}{x}$$

$$(47)(13) = (35)(x)$$

$$611 = 35x$$

$$\tfrac{1}{35} \cdot 611 = \tfrac{1}{35} \cdot 35x$$

$$17.5 = x \quad \text{(rounded)}$$

Answer: They can spend 17 days. If this is rounded to 18 days, the Smiths will go over their budget!

Now, let us look into a different situation. Machine shops use gears and pulleys to change the speeds of machines. In Fig. 6-8, a 10-in. pulley is being used to turn a 5-in. pulley. When pulley 1 turns once, pulley 2 will

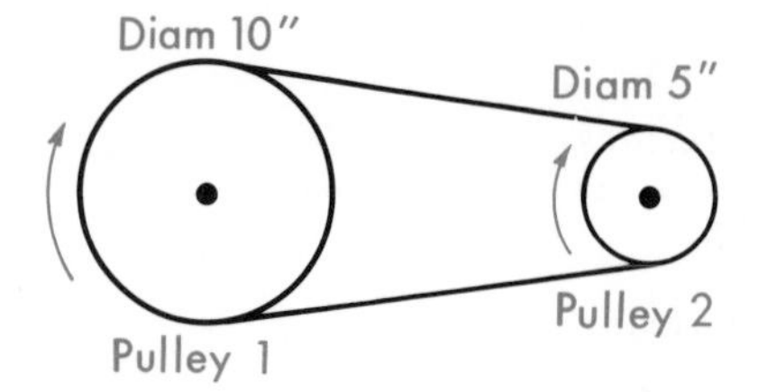

Fig. 6-8. Turning a small pulley.

have to turn twice to keep up with it, because the same belt goes over both pulleys. (A 5-in. pulley is really 5.0 in.)

Now look at Fig. 6-9. When pulley 1 turns once, pulley 2 makes only half a turn!

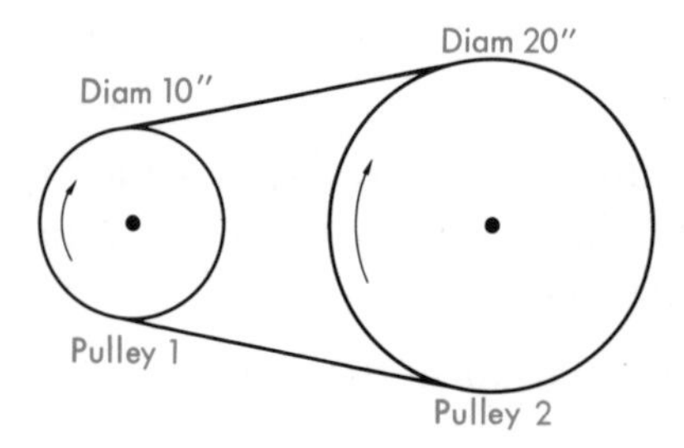

Fig. 6-9. Turning a big pulley.

If we made a table of the speeds of these three pulleys, it might look something like this.

Size of pulley (in. diameter)	5	10	20
Speed of pulley	2	1	0.5

Notice that

$$\underset{speed}{\frac{2}{1}} = \underset{size}{\frac{10}{5}}, \qquad \underset{speed}{\frac{2}{0.5}} = \underset{size}{\frac{20}{5}}$$

As the size of the pulley goes *up*, the speed goes *down* in proportion. If the size is multiplied by 4, the speed is divided by 4! This is called an *inverse proportion*.

Definition. If the numbers in one line of a table go *up* while the others go *down* in proportion, we say that they are in *inverse proportion.*

In other words, if you take any two columns of this kind of table:

size of pulley (in. diameter)	. . . .	12	. .	15	. . .
speed of pulley (rpm)	. . . .	500	. .	400	. . .

you can write:

$$\frac{12}{15} = \frac{400}{500}$$

and it will be a true proportion! If you compare this with the *direct proportion* type, you will see that one of the fractions seems to be *inverted* (turned upside down).

Problem 3. A 12-in. pulley turns at 500 rpm. How fast will a 5-in. pulley turn if it is connected to this 12-in. pulley by a belt? (5 in. = 5.0 in.)

Solution: We will assume that the speed changes in *inverse* proportion.

Let x = number of rpm for a 5-in. pulley.

$$\frac{12}{5} = \frac{x}{500}$$

↑ *size* ↑ *speed*

$$(5)(x) = (12)(500)$$

$$5x = 6000$$

$$\tfrac{1}{5} \cdot 5x = \tfrac{1}{5} \cdot 6000$$

$$x = 1200$$

Answer: The 5-in. pulley will turn at 1200 rpm.

Problem 4.

A 24-tooth gear turns at 2500 rpm. What size gear should be connected to it, to change the speed to 1300 rpm?

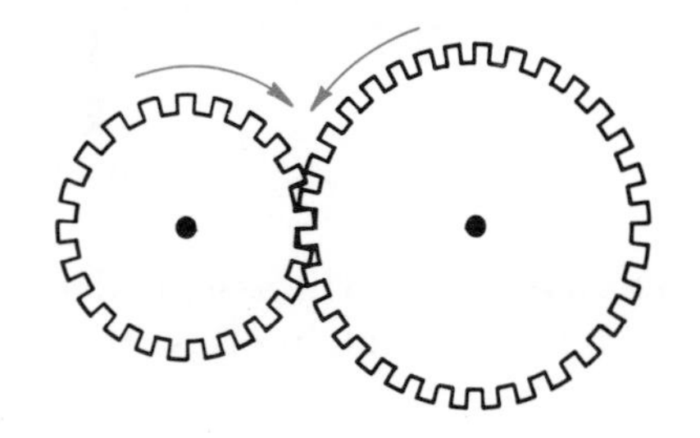

Solution: We will assume that the speed changes in *inverse* proportion. (The size of a gear can be measured by the number of teeth.)

Let x = number of teeth on the new gear.

$$\frac{24}{x} = \frac{1300}{2500}$$

$$\underset{\textit{size}}{\uparrow} \qquad \underset{\textit{speed}}{\uparrow}$$

For convenience, reduce $\frac{1300}{2500}$ to $\frac{13}{25}$:

$$\frac{24}{x} = \frac{13}{25}$$

$$(x)(13) = (24)(25)$$

$$13x = 600$$

$$\frac{1}{13} \cdot 13x = \frac{1}{13} \cdot 600$$

$$x = 46.2$$

Answer: Use a 46-tooth gear.

Obviously, you cannot have a piece of a tooth. Notice that the numerical solution is not always sensible. A problem should be answered in *words.*)

The following problems are additional examples of *important* cases of *inverse proportions.*

Problem 5. John and Mary are *exactly balanced* on a see-saw. John, who weighs 85 pounds is 5 ft. from the *fulcrum* (where the see-saw is supported). Mary is 7 ft. from the fulcrum. How much does Mary weigh? (2 s.f.)

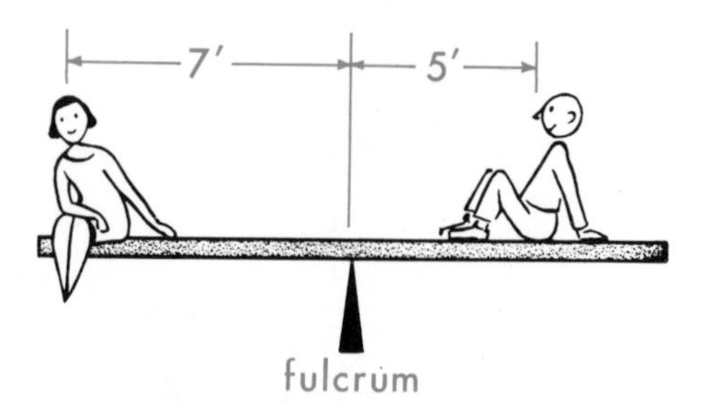

Solution: We will assume that the heavier person must be at less distance from the fulcrum, in proportion.

Let x = number of pounds for Mary.

$$\frac{85}{x} = \frac{7}{5}$$

$$(x)(7) = (5)(85)$$

$$7x = 425$$

$$\tfrac{1}{7} \cdot 7x = \tfrac{1}{7} \cdot 425$$

$$x = 60.7$$

Answer: Mary weighs about 61 pounds.

Problem 6. A man applies a force of 60 lb. to the end of a pair of pliers. The handles of the pliers are 5 in. long, and the jaws are 2 in. long. How much force is there, at the jaws? (Assume 2 s.f.)

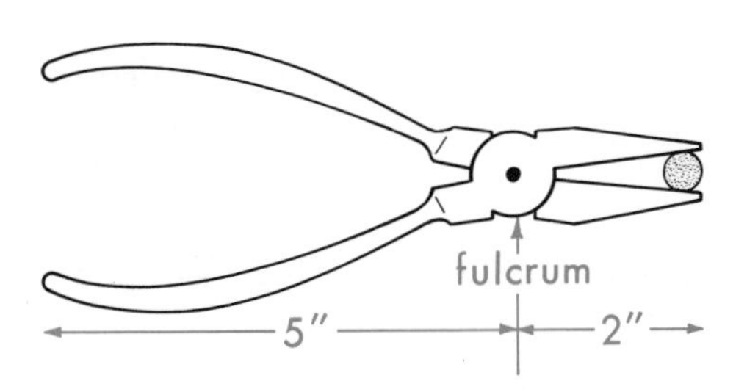

Solution: Let x = number of pounds of force.

$$\frac{60}{x} = \frac{2}{5}$$

force distance

$$(x)(2) = (60)(5)$$

$$2x = 300$$

$$\tfrac{1}{2} \cdot 2x = \tfrac{1}{2} \cdot 300$$

$$x = 150$$

Answer: There is a force of about 150 lb. (2 s.f.) at the jaws of the pliers.

Test: Section 8

Part A. In the following problems, assume that the total cost is *directly* proportional to the number of items.

1 Eight items cost $15. How much would 20 items cost?

2 Seven items cost $20. How much would 17 items cost?

3 Three items cost $5. How much would five items cost?

4 Four items cost $9. How much would three items cost?

5 Seven items cost $5. How many could be bought for $8?

6 Nine items cost $12. How many could be bought for $18?

7 Twelve items cost $28. How many could be bought for $10?

8 Eighteen items cost $90. How many could be bought for $51?

Part B. In the following problems, assume that the speed of a pulley or gear is *inversely* proportional to its size. The size of a pulley is measured by its diameter, and the size of a gear is measured by the number of teeth.

1 A 16-tooth gear makes 1200 rpm. How fast would a 28-tooth gear attached to it, turn?

2 A 22-tooth gear makes 1500 rpm. How fast would a 32-tooth gear attached to it, turn?

3 A 20-tooth gear makes 1900 rpm. How many teeth should a gear attached to it have, to get 1600 rpm?

4 A 36-tooth gear makes 700 rpm. How many teeth should a gear attached to it have, to produce 1000 rpm?

5 A 10-in. pulley makes 520 rpm. How fast would a 14-in. pulley belted to it, go?

6 An 8-in. pulley makes 615 rpm. How fast would a 6-in. pulley belted to it, go? (Express answer to the nearest hundredth.)

7 A 4-in. pulley makes 300 rpm. What size pulley should be used with it to obtain 550 rpm? (Express answer to the nearest hundredth.)

8 A 6-in. pulley makes 150 rpm. What size pulley should be belted to it, to obtain 110 rpm? (Express answer to the nearest hundredth.)

Part C. In the following problems, (D) means it is a *direct* proportion and (I) means it is an *inverse* proportion. In (7) – (10) assume 2 s.f.

1 (D) At a temperature of 250° absolute, the volume of a certain gas is 1150 qt. What would be its volume at 400° absolute?

2 (D) At a temperature of 300° absolute, the volume of a certain gas is 870 cc (cubic centimeters). What would be its volume at 130° absolute?

3 (I) At a pressure of 1.75 atmospheres, the volume of a certain gas is 420 cc. What would be its volume at 3.00 atmospheres?

4 (I) At a pressure of 0.35 atmospheres, the volume of a certain gas is 18.00 liters. What would be its volume at 1.50 atmospheres?

5 (D) To accelerate a certain object at a rate of 50 mph. per hour, requires a force of 10,000 foot-pounds. How much force would be required to make it accelerate at a rate of 75 mph. per hour?

6 (D) To accelerate a certain object at a rate of 25 mph. per hour, requires a force of 7000 foot-pounds. How much force would be required to make it accelerate at a rate of 40 mph. per hour?

7 (I) John and his father are balanced on a see-saw. John is 7 ft. from the fulcrum, and his father is 2 ft. from the fulcrum. If John weighs 60 pounds, how much does his father weigh?

8 (I) Sue and her mother are balanced on a see-saw. Sue is 6 ft. from the fulcrum, and her mother is 4 ft. from the fulcrum. If Sue weighs 80 pounds, how much does her mother weigh?

9 (I) A pair of pliers has a 4-in. handle, and 1-in. jaws. If the handles are squeezed with a force of 50 lb., what is the force at the jaws?

10 (I) A pair of pliers has a 7-in. handle, and 3-in. jaws. If the handles are squeezed with a force of 120 lb., what is the force at the jaws?

9 THE LANGUAGE OF VARIATION

To use the proportion method, you must know three of the four quantities. Ordinarily, this is quite satisfactory. In many cases, however, scientists find that it is not the best method for their own work. They prefer to use a formula of some kind. Here is how they do it.

Suppose the scientist has a set of data (dā′tȧ) as in the following table:

P	1	2	3	4	5	6
Y	5	10	15	20	25	30

You will recognize this as the *direct proportion* type of situation. You will also see that

$$Y = 5P$$

is the formula for the table. In this formula, 5 is called the *constant of variation,* and we say that

Y varies directly with P

Problem 1. A scientist discovers that in a gas, under certain conditions, pressure varies *directly* with absolute temperature. What kind of formula can he write?

Solution: $P = kT$, where k is a constant.

Problem 2. A scientist discovers that power in an electric circuit varies *directly* with the square of the resistance. What kind of formula can he write?

Solution: $P = kR^2$, where k is a constant.
Here is another set of data.

Q	1	2	3	4	5	6
M	18	9	6	4.5	3.6	3

You may recognize this as an *inverse proportion.* It is also true that

$$M = \frac{18}{Q}$$

For example, when $Q = 3$, $M = 6$. The scientist says that *M varies inversely* with Q.

Problem 3. A scientist discovers that under certain conditions in a gas, pressure varies *inversely* with volume. What kind of formula can he write?

$$P = \frac{k}{V}, \text{ where } k \text{ is a constant.}$$

Problem 4. The inverse square law states that the amount of illumination (I) from an electric light bulb, varies *inversely* as the square of the distance (r) from the bulb. What sort of formula is this?

Solution: $I = \dfrac{k}{r^2}$, where k is a constant.

The usual scientific problem has many more than two variables, but these are just as easy to handle.

Problem 5. The pressure of a perfect gas varies *directly* with the absolute temperature, and *inversely* with the volume. What sort of formula is this?

Solution: $P = \frac{kT}{V}$, where k is a constant.

Problem 6. The period (t) of a pendulum varies *directly* with the square root of its length (l), and *inversely* with the square root of the acceleration of gravity, (g). What sort of formula is this?

Solution: $t = \frac{k\sqrt{l}}{\sqrt{g}}$, where k is a constant.

If you are reading a scientific formula, you may find it interesting to write it in full form.

Problem 7. Explain the formula $e = \frac{kPl}{A}$, where e is the elongation of a bar of steel, P is the pressure on the bar, l is its length, A is its cross-section, and k is a constant.

Solution: The elongation of a bar of steel varies directly with the pressure on it and its length, and inversely with its cross-section area. This means that if the pressure increases, or the length increases, or both, then the elongation will increase. If the cross-section increases, the bar will stretch less.

Test: Section 9

Part A. Tell whether the following sets of numbers are in direct or inverse proportion, then write formulas for each.

1

M	1	2	3	4	5
P	2	4	6	8	10

2

Q	1	2	3	4	5
R	3	6	9	12	15

3

S	2	5	8	11	12
T	8	20	32	44	48

4

U	3	4	6	7.5	9.1
V	15	20	30	37.5	45.5

5

A	1	2	4	8
N	8	4	2	1

6

B	1	2	3	4	5	6
P	6	3	2	1.5	1.2	1

7

C	2	5	8	12	15
R	30	12	7.5	5	4

8

D	2	3	4	5	6
T	6	4	3	2.4	2

Part B. Translate the following into algebraic form.

1 A varies directly as B.
2 C varies directly as D.
3 M varies inversely as P.
4 N varies inversely as Q.
5 L is in direct proportion to T.
6 R is in direct proportion to X.
7 B varies inversely as Y.
8 I is in inverse proportion to R.
9 F varies directly with m, and with a.
10 W varies directly with F, and with d.
11 E varies directly with the square of v, and inversely with g.
12 P varies directly with the square of I, and inversely with C.

Part C. In the following, E means *energy*, F means *force*, w means *weight*, v means *speed* (velocity), P means *pressure*, V means *volume*, T means *absolute temperature* and g means *acceleration of gravity*; k is a constant. Explain each in full form.

1 For fixed v, $E = km$.
2 For fixed m, $E = kv^2$.
3 For fixed $\overline{V}$, $P = kT$.
4 For fixed T, $P = \frac{k}{V}$.
5 $P = \frac{kT}{V}$.
6 For fixed w, $F = \frac{ka}{g}$.

10 SOLVING SCIENTIFIC PROBLEMS INVOLVING VARIATION

So far, we have showed you how the scientist made a formula, say $R = kS$, and what this formula means.

This formula is useless to him unless he knows how much k is.

Here is the problem. Suppose he does an experiment and gets the following results:

S	1.1	1.9	3.1	3.9
R	1.9	4.1	6.1	7.9

It is not easy to see what k is for this table. If the table had a hundred of these numbers, all with five significant figures, matters would be even worse!

But things are not as bad as they seem. The first thing to do (if there are only two variables), is to draw a smooth graph (like we did in Section 3, p. 174). From the graph he picks two values. Let us say that he reads $S = 2$, and $R = 4$.

Assuming that this is *direct variation,* he can now substitute as follows:

Formula	$R = k \quad S$
	$\downarrow \quad \downarrow \quad \downarrow$
Substitution	$4 = k \cdot 2$
	$4 = 2k$
	$\frac{1}{2} \cdot 4 = \frac{1}{2} \cdot 2k$
Value of k	$2 = k$

Now he knows the value of k. The formula is therefore

$$R = 2\ S$$

Problem 1. A scientist does an experiment and gets the following table of results:

T	2.1	5.9	10.1	31.9
P	1.1	2.9	5.1	15.9

After drawing a graph, he picks the values $P = 5$, and $T = 10$, from it.

a What sort of variation is this?

b What is the general formula?

c What is the value of k?

d What is the formula?

e What is the value of P when $T = 50$?

Answer: (*a*) Direct. (*b*) $P = kT$. (*c*) By substituting, you get $k = 0.5$ (*d*) $P = 0.5T$. (*e*) By substituting, you get $P = 25$.

Problem 2. A scientist does an experiment and gets the following table:

P	60.2	29.8	15.2	19.8
V	1.8	2.2	3.8	3.2

After drawing a graph, he chooses the values $P = 20$, and $V = 3$, from it.

a What sort of variation is this?

b What is the general formula?

c What is the value of k?

d What is the formula?

e What is the value of P when $V = 4$?

Answer: (*a*) Inverse. (*b*) $V = \frac{k}{P}$. (*c*) By substituting, $k = 60$. (*d*) $V = \frac{60}{P}$. (*e*) When $V = 4$, $P = 15$.

Problem 3. The distance (s) covered by a body falling in a vacuum is proportional to the square of the number (t) of seconds of fall.

a Write a formula for this statement.

b In one case, it was noted that a body fell 144 ft. in 3 sec. Find k.

c What is the formula?

Answer: (*a*) $s = k\,t^2$. (*b*) By substituting, $k = 16$. (*c*) $s = 16\,t^2$. This is called the *Law of Falling Bodies.*

Problem 4. The force of attraction (F) between two bodies varies inversely as the square of the distance (d) between them.

a Write a general formula for this statement.

b From a graph, it was noted that a force of 4 lb. was present at a distance of 3 in. Find k.

c What is the formula?

d How much force will there be at 6 in?

Answer: (*a*) $F = \frac{k}{d^2}$. (*b*) By substituting, $k = 36$. (*c*) $F = \frac{36}{d^2}$.

(*d*) $F = \frac{36}{d^2}$

$$F = \frac{36}{(6)(6)}$$

$$F = \frac{36}{36}$$

$F = 1$ . . There will be a force of 1 lb.

Test: Section 10

Part A. In the following, you are given formulas involving variation. A sample pair of values is given. Find k, then write the correct formula.

1. $A = kw$. When $w = 3$, $A = 6$.
2. $B = kv$. When $v = 7$, $B = 21$.
3. $C = kr$. When $r = 3$, $C = 15$.
4. $D = kt$. When $t = 5$, $D = 35$.
5. $E = kR$. When $R = 8$, $E = 2$.
6. $F = kd$. When $d = 16$, $F = 4$.
7. $G = \frac{k}{m}$. When $m = 3$, $G = 6$.
8. $H = \frac{k}{p}$. When $p = 2$, $H = 5$.
9. $I = \frac{k}{L}$. When $L = 3$, $I = 8$.
10. $J = \frac{k}{s}$. When $s = 4$, $J = 5$.
11. $M = \frac{k}{n^2}$. When $n = 2$, $M = 3$.
12. $N = \frac{k}{t^2}$. When $t = 3$, $N = 1$.

Part B. In each of the following problems, *do five things*: (a) tell what kind of variation is shown in the table; (b) write the general formula; (c) find the value of k. (d) rewrite the formula; (e) use the rewritten formula to answer the question in the problem.

1.

L	2	5	6	9
A	12	30	36	54

Find A when $L = 8$.

2.

L	3	8	17	20
Q	24	64	136	160

Find Q when $L = 15$.

3.

T	2	5	9	18
M	14	35	63	126

Find M when $T = 1$.

4.

T	3	7	8	15
N	36	84	96	180

Find N when $T = 4$.

5

U	2	4	8	24
R	12	6	3	1

(HINT: What is $U \times R$ in *each case?*)

Find R when $U = 5$.

6

U	5	15	30	60
H	6	2	1	0.5

(HINT: What is $U \times H$ in *each case?*)

Find H when $U = 6$.

7

W	6	8	18	24
L	12	9	4	3

(HINT: What is $W \times L$ in *each case?*)

Find L when $W = 36$.

8

W	3	6	8	10
P	40	20	15	12

(HINT: What is $W \times P$ in *each case?*)

Find P when $W = 15$.

Part C. In the following, you are given a statement involving variation: (a) translate it into a mathematical formula; (b) using the information given, find k; (c) use the formula to answer the question.

1 The force (F) of a punch varies directly with its acceleration (a). In one case, the force was 16 lb. when the acceleration was 24 feet per second per second. What would the force have been for an acceleration of 32 feet per second per second?

2 The work (W) done by a piston is proportional to the distance (d) that it travels. In one case, the work done was 100 ft-lb. for a distance of 2 ft. What would the work be for a distance of 3 ft?

3 The speed (R) of a gear varies inversely with the number (T) of teeth. In one case, the gear had 20 teeth, and turned at 500 rpm. How fast would a 50-tooth gear go? It is assumed that the two gears are attached.

4 The speed (R) of a pulley varies inversely with its diameter (D). In one case, the pulley had a diameter of 7 in., and turned at 30 rpm. If a 9-in. pulley is belted to this one, how fast will it go?

5 The light (I) from a flash gun varies inversely as the square of the distance (d) between the flash and the object. In one case, an object 2 ft. away received 9 units of light. How many units would an object receive if it were 3 ft. away from the same flash gun?

6 The resistance (R) of a motor of fixed horsepower varies inversely as the square of the current (I). In one case, the motor had a resistance of 100 ohms when the current was 5 amperes. What will be the resistance when the current is 8 amperes?

7 The surface area (S) of a ball varies directly with the square of its diameter (D). One ball had a surface area of about 12 sq. in. when the diameter was 2 in. What would be the surface area of a ball with a diameter of 5 in?

8 The period of a pendulum is the time it takes to make one full swing. The length of the pendulum (l) varies directly with the square of the period (t). A 20-ft. pendulum has a period of about 5 sec. What length would a pendulum have to be to have a period of 1 sec?

7

THE MATHEMATICS LABORATORY

"How do mathematicians get all those laws and formulas?" asked the student.

"Well, every law starts with a guess of some kind," replied the teacher. "This guess may be verified by an experiment and then proved by mathematical methods."

"But how," demanded the student, "do they get the guess?"

The teacher shrugged this off. "No one really knows where a guess comes from. It's just a 'hunch.' "

"Well, how do you know whether your hunch is right?"

"That," the teacher answered, "is what we're going to spend some time on. We'll use the scientific method of finding out — experimentation."

The student was not satisfied. "Does that tell you whether it's a correct guess?"

"No," said the teacher. "It tells you only whether it's a good guess. The

Fig. 7-1. A scale with millimeter marks.

matter of proof is taken up at the end of the course. Let's concentrate on experiments. This involves observation, counting and measurement. Be sure that you get four mathematical tools for yourself: a 6-in. ruler marked in millimeters (Fig. 7-1); a protractor (Fig. 7-2), compasses, and a small

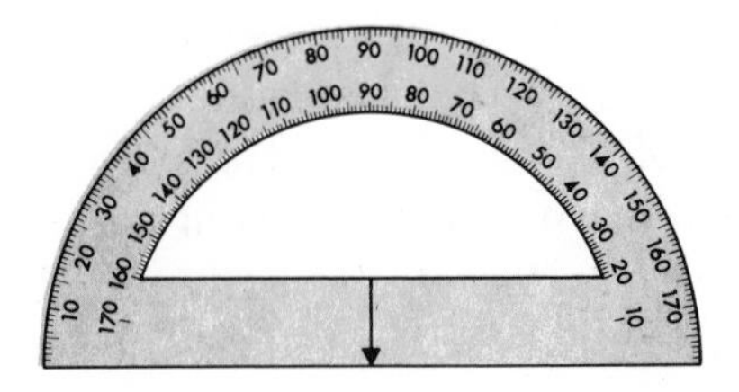

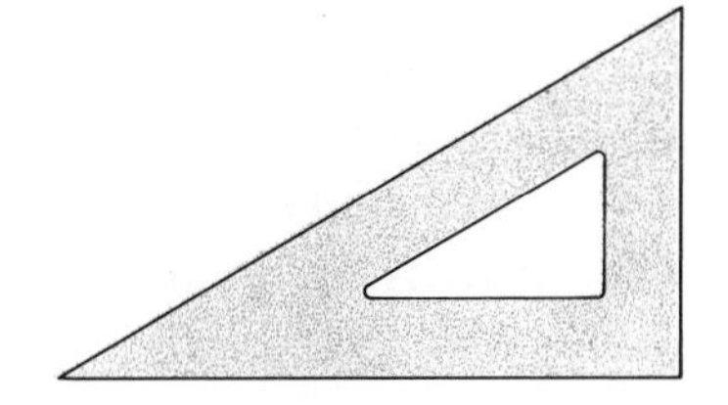

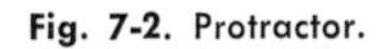

Fig. 7-2. Protractor.

Fig. 7-3. Draftsman's triangle.

30°-60°-90° celluloid triangle (Fig. 7-3). These will cost you less than a dollar, and provided you don't lose them, last for a long time.

"Now, before we get to mathematical experiments, let us talk about two important problems involved in all experimentation."

1 THE PROBLEM OF INVESTIGATING

The general manager of a large department store was very annoyed. That week he had received a dozen letters complaining about the elevator service. He sent for his assistant and told him to investigate the whole elevator situation.

The assistant thought about what to do. There were eight elevators, each running on two shifts. Each day, some twelve thousand customers came to the store. It looked like an impossible situation.

First, he thought he would send a letter to each customer asking for opinions on the elevator service. But this was no good for many reasons. (1) Only a small percentage of people answer questionnaires; those who do so, are those especially interested. (2) The store had addresses for "charge" customers only, so this method would only reach and represent the opinions of a certain section of the customers.

An investigation is *fair* only if it represents *all* parts of the population involved in the problem.

The assistant's second idea was to have clerks stand at the exits, and for one whole week, ask each customer whether the elevator service was satisfactory. This would have been a "fair" investigation, but not practical. It would have cost too much in terms of time and money.

His third idea was to have the clerks do this only between 8:30 AM and 9:30 AM when the store was not very busy. This was no good either, because only certain types of people shop early in the morning; for example, people who work on afternoon and evening shifts. Besides, different elevator operators worked in the morning and the afternoon, and the *operators* were responsible for the service. This would not be a *fair* investigation.

Finally, the assistant decided on the following scheme. He had the stock clerks stand at the exits for five minutes of each hour throughout the time the store was open. As the customers went out, the stock clerks asked them whether they had used an elevator, and whether they were satisfied with the service.

In this way, the store was able to *sample* the customers. The store received $\frac{5}{60}$ or $\frac{1}{12}$ of all the customers' opinions, about one thousand a day. The people represented all kinds of customers: rich and poor, morning and afternoon, men and women.

In any investigation, it is important that a *fair sample* be taken: one that represents all kinds of whatever it is you are measuring. The sample must be *adequate*; it must be large enough to avoid "accidental results." One case is never enough. In mathematics, five or six or seven cases, are usually "adequate." In scientific work, such as the Salk polio experiment, the sample ran to thousands of cases. The more cases there are in the sample, the safer the results.

Test: Section 1

In each of the following situations, something is wrong with the method of investigation. In each case, tell what is wrong, and suggest a method for correcting it.

1 The Republocrats wanted to find out how the voters felt about an amendment to the State constitution. They telephoned every tenth number in the telephone book. (Do all voters have telephones?)

2 Mr. Rich wanted to know what the people of Xville thought about a slum clearance project. He had investigators go to the Main Street Theater — the best theater in town — on Saturday and interview people as they left at 11:00 PM. (What kinds of voters do not go to this theater on Saturday night?)

3 Mr. Pater wanted to know whether his son was behaving himself in school, so he asked all his son's friends.

4 The school honor society was investigating a candidate for admission. This candidate had just become class president. They asked the three people who ran against him to tell what they thought of him.

5 Mrs. Farmer wanted to find out whether a certain bottle of fresh (not

homogenized) milk was creamy, so she took a spoonful from the top, and tasted it.

6 A visitor to a chemical factory saw the chemist test a drum of potassium sulfate by taking portions from all parts of the drum. He said, "Why don't you save yourself work and just take a sample from the top?"

7 The Buyer's Testing Service bought one Oldsmoford car, and reported that careful tests showed that Oldsmoford cars had poor heaters.

8 Dr. *M* was experimenting with the intelligence of chimpanzees. He acquired a young chimp and trained it to ride a bicycle. He then tried the same thing with a monkey, but failed. He concluded that chimps are much smarter than monkeys.

9 The producer of a television show wanted to measure its popularity. He called twenty-five people in various occupations: one teacher, one doctor, one plumber, one housewife, etc. He collected their opinions and drew his conclusions from them.

10 The Vocational High School had a population of 500 boys, and 100 girls. The principal decided to find out how popular the shop courses were. He selected five boys and five girls. One boy liked Wood Shop, two liked Machine Shop, one liked Auto Shop and one liked Printing Shop. All five girls like Beauty Culture. The principal concluded that Beauty Culture was the most popular shop in school.

2 THE SCIENTIFIC METHOD

The scientific method has the following five steps:

1. Making a statement concerning what is being tested
2. Getting a *fair* and *adequate* sample
3. Doing the measuring and counting
4. Preparing the results
5. Drawing a conclusion.

The following are examples of scientific investigations.

Problem 1. A certain brand of cereal advertises that it contains 29.0 milligrams of calcium, per ounce (1 oz. is approximately 28,350 milligrams). To check this, a school laboratory weighed out four 1-oz. samples from different boxes, and measured the amount of calcium in each sample. The results were:

27.0 mg.	29.6 mg.
26.3	28.5

Adding these and dividing by four, the *average* was 27.9 milligrams. The *difference* between the average and what was claimed was 29.0 − 27.9 = 1.1 mg.

Now, 1.1 mg. is a very small amount, but so is the 29.0 milligrams claimed! To find out whether the difference is "important," we convert the difference to per cent form. This is called the *per cent error.*

$$\textit{Error Formula}: \text{per cent error} = \frac{\text{difference} \times 100}{\text{claimed value}}$$

In this case, the per cent error was

$$\frac{1.1 \times 100}{29} = \frac{110}{29} = 3.8\%$$

In this particular laboratory, only 2% error was allowed. Therefore, it was *concluded* that the boxes of cereal tested did not contain what was claimed. The report form is shown in Fig. 7-4.

Problem 2. A TV advertiser claimed that his commercial took only 30 seconds. To test his claim, a group of students timed the commercials with stop-watches. Their results are shown in Fig. 7-5. As you can see, the investigation showed that the advertiser was telling the truth within 2% error.

• Test: Section 2

In each of the following, write a report showing the results and conclusions as in Figs. 7-4 and 7-5. If the per cent error is less than 2%, you may accept the statement tested. If the per cent error is 2% or more, you must reject the statement tested.

1. A food product advertises a butter fat content of 4.0, and tests show 3.8, 4.0, 4.2, and 3.8.
2. Maple sugar has 2.8 parts of water per hundred. A certain sugar claimed to be maple sugar is tested, and shows 2.6, 2.4, 2.5, and 2.2 parts per hundred.

Experiment No. 1

Testing: *Claim: The cereal has 29.0 mg. of calcium per oz.*

Results:
1. 27.0
2. 26.3
3. 29.6
4. 28.5
5. ——
6.
7.
8.
9.
10.

Total: 111.4

Average: 27.9

Difference: $29.0 - 27.9 = 1.1$

Per Cent Error: $\frac{1.1 \times 100}{29} = 3.8\%$

Conclusion: *Within 2% error, the cereal does not have 29.0 mg. of calcium per oz.*

Fig. 7-4. Report on Problem 1.

Experiment No. 2

Testing: *Claim: The commercials are 30 seconds long.*

Results:
1. 31.7
2. 32.0
3. 30.8
4. 30.0
5. 32.0
6. 33.1
7. 27.8
8. 28.5
9. 30.1
10. 29.1

Total: 305.1

Average: 30.5

Difference: $30.5 - 30.0 = 0.5$

Per Cent Error: $\frac{0.5 \times 100}{30} = 1.7\%$

Conclusion: *Within 2%, the commercials are 30 seconds long.*

Fig. 7-5. Report on Problem 2.

3 Vinegar contains about 20 grams (gm.) of acetic acid to a pint. A liquid claimed to be vinegar measures 16.5, 17.8, 17.1, 16.8, and 17.9 gm. per pint.

4 The label on a certain brand of breakfast cocoa says it contains 22% cacao fat. Analysis of five cans shows 21.8, 23.9, 20.4, 27.6, and 31.6%.

5 A perfumer says his bottles contain exactly 2.5 oz. Actual tests show 2.4, 2.4, 2.3, 2.5, 2.6, 2.4, 2.6, 2.4, 2.3 and 2.5 oz.

6 "I always weigh 152 pounds," said the man, "no matter what I eat." Actual records in different months showed the following weights: 149.2, 150.4, 150.5, 150.7, 151.8, 151.9, 152.6, 153.5, 154.1, and 157.2 pounds.

3 ANGLES

Our first venture into mathematical experimentation will be experiments with *angles*. Angles are figures formed by a pair of lines (Fig. 7-6). To

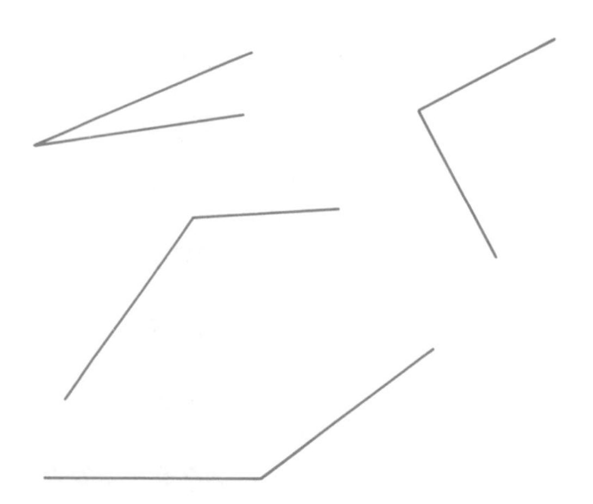

Fig. 7-6. Angles.

experiment with angles, we shall have to learn how to measure them, and we shall have to learn enough about different kinds of angles to tell us how to make a fair sample.

The measurement of an angle is taken with a protractor (Fig. 7-7), an instrument marked in *degrees*. The protractor has *two* sets of measurements. One set starts at *left zero*, and continues to 180° (degrees) in the *outside track*. The second set starts at *right zero*, and continues to 180° on the *inside track*. Here is how the protractor is used:

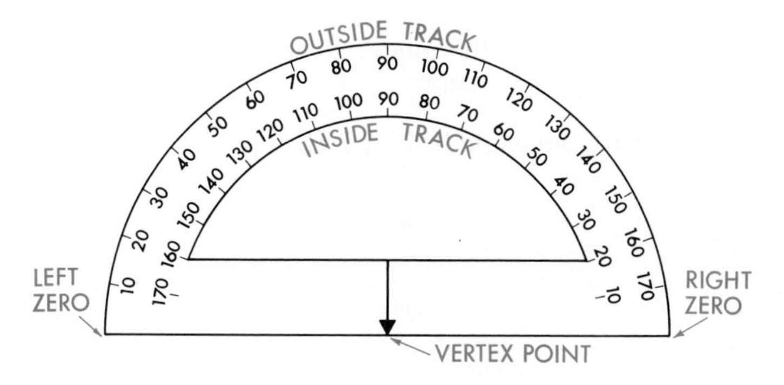

Fig. 7-7. Parts of the protractor.

Problem 1. Measure the angle in Fig. 7-8a.

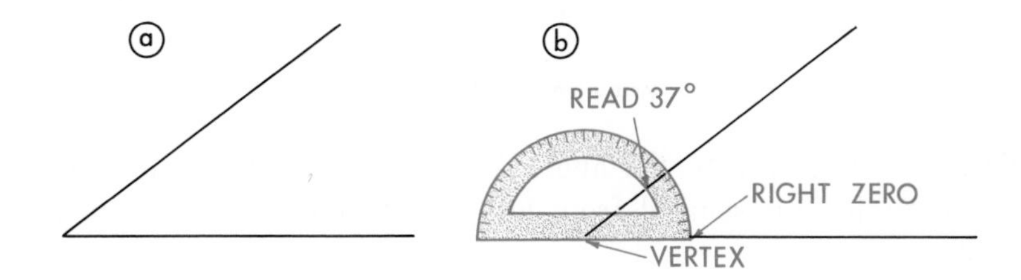

Fig. 7-8. Measuring an angle that opens to the right.

Solution: Place the *arrow* of the protractor on the *vertex* (point) of the angle. Rest the protractor on one *side* of the angle. Read the *inside track* where the other side of the angle crosses. The angle is 37°.

Problem 2. Measure the angle in Fig. 7-9a.

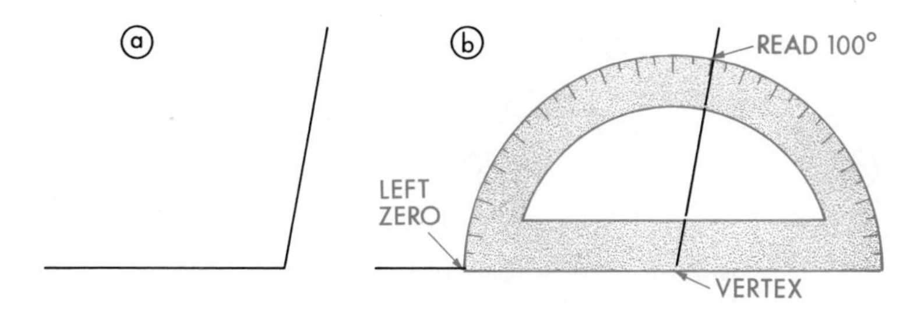

Fig. 7-9. Measuring an angle that opens to the left.

Solution: Place the arrow of the protractor on the vertex of the angle. Rest the protractor on one side of the angle. Read the outside track where the other side crosses. The angle is 100°.

Problem 3. Measure the angle in Fig. 7-10a.

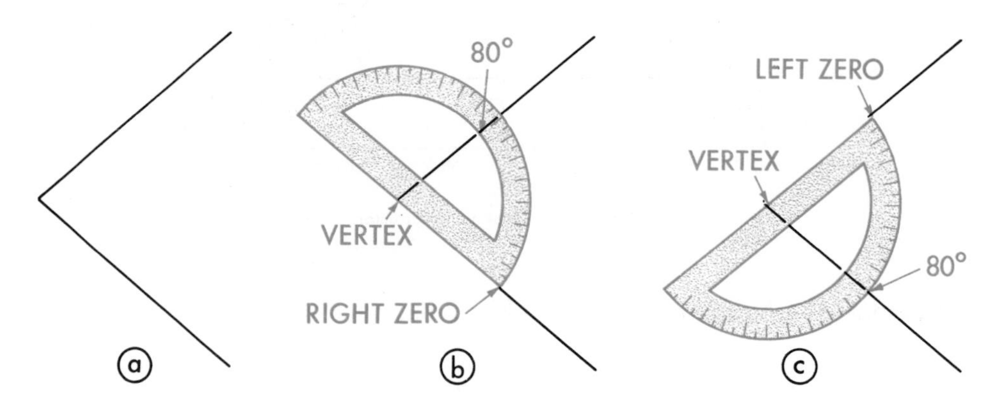

Fig. 7-10. Measuring an angle from either side.

Solution: In Fig. 7-10b, the angle is measured from right zero. In Fig. 7-10c, the angle is measured from left zero. Either way, the answer is the same: 80°.

The protractor may also be used to make angles, as in the following examples.

Problem 4. Make an angle of 90°. This is called a *right angle.*

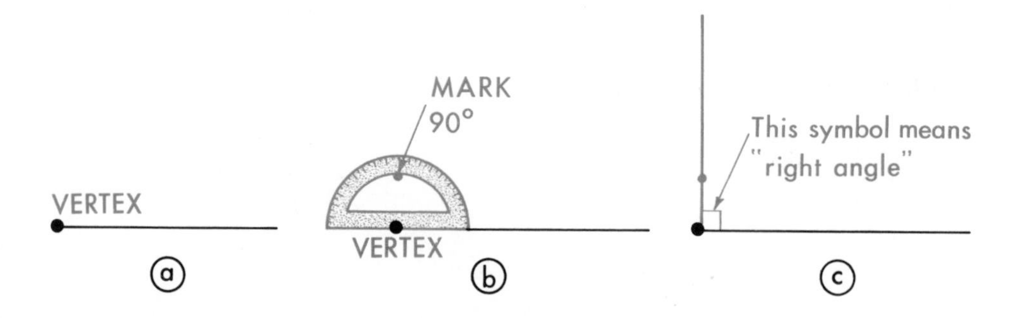

Fig. 7-11. Making a right angle opening to the right.

Solution 1: (Fig. 7-11) (*a*) Draw any line and mark a point for the vertex; (*b*) place the protractor with its arrow at the vertex, and make a mark at 90°; (*c*) Remove the protractor, and connect the two points.

Solution 2: Figure 7-12 shows how to make a right angle opening to the

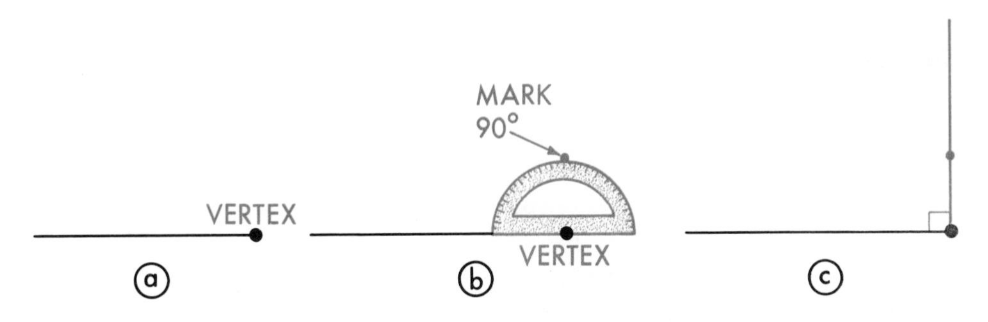

Fig. 7-12. Making a right angle opening to the left.

left. The little "box" is a mathematical symbol to remind us that this is a right angle.

Problem 5. Make an angle of 52°.

Solution 1: See Fig. 7-13.

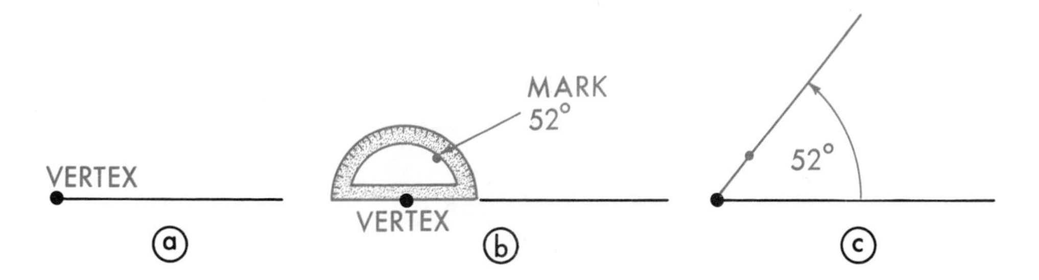

Fig. 7-13. Making an angle of 52° opening to the right.

Solution 2: See Fig. 7-14.

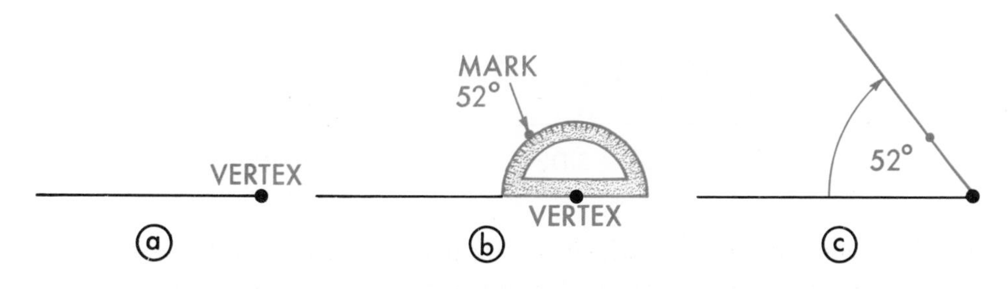

Fig. 7-14. Making an angle of 52° opening to the left.

Problem 6. Make an angle of 112°.

Solution 1: See Fig. 7-15.

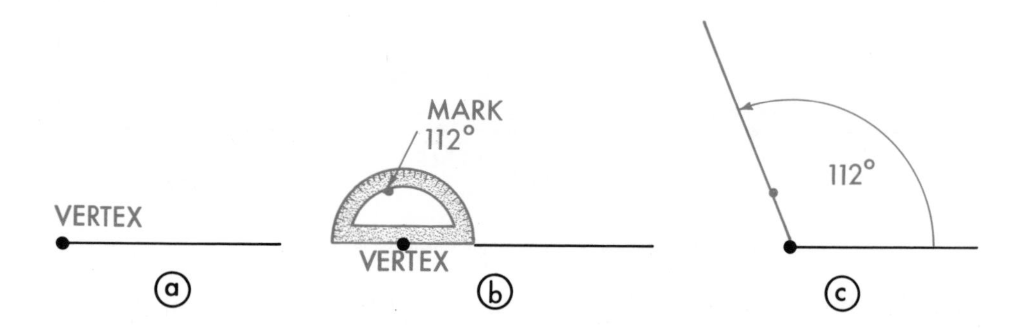

Fig. 7-15. Making an angle of 112° opening to the right.

Solution 2: See Fig. 7-16.

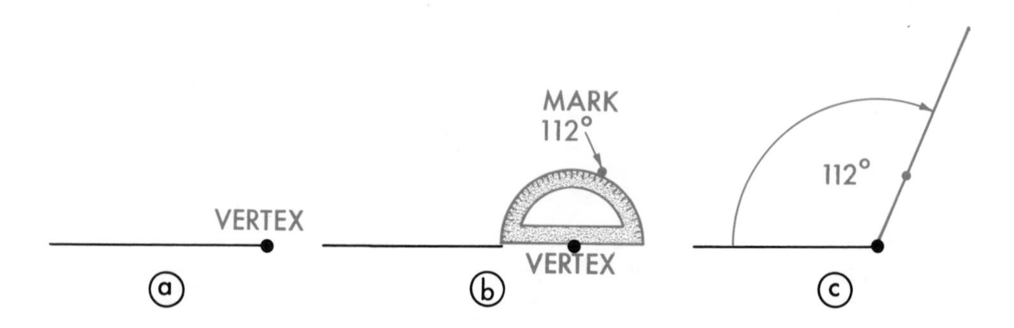

Fig. 7-16. Making an angle of 112° opening to the left.

To make an angle of 180°, you do not really need a protractor at all; it

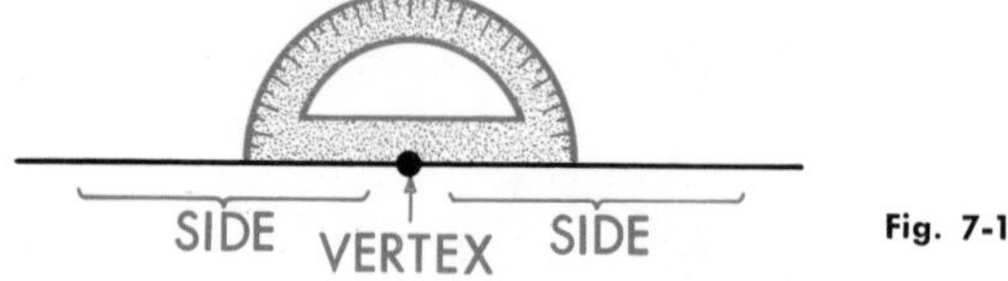

Fig. 7-17. A straight angle.

can be made with a ruler, which is why it is called a *straight angle* (Fig. 7-17). An angle of more than 180° can easily be made by dividing a straight line into two parts, as shown in the following problem.

Problem 7. Draw an angle of 210°.

Solution: 210° = 180° + 30°. So we make a 180° angle by drawing a straight angle, then add on 30° (Fig. 7-18).

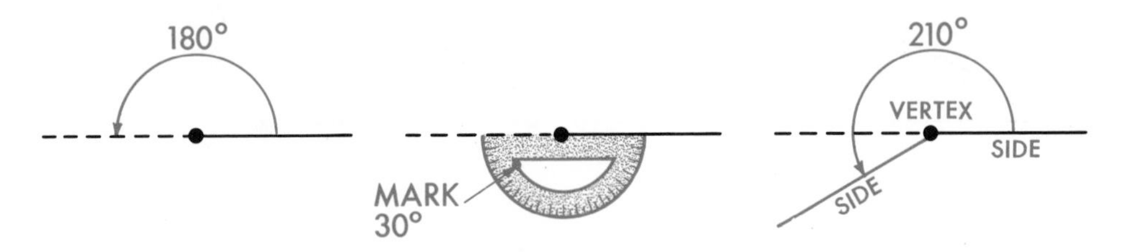

Fig. 7-18. Making an angle of 210°.

This can be made to open either to the right or to the left, just as the other angles.

Angles are classified as follows:

Name of Angle	*Size*	*Examples*
Acute angle	below 90°	38°, 57°, 80°
Right angle	90°	90°
Obtuse angle	above 90°, below 180°	110°, 150°, 178°
Straight angle	180°	180°
Reflex angle	above 180°	210°, 310°, 350°

Test: Section 3

Part A. Name the angle in each of the following:

1 27° 2 42° 3 90° 4 180° 5 115°
6 168° 7 227° 8 270° 9 288° 10 190°

Part B. Draw angles of the following sizes:

1 35° 2 47° 3 90° 4 180°
5 125° 6 148° 7 220° 8 270°

Part C. On your own paper, copy the angles given here and measure them. (*Do not write in this book!*)

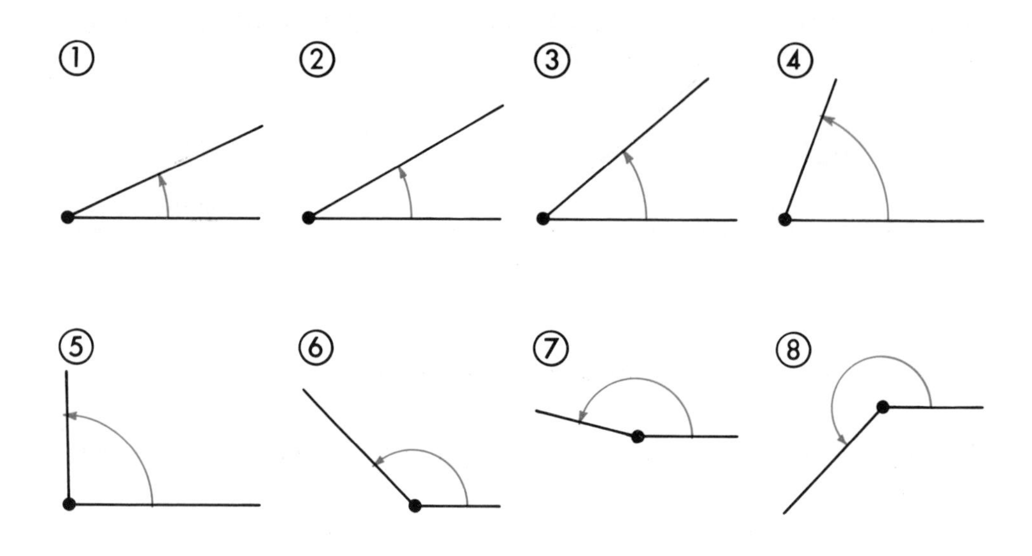

4 EXPERIMENTS ON ANGLES

If we draw two lines as shown in Fig. 7-19, they form pairs of angles called *opposite vertical angles*. In the figure, $\angle 1$ (angle No. 1) and $\angle 2$ are one pair of opposite vertical angles, and $\angle 3$ and $\angle 4$ are another pair of

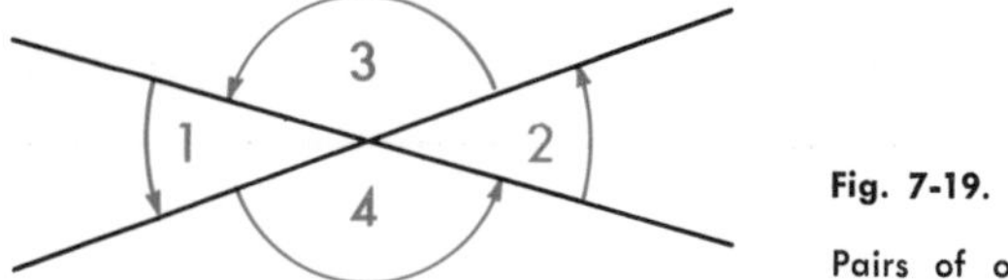

Fig. 7-19.

Pairs of opposite vertical angles.

opposite vertical angles. The first scientific step is to make a guess about these angles. Does it seem reasonable to guess that $\angle 1 = \angle 2$, and $\angle 3 = \angle 4$? What we are guessing is:

Experiment A-1. Opposite Vertical Angles are Equal.

In keeping with our outline for experimental work, we must first make different *kinds* of opposite vertical angles to be sure that we have a *fair sample* of these angles. This is done in Fig. 7-20.

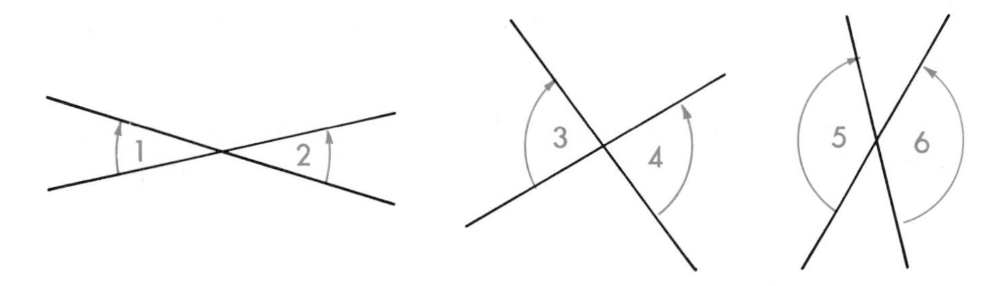

Fig. 7-20. A fair sample of opposite vertical angles.

Now let us measure the angles marked, and make a report (Fig. 7-21).

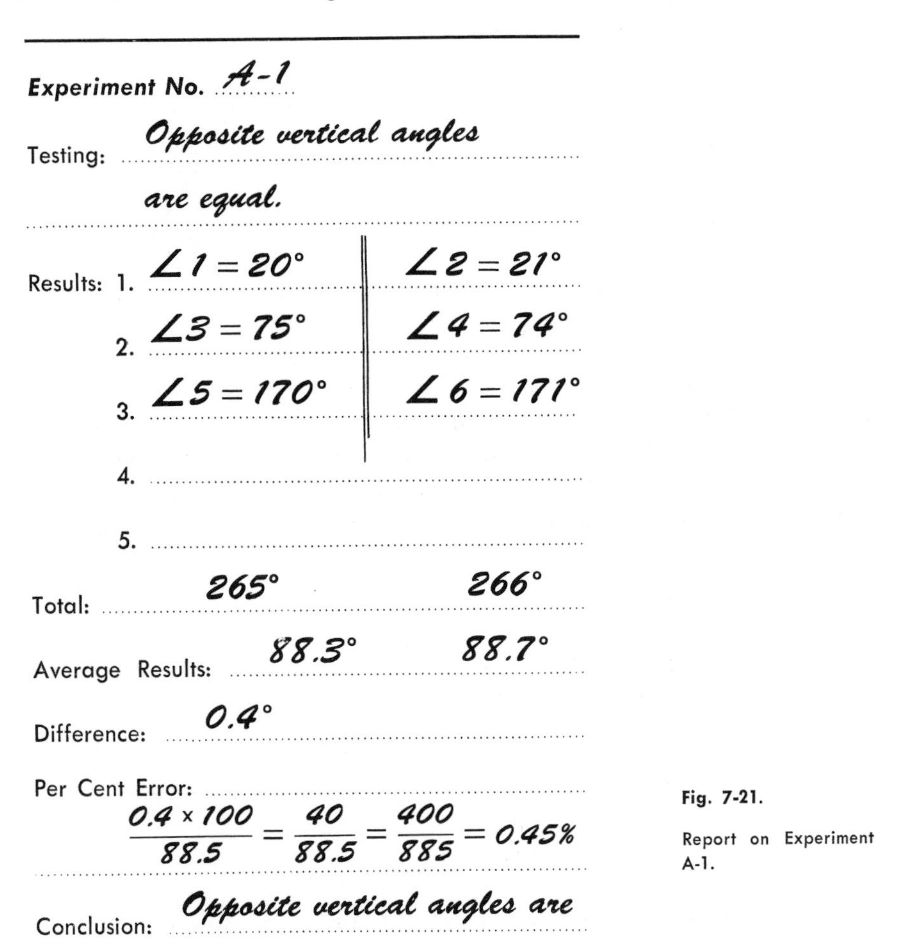

Experiment No. A-1

Testing: Opposite vertical angles are equal.

Results:

1.	$\angle 1 = 20°$	$\angle 2 = 21°$
2.	$\angle 3 = 75°$	$\angle 4 = 74°$
3.	$\angle 5 = 170°$	$\angle 6 = 171°$
4.		
5.		

Total: 265° 266°

Average Results: 88.3° 88.7°

Difference: 0.4°

Per Cent Error:

$$\frac{0.4 \times 100}{88.5} = \frac{40}{88.5} = \frac{400}{885} = 0.45\%$$

Conclusion: Opposite vertical angles are equal within 2% error.

Fig. 7-21.

Report on Experiment A-1.

In figuring per cent error, the denominator, 88.5, was found by averaging 88.3°, and 88.7°.

Experiment A-2: If two angles add up to 90°, the two angles are called *complements* of each other. In Fig. 7-22, ∠1 and ∠3 are complements of

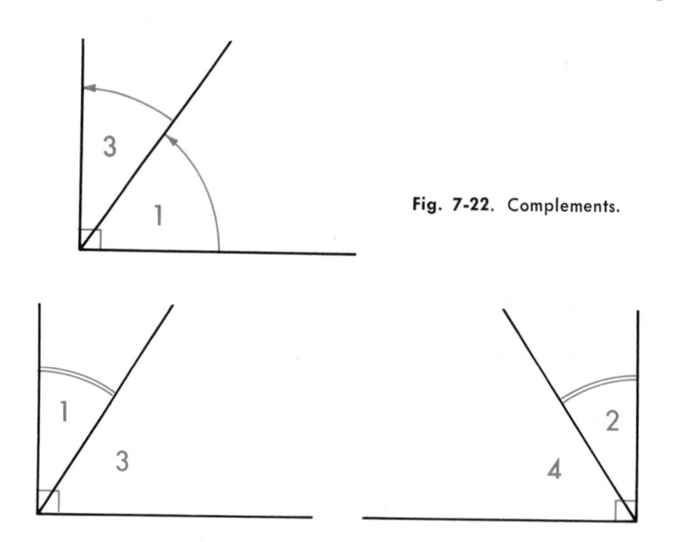

Fig. 7-22. Complements.

Fig. 7-23. Complements of equal angles.

each other. Now suppose (Fig. 7-23) we know that ∠1 = ∠2. (To remember this, we mark these angles with double lines.) What do you think is true of ∠3 and ∠4? Would you guess that they are equal?

The experiment is started as follows. First, make two 90° angles (Fig.

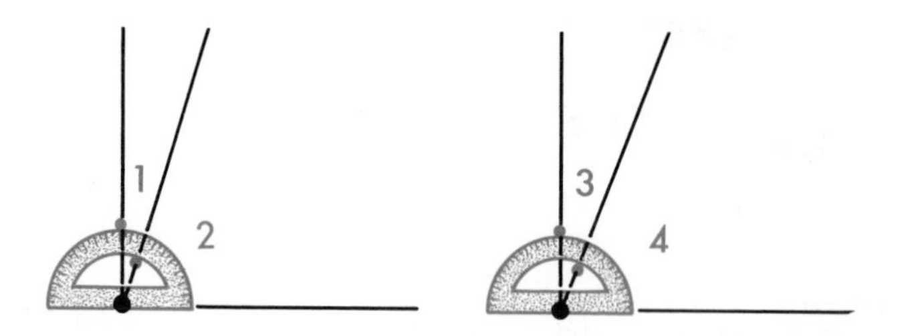

Fig. 7-24. Starting Experiment A-2.

7-24) and measure off equal angles, ∠1 and ∠3. Now measure ∠2 and ∠4, and complete the report after testing several cases. Is it true, within 2% error, that *complements of equal angles are equal?*

Experiment A-3. If two angles add up to 180°, the two angles are called *supplements* of each other. In Fig. 7-25, $\angle 5$ and $\angle 6$ are supplements of each other.

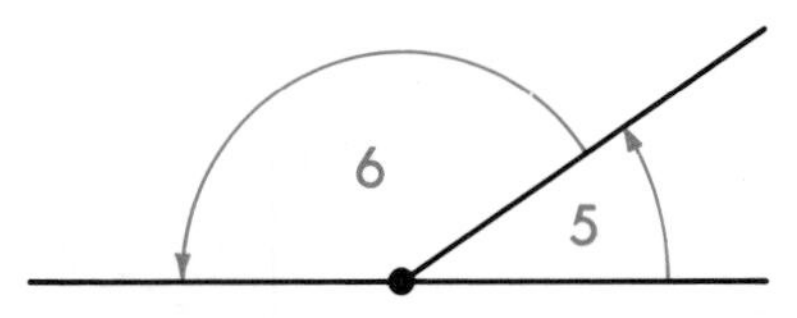

Fig. 7-25. Supplements.

Now suppose we know that in Fig. 7-26, $\angle 7 = \angle 8$. What would be your guess about $\angle 9$ and $\angle 10$? Is it true (within 2% error) that *supplements of equal angles are equal*?

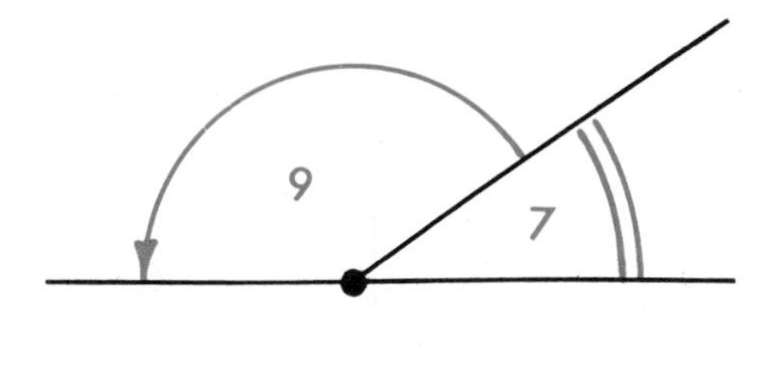

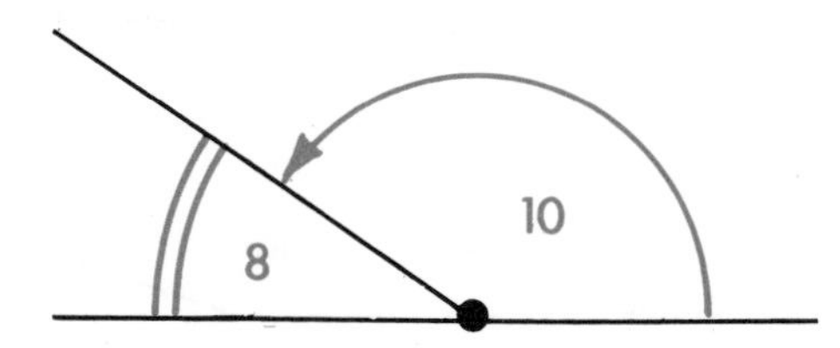

Fig. 7-26. Supplements of equal angles.

Test: Section 4

Part A. Using the definitions, find each of the following:

1 Complement of 20°
2 Complement of 40°
3 Complement of 60°
4 Complement of 80°
5 Supplement of 30°
6 Supplement of 50°
7 Supplement of 100°
8 Supplement of 140°
9 Complement of 27.5°
10 Supplement of 138.5°

Part B. Perform experiments to verify the following laws. In each case, use at least five different diagrams.

1 Complements of unequal angles are unequal.
2 Supplements of unequal angles are unequal.

Part C. In each of the following, use the definitions and the laws verified by experiment to find the sizes of the angles marked with letters.

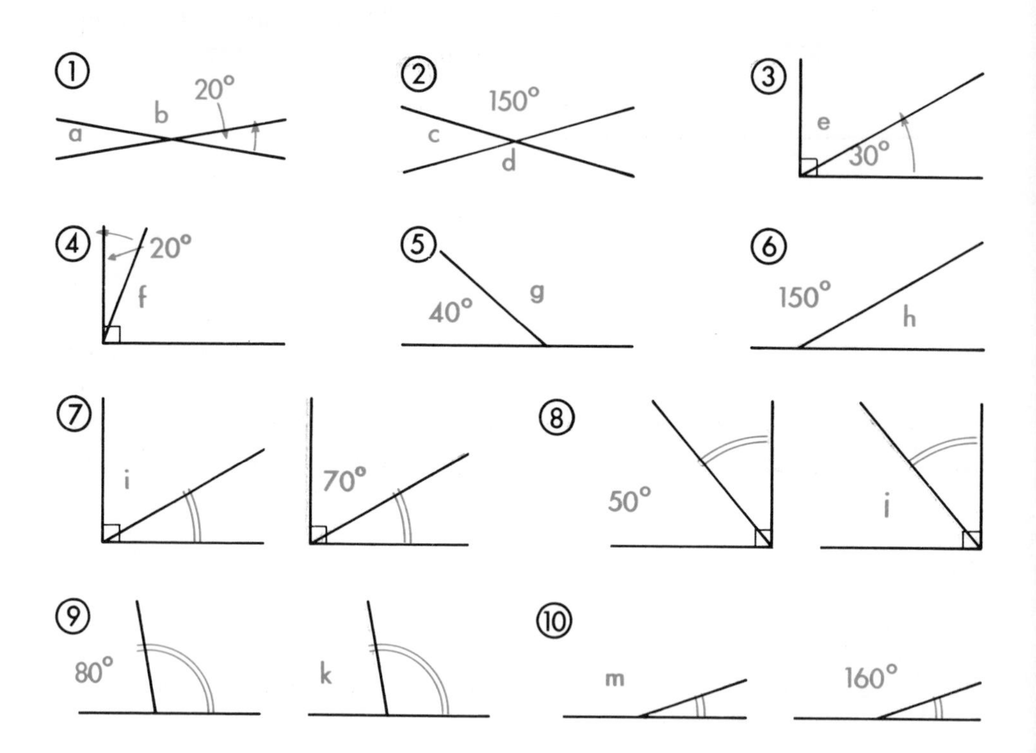

5 EXPERIMENTS WITH LINE SEGMENTS

A line segment is simply a "piece" of a line. It is named by its endpoints.

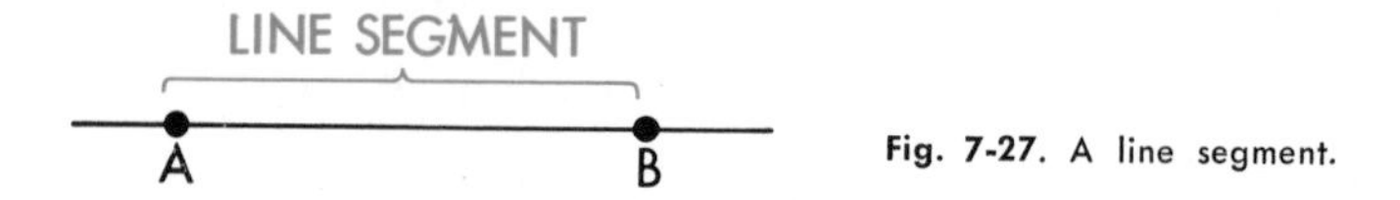

Fig. 7-27. A line segment.

In Fig. 7-27, the piece of the line between points A and B is called either AB, or BA.

If two lines form right angles (Fig. 7-28), they are said to be *perpendicular* (pûr′pĕn·dĭk′ū́·lẽr) to each other, and this is written

$AB \perp CD$ (read: AB is perpendicular to CD) or

$CD \perp AB$ (read: CD is perpendicular to AB)

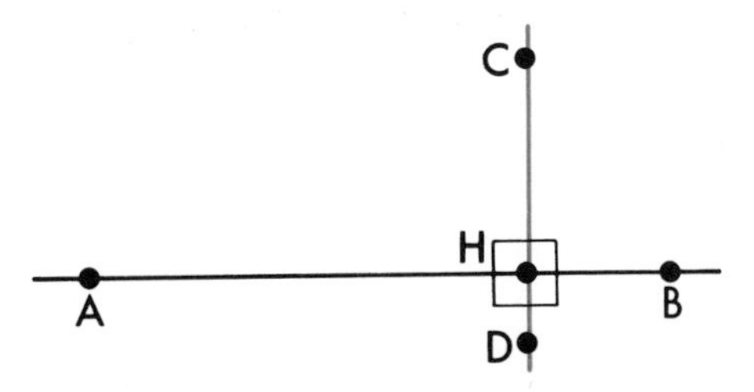

Fig. 7-28. $CD \perp AB$, or $AB \perp CD$.

If a line cuts a line segment into two equal parts, the line segment is said to be *bisected* (bī′sĕkt′ed). The two equal parts are marked (Fig. 7-29) by short marks called *hatch marks*. *M* is called the *midpoint* of segment *AB*.

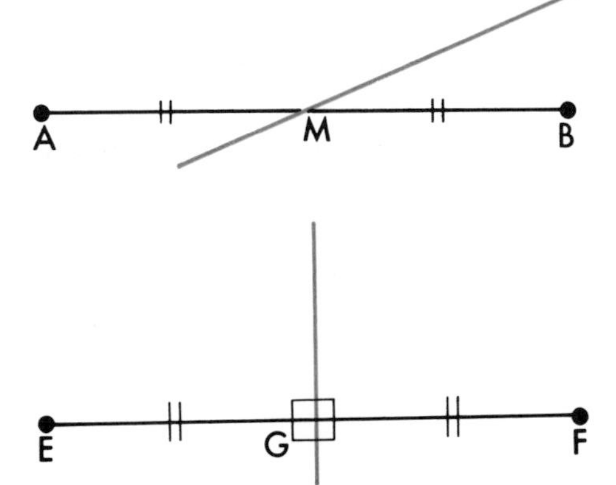

Fig. 7-29. The line bisects *AB*, so that $AM = MB$.

Fig. 7-30. Perpendicular bisector of *EF*.

Sometimes, the line that does the bisecting is also at right angles (Fig. 7-30). In this case, it is called the *perpendicular bisector*.

It is possible for two line segments to bisect each other (Fig. 7-31), or even to be perpendicular bisectors of each other (Fig. 7-32). Notice the hatch marks.

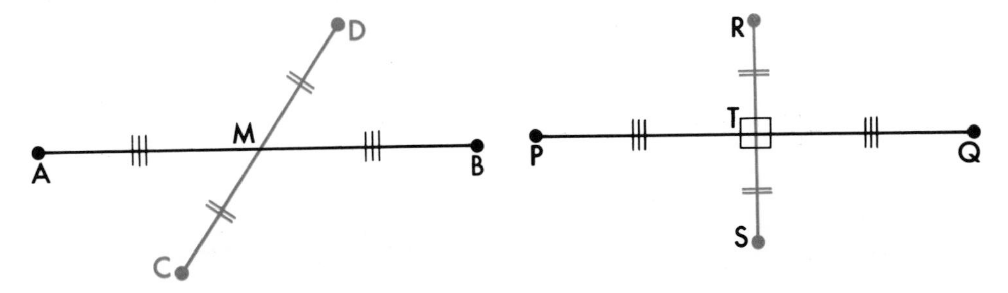

Fig. 7-31. *AB* and *CD* bisect each other.

Fig. 7-32. *PQ* and *RS* are perpendicular bisectors of each other.

Problem 1. Given a line segment 2 in. long, construct the perpendicular bisector.

Solution: First (Fig. 7-33a) make a 2-inch line segment, and mark the

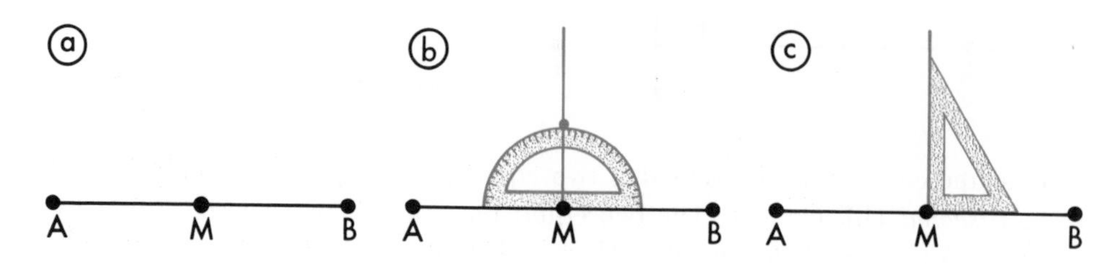

Fig. 7-33. Two methods for constructing a perpendicular bisector.

midpoint, M. Then, using either a protractor (b) or a draftsman's triangle (c), make the perpendicular at point M.

A line may also be used to cut an angle into two or more equal parts, as in Problems 2 and 3.

Problem 2. Draw the angle-bisector for an angle of 36°.

Solution: (Fig. 7-34) Mark the 36° point, divide by 2, and mark the 18° point. Remove the protractor and draw the lines.

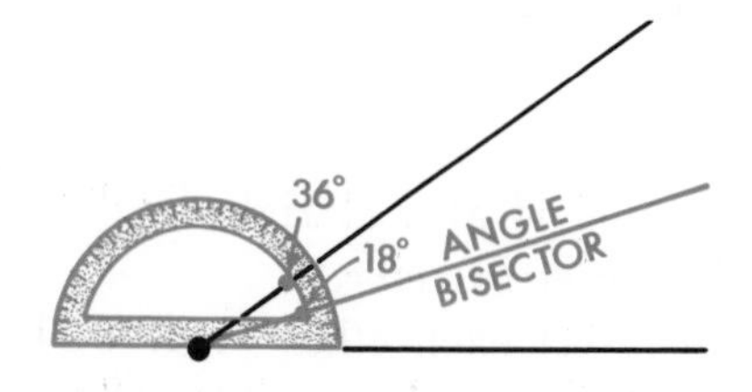

Fig. 7-34. Bisecting an angle.

Problem 3. Draw the angle-trisectors for an angle of 60°. (To *trisect* is to divide into three equal parts.)

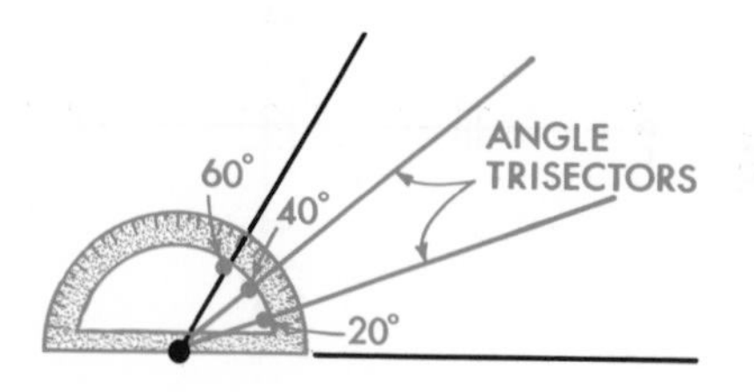

Fig. 7-35. Trisecting an angle.

Solution: (Fig. 7-35). Mark 20°, 40°, and 60°, and draw the lines.

Our first experiments have to do with *distances*.

Experiment L-1. Draw a line segment between two points, A and B, and measure it. (It will make things much easier if you use the *millimeter* scale on your ruler.)

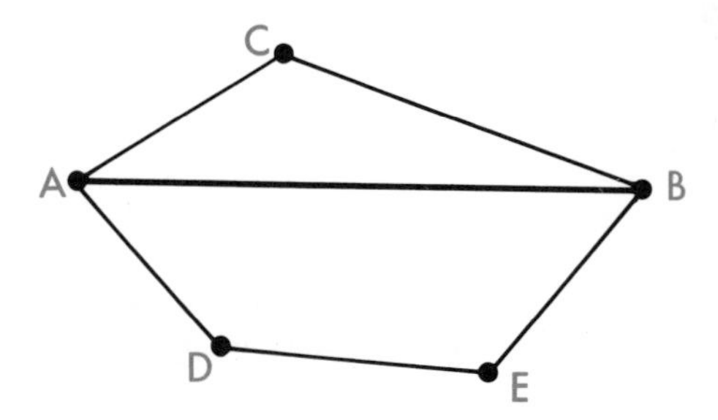

Fig 7-36.

The path between two points.

Now draw *any* other "paths" between A and B, *like* $AC + CB$, $AD + DE + EB$ (Fig. 7-36), and measure the total length of each path. You should soon verify the law that AB is the shortest path. In mathematics, we call the shortest path the *distance*, so that we can now say that

- *The distance between two points is the length of the line segment between them.*

Experiment L-2. Make an angle of any size and draw the angle bisector (Fig. 7-37). Now choose any point, P, on the angle-bisector, and go from P

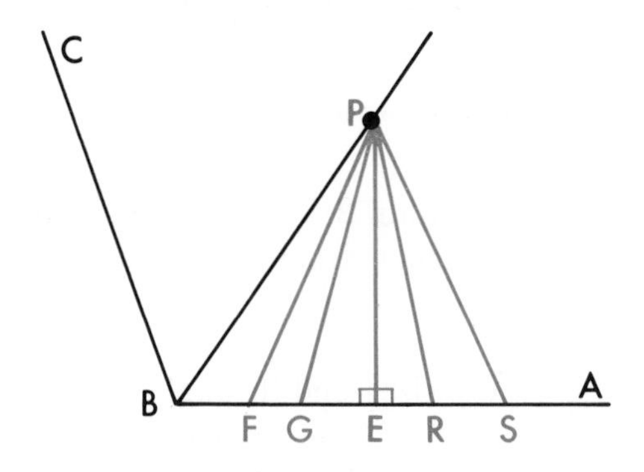

Fig. 7-37. The path from a point to a line.

to one of the sides by drawing line segments. When PR, PE, PF, and PG are measured, it is found that the shortest path is the one that is perpendicular to AB. We say that

- *The distance between a point and a line is the length of the perpendicular line segment.*

The easiest way to make this perpendicular line segment is with a draftsman's triangle (Fig. 7-38).

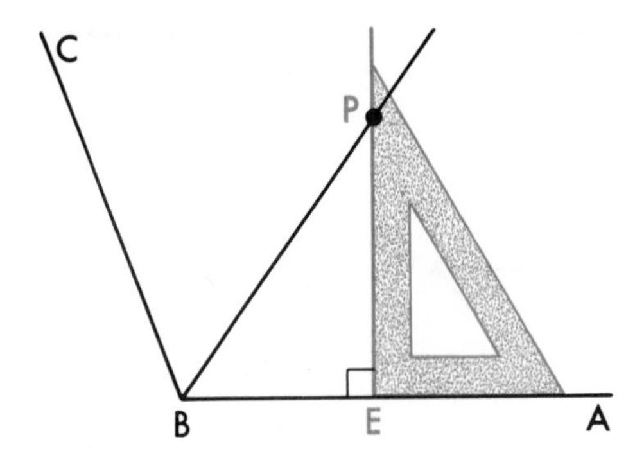

Fig. 7-38. Finding the perpendicular line segment.

Experiment L-3. Make a line segment 8 cm (80 mm) long (or else make it 3 in. long). Now make a perpendicular bisector (Fig. 7-39). Choose any point P on the perpendicular bisector, and draw PA and PB. No matter

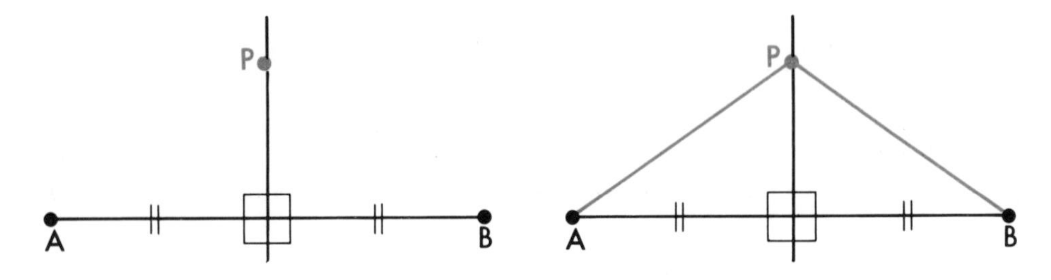

Fig. 7-39. Point on the perpendicular bisector of a line segment.

where P is, you will find that $PA = PB$, within 2% error. We say that P is *equidistant* (ē′kwĭ·dĭs′tănt) (equally distant) from the ends of the line segment.

Experiment L-4. Make an angle (any size) and its angle bisector, as in Fig. 7-40. Now choose any point, P, on the angle bisector, and draw the distances to the sides of the angle. Measure them. Do you find that the following is true within 2% error?

- *Any point, P, on the angle-bisector is equidistant from the sides of the angle.*

The usefulness of these laws is shown in the following problem.

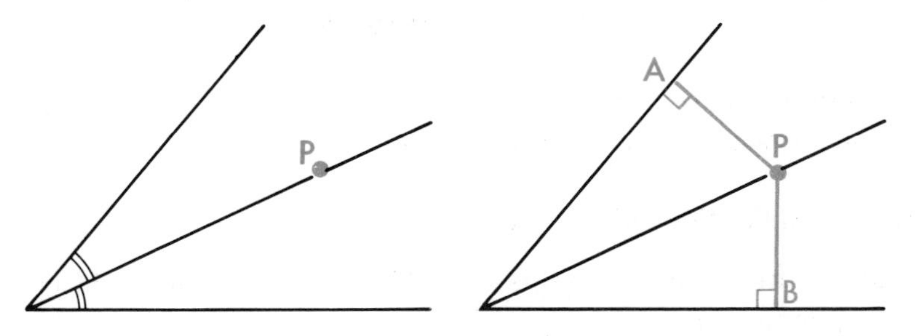

Fig. 7-40. Any point on an angle-bisector.

Problem 4. A manufacturer wishes to build a factory equally distant from two towns, Abbey, and Bounty, and also equally distant from two rivers (Fig. 7-41). Where should the factory be built?

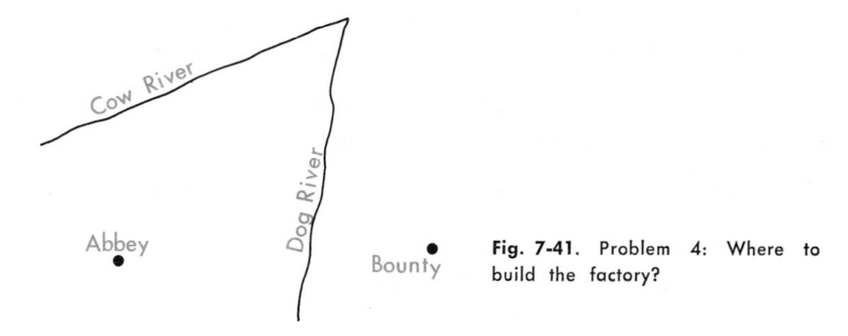

Fig. 7-41. Problem 4: Where to build the factory?

Solution: (Fig. 7-42) First, draw AB and its perpendicular bisector. Then draw the angle-bisector for the two rivers. Point F is the best location for the

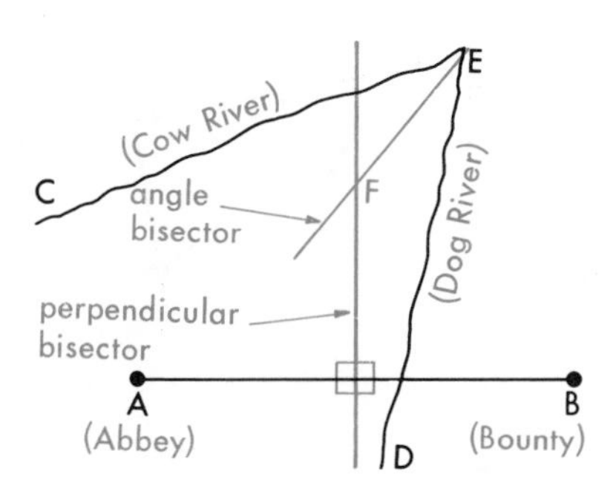

Fig. 7-42. The solution to Problem 4.

plant. By Experiment L-3, F is equally distant from the two towns because it is on the perpendicular bisector. By Experiment L-4, F is equally distant from the two rivers because it is on the angle-bisector. In this way, both conditions are satisfied.

Test: Section 5

In the following, you may use either the inch scale or the millimeter scale. The millimeter scale is much easier to use.

Part A. Make the following drawings:

1. Make a line segment 7 units long. One unit from the right end, make a perpendicular.
2. Make a line segment 5 units long. One unit from the left end, make a perpendicular.
3. Make a line segment 10 units long. Find its midpoint. Draw any line bisecting the segment.
4. Make a line segment 8 units long. Find its midpoint. Draw any line bisecting the segment.
5. Make a line segment 12 units long. Make the perpendicular bisector.
6. Make a line segment 9 units long. Make the perpendicular bisector.
7. Draw two line segments bisecting each other.
8. Draw two line segments that are perpendicular bisectors of each other.
9. Make an angle of 120°, and bisect it.
10. Make an angle of 150°, and bisect it.

Part B. Using the conclusions reached in this section, find the lengths marked by letters in the following diagrams.

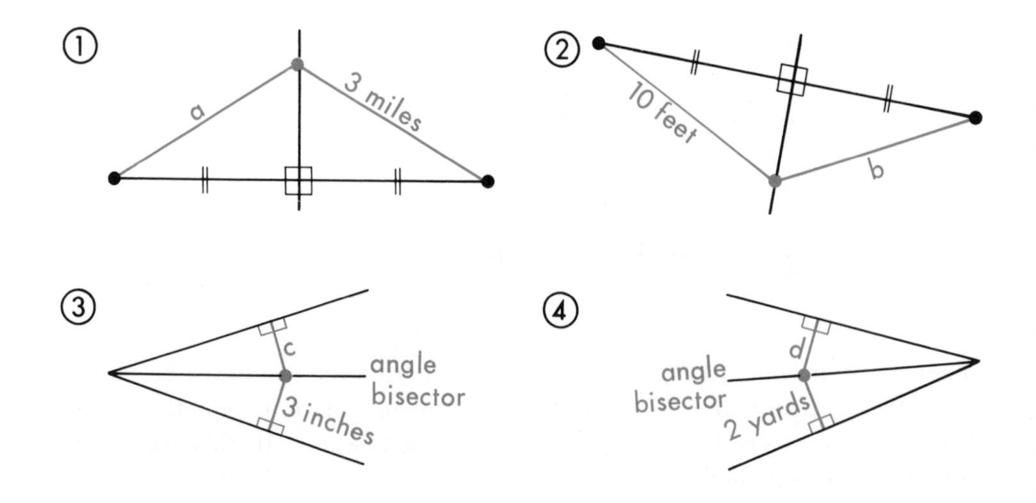

Part C. In each of the following cases, where should the manufacturer build his factory?

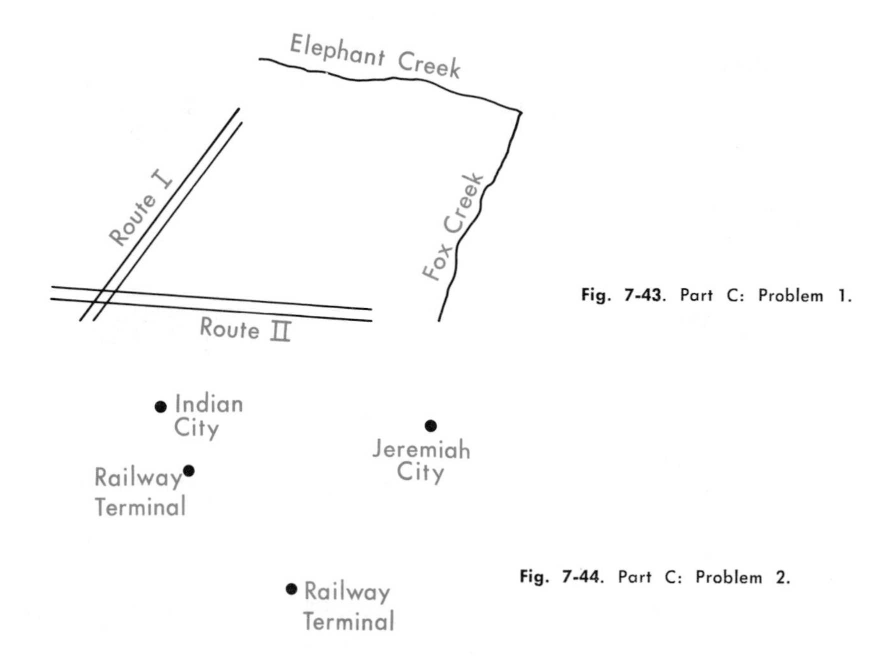

Fig. 7-43. Part C: Problem 1.

Fig. 7-44. Part C: Problem 2.

1 In Fig. 7-43, he wishes to be equidistant from the two creeks, and equidistant from the two highways.

2 In Fig. 7-44, he wishes to be equally distant from the two terminals, and equally distant from the two cities.

6 TRIANGLES

Any closed figure made up of straight-line segments (Fig. 7-45) can be split into three-sided figures. These three-sided figures are called *triangles.* They are so important that we shall show the different kinds of triangles

Fig. 7-45.

Splitting a closed figure into triangles.

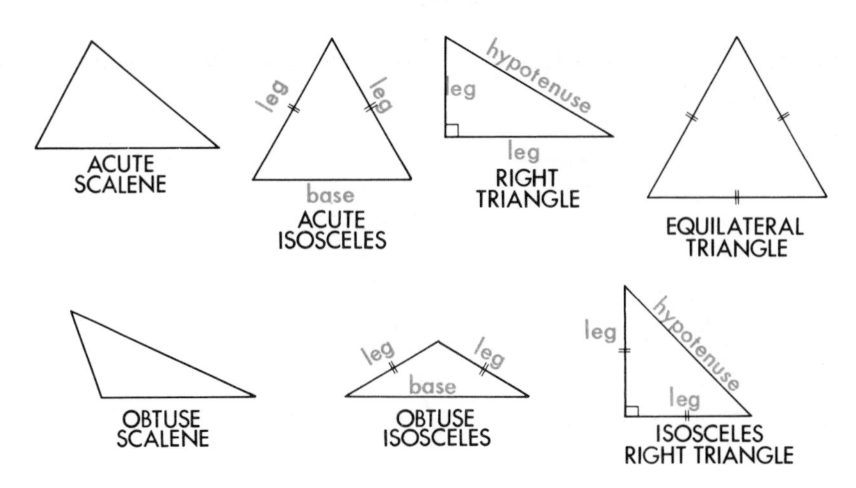

Fig. 7-46. Kinds of triangles.

(Fig. 7-46). In an experiment involving triangles, at least one of each kind should be used.

Triangles are classified as follows:

- An *acute scalene* triangle has unequal sides and three acute angles.
- An *obtuse scalene* triangle has unequal sides and one obtuse angle.
- An *acute isosceles* triangle has two equal sides and three acute angles.
- An *obtuse isosceles* triangle has two equal sides and one obtuse angle.
  The equal sides of an isosceles triangle are called *legs*, and the third side is called the *base*.
- A *right* triangle has a right angle.
  The side opposite the right angle is called the *hypotenuse*, and the other two sides are called *legs*.
- An *isosceles right* triangle has a right angle and equal legs.
- An *equilateral* triangle has three equal sides.

To do experiments with these, we shall have to learn how to draw them using ruler, compasses, and a protractor. This is done in the following problems.

Problem 1. Draw a scalene triangle with sides of $2\frac{1}{2}$, 3, and 4 units.

Solution: (Fig. 7-47) (*a*) Make a line segment 3 units long, and label the ends A and B. (*b*) Place the point of your compasses at the beginning of the ruler, and the pencil point at $2\frac{1}{2}$. (*c*) Now, lift the compasses *carefully*. Place the point on A, and draw an arc (curved line). (*d*) Now place the point of the compasses at the beginning of the ruler again, and adjust the pencil point until it is at 4 units. Lift the compasses *carefully*, place the

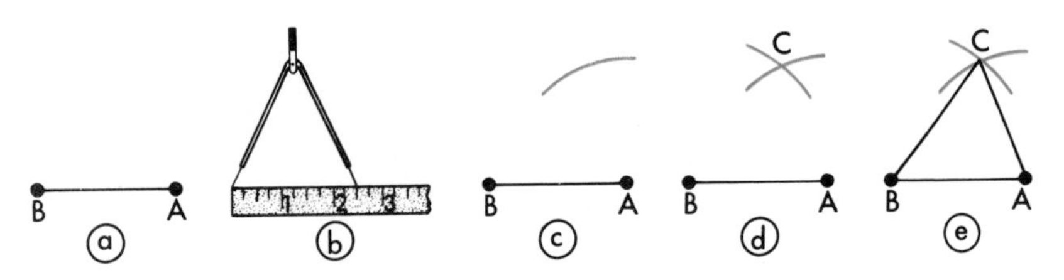

Fig. 7-47. Making a scalene triangle.

point on B, and draw another arc. Where the two arcs meet, write "C." (e) With your ruler, draw AC, and BC.

Triangles are named by their endpoints or *vertices* (vûr′tĭ•sēz). This one may be called $\triangle ABC$ (triangle ABC), or $\triangle BCA$, or $\triangle CAB$, etc.

Problem 2. Construct an isosceles triangle with base = 5 units, and leg = 3 units.

Solution: See Fig. 7-48.

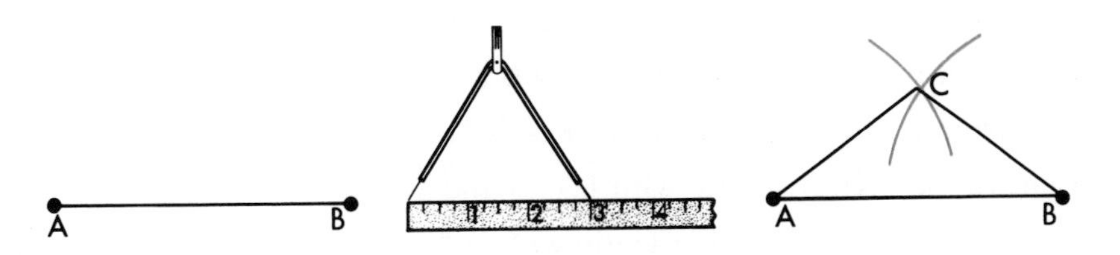

Fig. 7-48. Constructing an isosceles triangle.

Problem 3: Construct a right triangle with legs equal to 3, and 4 units.

Solution: See Fig. 7-49.

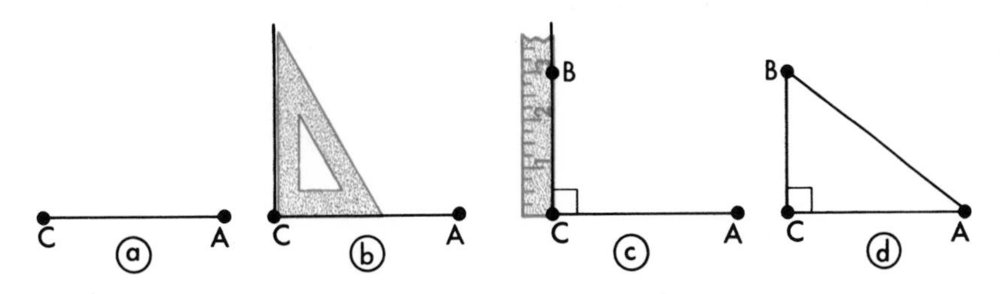

Fig. 7-49. Constructing a right triangle.

Problem 4. Construct an equilateral triangle with side equal to 6 units.

Solution: See Fig. 7-50.

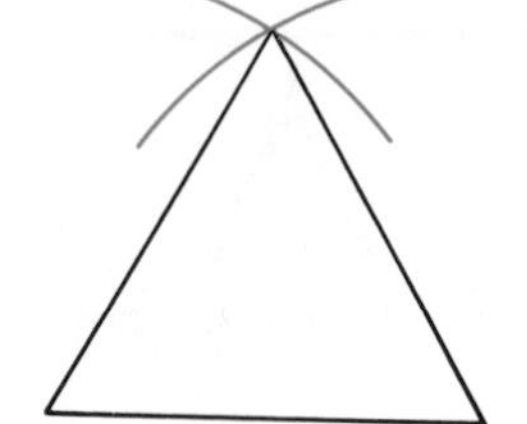

Fig. 7-50.
Constructing an equilateral triangle.

Test: Section 6

1. Construct a scalene triangle with sides 5, 7, and 8 units.
2. Construct a scalene triangle with sides 5, 7, and 11 units.
3. Construct an isosceles triangle with base 10, and legs 7.
4. Construct an isosceles triangle with base 8, and legs 6.
5. Construct an isosceles triangle with base 8, and legs $4\frac{1}{2}$.
6. Construct an isosceles triangle with base 9, and legs 5.
7. Construct a right triangle with legs 5 and 12.
8. Construct a right triangle with legs 6 and 8.
9. Construct a right triangle with legs 8 and 8.
10. Construct a right triangle with legs 5 and 5.
11. Construct an equilateral triangle with sides 6 units.
12. Construct an equilateral triangle with sides 11 units.

7 EXPERIMENTS WITH TRIANGLES

You have now had enough practice with experiments to do them by yourself. Before suggesting these experiments, though, there are some new names to learn.

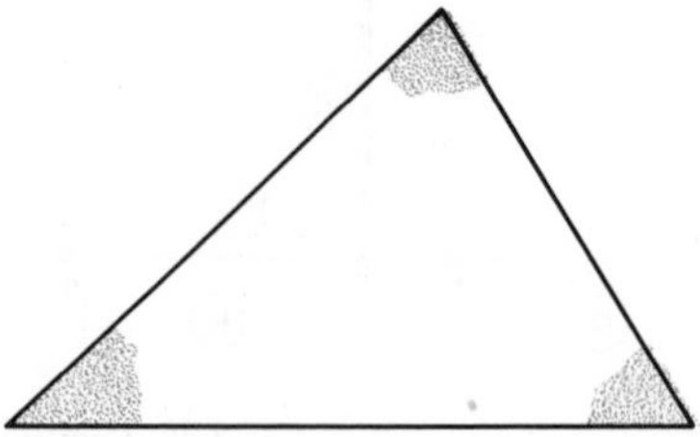

Fig. 7-51.
The interior angles of a triangle.

The *interior angles of a triangle* are those inside the triangle (Fig. 7-51). The *exterior angles of a triangle* are those formed when the sides are *extended* (made longer) as shown in Fig. 7-52 (either *a* or *b*).

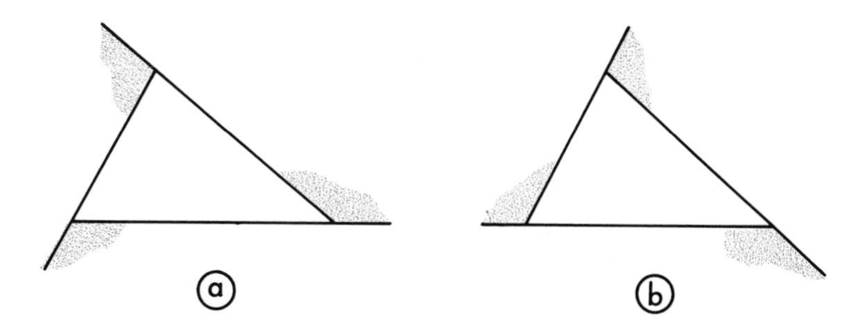

Fig. 7-52. The exterior angles of a triangle.

Test: Section 7

Part A. Verify each of the following by using several triangles.

1 The hypotenuse of a right triangle is longer than either of the legs. (Use scalene and isosceles right triangles.)

2 Each acute angle of an isosceles right triangle is 45°.

3 The acute angles of a right triangle are complements of each other.

4 Each angle of an equilateral triangle is 60°.

5 The sum of the interior angles of a triangle is 180°.

6 The sum of the exterior angles of a triangle is 360°.

7 Draw various kinds of isosceles triangles. The angles at the base are called *base angles* (Fig. 7-53). Measure the base angles, and come to some conclusion.

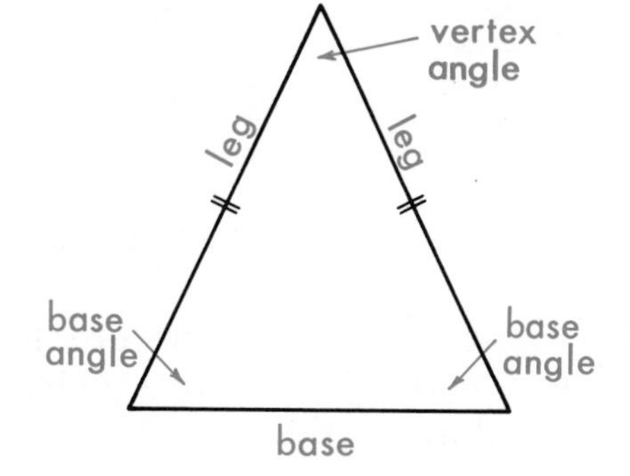

Fig. 7-53. Base angles and vertex angle.

8 Draw each of the seven kinds of triangle shown in Fig. 7-46. Extend one side of each, and measure the exterior angle formed (Fig. 7-54). Now measure each of the interior angles. You should be able to get *two*

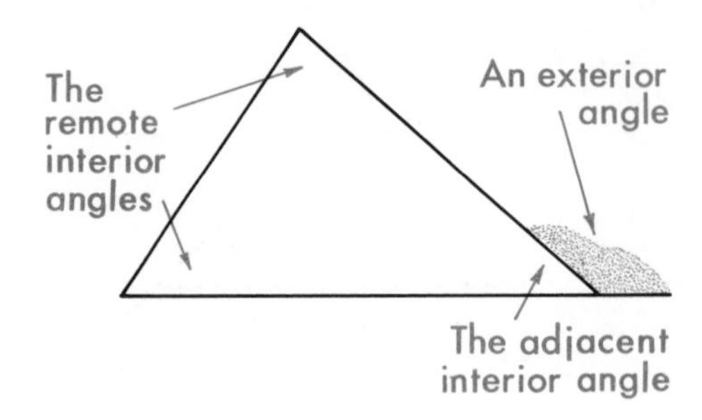

Fig. 7-54.

Remote and adjacent interior angles.

conclusions, one for the exterior angle and the adjacent interior angle, and one for the exterior angle and the remote interior angles.

Part B. Using the laws verified in Part *A*, find the sizes of the angles marked by letters in the following diagrams.

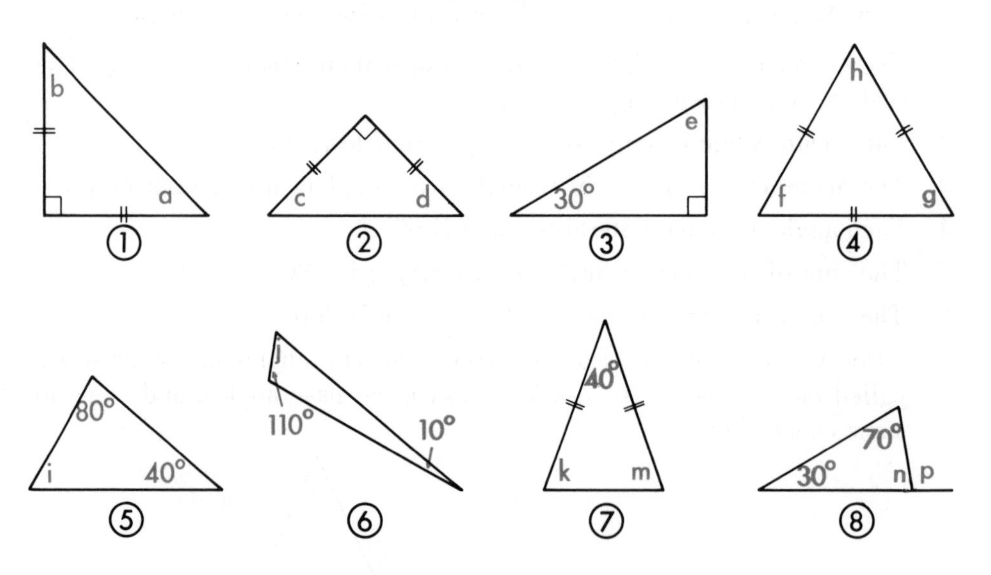

8 LINES OF A TRIANGLE

Certain lines and line segments of a triangle are also very important in mathematical work. The following problems show how these lines and line segments are drawn.

Problem 1. In $\triangle ABC$, draw the median to side BC.

Solution: The *median* to side BC runs from the midpoint of BC to the opposite vertex (point). First, find the midpoint of side BC with a ruler

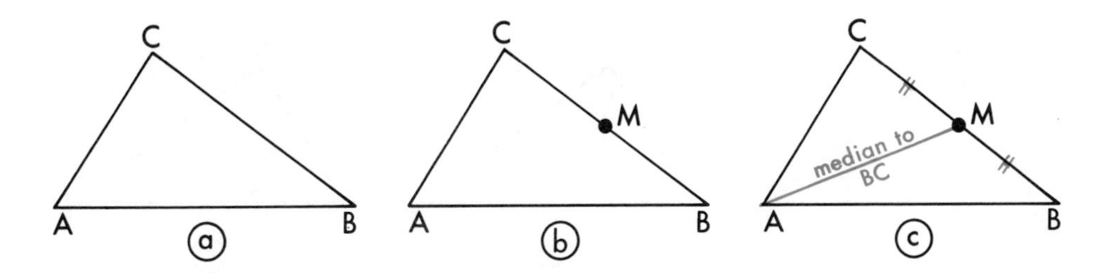

Fig. 7-55. Median to side *BC*.

(Fig. 7-55b). Then draw AM (Fig. 7-55c). There are also medians to sides AC and AB.

Problem 2. In $\triangle ABC$, draw the angle-bisector of $\angle B$.

Solution: The angle-bisector of $\angle B$ divides this angle into two equal parts, and ends at the opposite side. First measure $\angle B$ with your protractor, divide by two, and mark the midpoint (Fig. 7-56b). Remove the protractor,

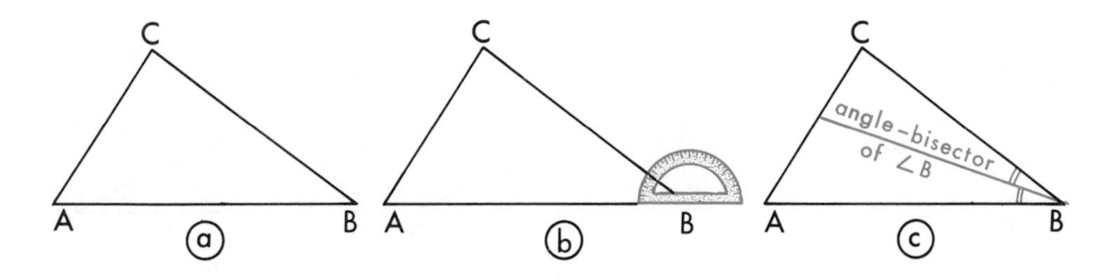

Fig. 7-56. Angle-bisector of ∠B.

and draw the angle-bisector (Fig. 7-56c). There are also angle-bisectors for $\angle A$ and $\angle C$.

Problem 3. In acute $\triangle ABC$, draw the altitude to side AB.

Solution: The altitude to side AB is a perpendicular line segment from AB

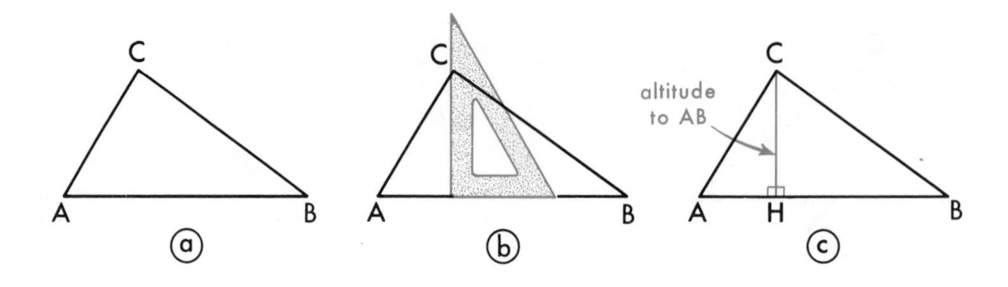

Fig. 7-57. Altitude in an acute triangle.

to the opposite vertex. Place the draftsman's triangle as shown in Fig. 7-57b, and draw CH. There are also altitudes to sides AC and BC.

Problem 4. In obtuse $\triangle ABC$, draw the altitude to side AB.

Solution: When you place the draftsman's triangle in position, you will

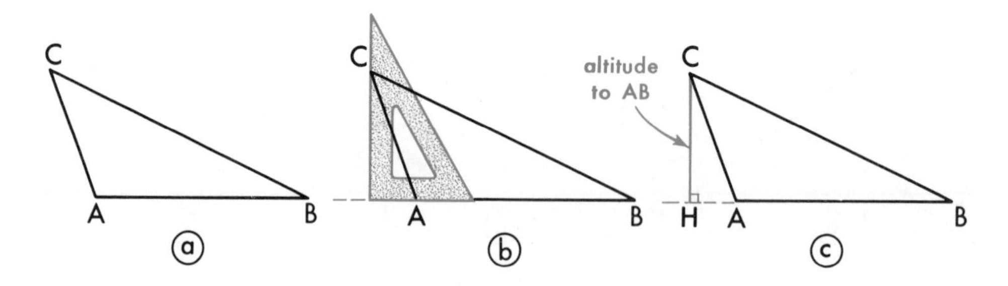

Fig. 7-58. Altitude in an obtuse triangle.

find that AB is not long enough. Make it long enough by drawing dotted lines as shown in Fig. 7-58b. There are also altitudes to sides AC and BC.

Problem 5. In $\triangle ABC$, draw the perpendicular bisector of side BC.

Solution: Find the midpoint of BC. Call it M. Place the draftsman's tri-

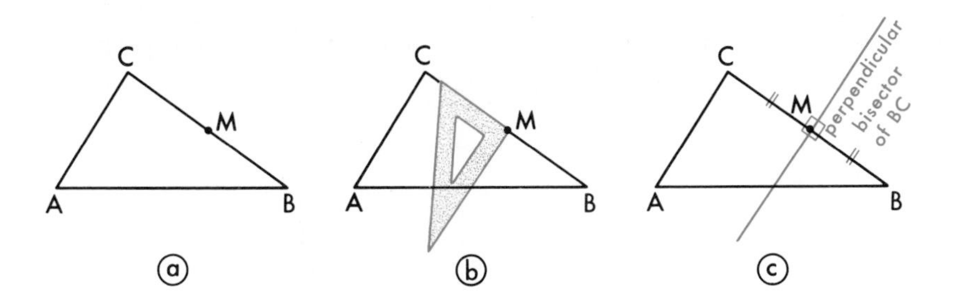

Fig. 7-59. Perpendicular bisector of the side.

angle in position (Fig. 7-59b) and draw the line. This line does not end in any special place. AC and AB also have perpendicular bisectors.

Test: Section 8

Part A. Using different kinds of triangles, make the following lines or line segments:

1. Median to AB
2. Median to BC
3. Angle-bisector to AC
4. Angle-bisector to AB
5. Altitude to AB
6. Altitude to AC
7. Perpendicular bisector of side BC
8. Perpendicular bisector of side AB

Part B. Verify each of the following, using different kinds of triangles.

1. In any triangle, the three medians meet at a point. (This point is called the *centroid*. If you make a triangle out of something stiff, you can balance the triangle on a pin at this point.)
2. In any triangle, the three angle-bisectors meet at a point. (The point is called the *incenter*.)
3. In any triangle, the three perpendicular bisectors meet at a point. (This point is called the *circumcenter*.)
4. In any triangle, the three altitudes meet at a point. (This point is called the *orthocenter*.)
5. If you have done 1, 2, and 3, answer the following question. Are all of these "centers" inside the triangle? Explain.

9 EXPERIMENTS WITH THE LINES OF A TRIANGLE

Some of the following experiments depend upon the fact that the medians meet in a point (Fig. 7-60), the angle-bisectors meet in a point (Fig. 7-61), the altitudes meet in a point (Figs. 7-62, and 7-63), and the perpendicular-bisectors meet in a point (Figs. 7-64, and 7-65).

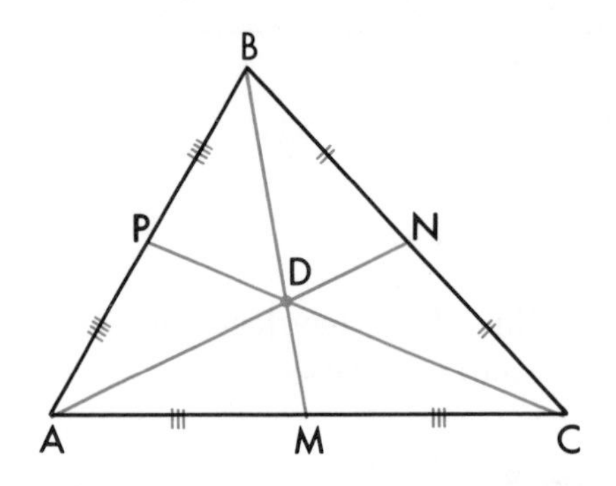

Fig. 7-60. The medians meet in a point.

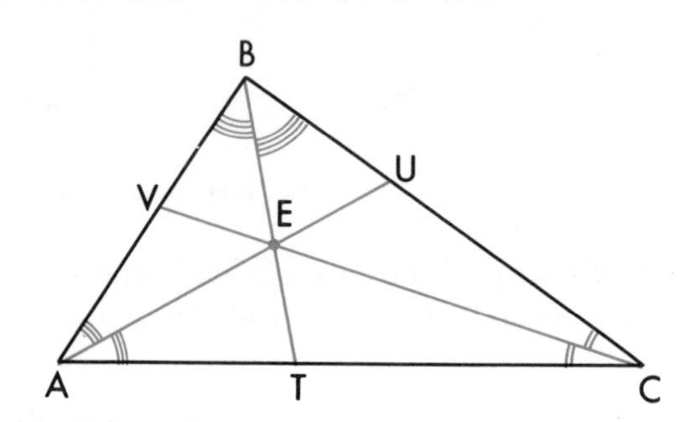

Fig. 7-61. The angle-bisectors meet in a point.

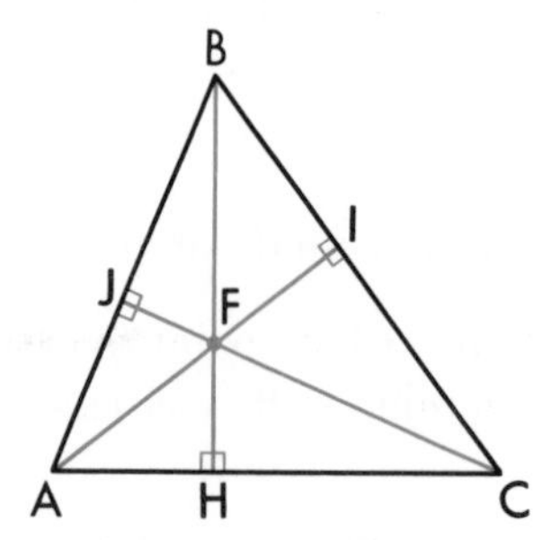

Fig. 7-62. The altitudes of an acute triangle meet inside.

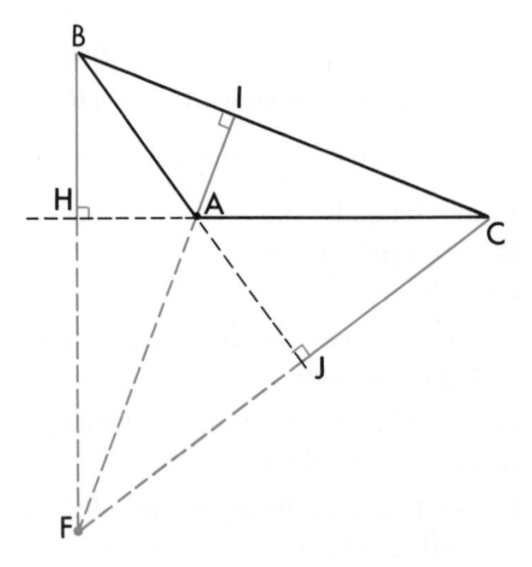

Fig. 7-63. The altitudes of an obtuse triangle meet outside.

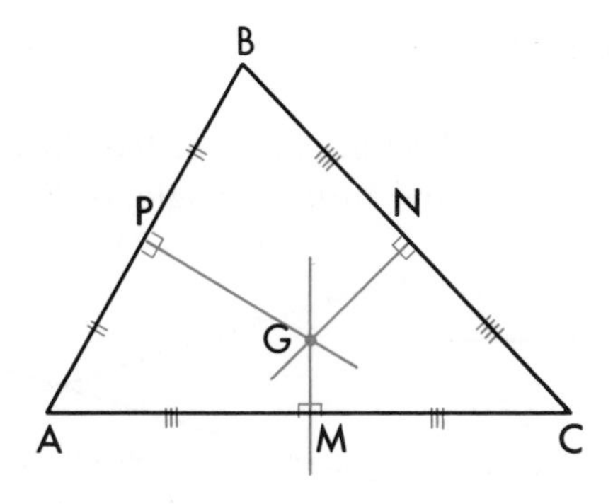

Fig. 7-64. The ⊥ bisectors of an acute △ meet inside.

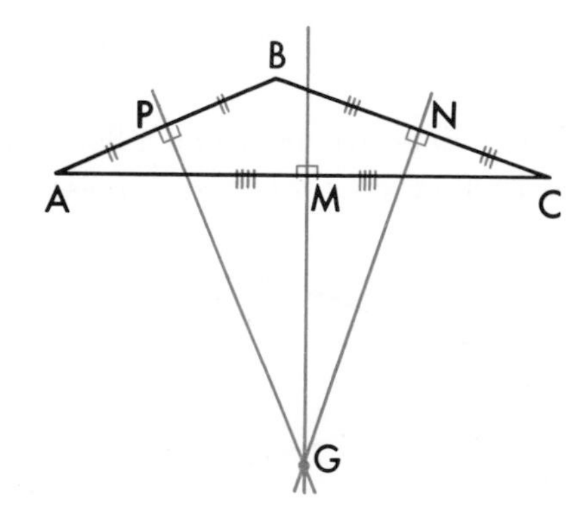

Fig. 7-65. The ⊥ bisectors of an obtuse △ meet outside.

Test: Section 9

Part A. Verify the following, using many different triangles.

1 The median, the altitude, and the angle-bisector to the base of any isosceles triangle, are the same line segment.

2 The three altitudes of a right triangle meet at the vertex of the right angle.

Part B. Make the following investigations.

1 Draw the three medians of any triangle, as in Fig. 7-60. Then BD is twice DM, AD is twice DN, and CD is twice DP.

2 Draw the three angle-bisectors of a large triangle. Label it as in Fig. 7-61. Find the distance (perpendicular line segment) from E to any side. Now take your compasses and open them to this distance. Place the point of the compasses on E, and draw a circle. What do you find? The circle is called the *inscribed circle of the triangle.*

3 Draw the three perpendicular bisectors for any large triangle. Label the triangle as in Fig. 7-64 or Fig. 7-65. Find the distance from G to any vertex. Now take your compasses and open them to this distance. Place the point of the compasses on G, and draw a circle. What do you find? This circle is called the *circumscribed circle of the triangle.*

10 PARALLELS

If two lines are drawn on a flat surface (like a sheet of paper, or the blackboard), they may *intersect* (cross) at some point and form an angle, or they

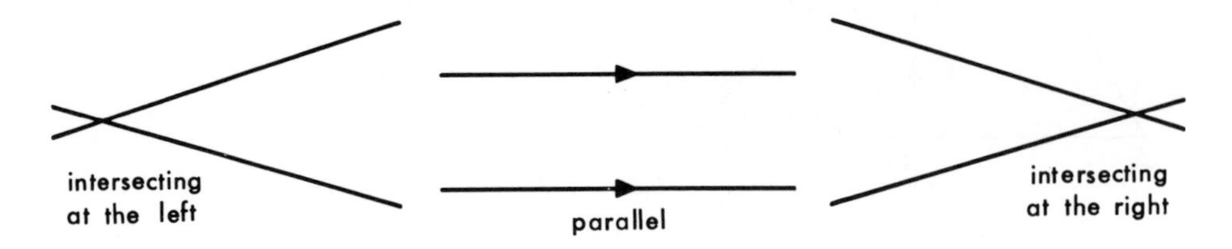

Fig. 7-66. Intersecting, and parallel lines.

may never intersect (Fig. 7-66). If they *never intersect,* no matter how long they are made, they are called *parallel lines.*

A convenient way to draw parallel lines is as follows:

Problem. Through point P, draw a line parallel to AB.

Solution: Place a draftsman's triangle with its leg under the line (Fig. 7-67b). Then place a long ruler so that it rests firmly along the hypotenuse

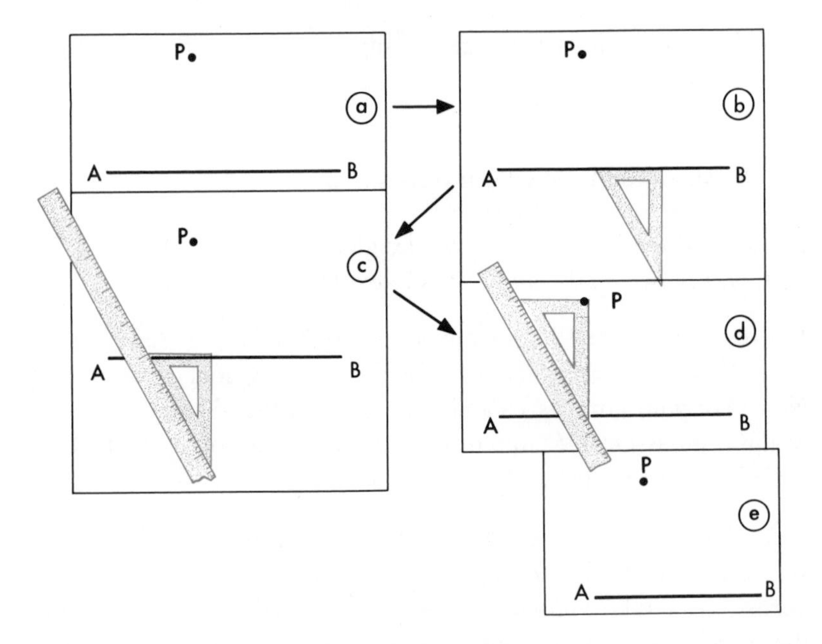

Fig. 7-67. Drawing parallel lines.

(Fig. 7-67c). Now, hold the ruler firmly with the left hand, and slide the triangle along it until the upper leg is at the correct point, P (Fig. 7-67d). Now draw the line through point P (Fig. 7-67e).

Now, let us draw a third line across these lines (Fig. 7-68b). This third line is called a *transversal* (trăns•vûr′săl).

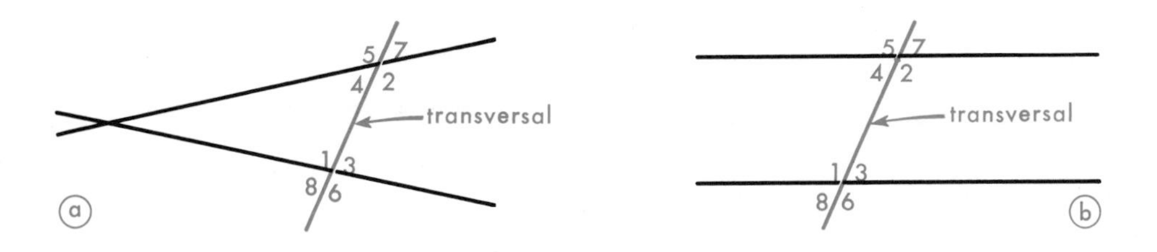

Fig. 7-68. Angles formed by a transversal.

The following pairs of angles (Fig. 7-68, a and b) have special names:

- $\angle 1$ and $\angle 2$, also $\angle 3$ and $\angle 4$ are called *alternate interior angles.*
- $\angle 1$ and $\angle 5$, $\angle 8$ and $\angle 4$, $\angle 3$ and $\angle 7$, and $\angle 6$ and $\angle 2$ are called *corresponding angles.*
- $\angle 1$ and $\angle 4$, and $\angle 2$ and $\angle 3$, are called *consecutive angles.*

Test: Section 10

Part A. Verify the following laws.

1 If two lines are parallel, any pair of alternate interior angles are equal.
2 If two lines are parallel, any pair of corresponding angles are equal.
3 If two lines are parallel, any pair of consecutive angles are supplementary.
4 If two lines are not parallel, the alternate interior angles are not equal.

Part B. Investigate the following.

1 Draw a pair of parallel lines. Make a transversal at right angles to one of them. Is it at right angles to the other also?

2 Draw a pair of parallel lines. The interior transversal perpendicular to these lines (Fig. 7-69) is the shortest path (distance). Draw other perpendiculars between the lines. Are they the same or different?

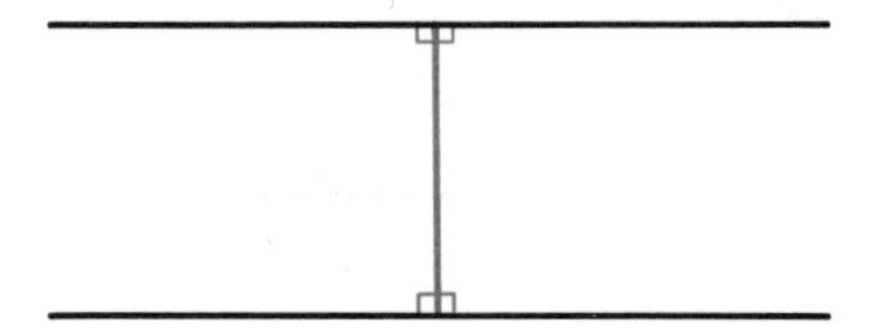

Fig. 7-69. The distance between parallel lines.

3 Draw $\triangle$ *ABC* (Fig. 7-70). Find the midpoint of *AB*. Through *M*, draw a line parallel to *BC*. Now compare *MN* and *BC*. Also compare *AN* and *NC*. What are your conclusions?

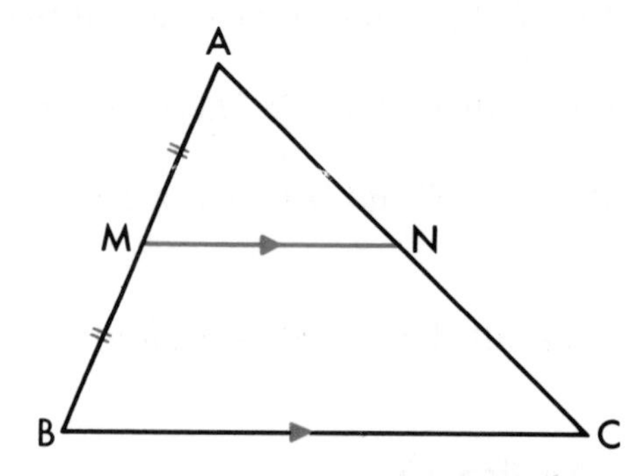

Fig. 7-70. A line parallel to the base of a triangle.

4 Draw $\triangle$ *ABC* (Fig. 7-71). Divide *AB* into three equal parts. Through *P* and *Q*, draw lines parallel to *BC*. Now compare *PR*, *QS*, and *BC*. Also compare *AR*, *RS*, and *SC*. What are your conclusions?

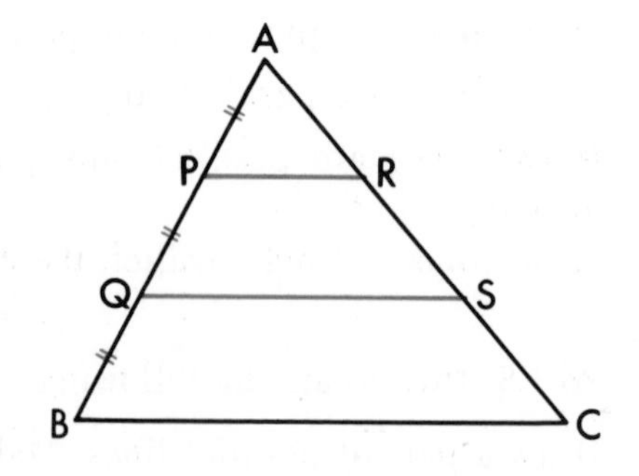

Fig. 7-71. Problem 4.

Part C. Using the laws verified in this section, find the value of the lines and angles marked by letters in the following diagrams.

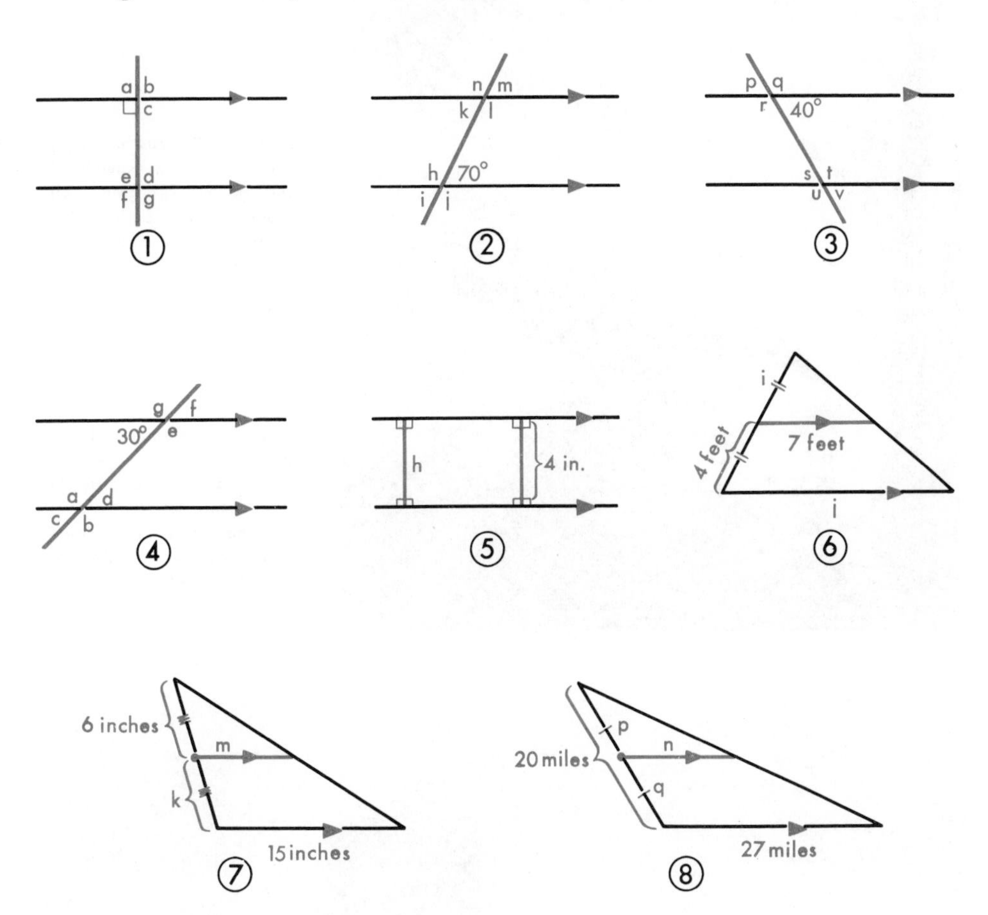

The Bronx-Whitestone Bridge, New York, is an example of the geometrical forms all around you. *Courtesy Triborough Bridge and Tunnel Authority.*

New York International Airport. How many geometrical forms can you identify in this picture of the arrival building tower and fountain? *Courtesy The Port of New York Authority.*

8

GEOMETRICAL FIGURES

All about you, you can see lines, angles and triangles. These are the basic figures of one of the oldest branches of mathematics: *geometry*. The word "geometry," actually means "earth-measurement," and the work in geometry was, in early times, connected with the problems of laying out fields, surveying, and other practical problems.

We shall now turn our attention to *closed* geometrical figures with more than three sides. Using the same methods of investigation that you have already practiced in Chapter 7, you will be able to find out the most important facts about these new types of figures.

1 QUADRILATERALS

Any closed figure made up of line segments is called a polygon (pŏl′ĭ·gŏn).

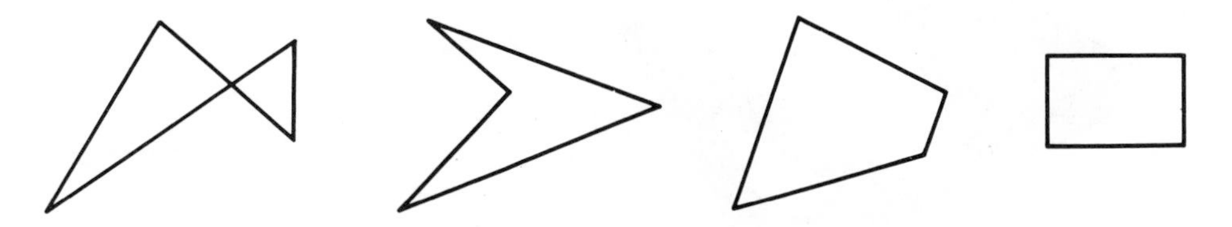

Fig. 8-1. Some quadrilaterals.

If it has exactly *four sides*, it is a *quadrilateral* (kwŏd′rĭ·lăt′ẽr·*a*l). Typical quadrilaterals are shown in Fig. 8-1.

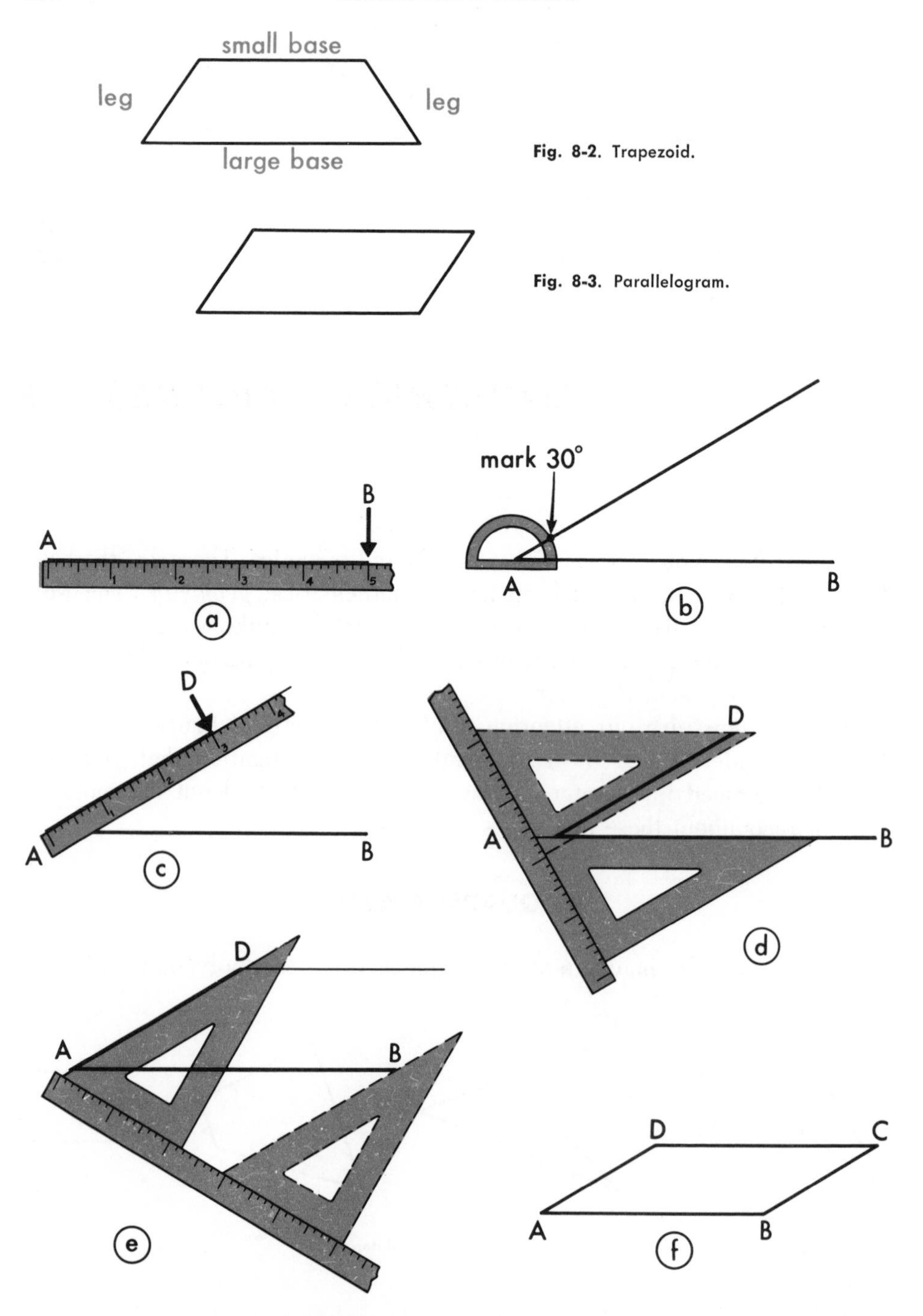

Fig. 8-2. Trapezoid.

Fig. 8-3. Parallelogram.

Fig. 8-4. Constructing a parallelogram.

Two basic quadrilaterals are the *trapezoid,* and the *parallelogram.* A trapezoid has only two sides parallel (Fig. 8-2). These two sides are called *bases,* and the other two, nonparallel, sides are called *legs.*

The parallelogram has *both* pairs of opposite sides parallel (Fig. 8-3). The illustrative problem shows how to draw one.

Problem 1. Draw a parallelogram with sides of 3, and 5 units, and an angle of 30°.

Solution: See Fig. 8-4.

(*a*) Rule a line segment 5 units long. (*b*) Mark off an angle of 30°. (*c*) Rule a side of 3 units. (*d*) Draw a parallel to AB. (*e*) Draw a parallel to AD. (*f*) The parallelogram is called $ABCD$. (Read the endpoints in any consecutive order. There are eight correct ways to name this parallelogram.)

The following figures are types of parallelograms (Fig. 8-5). The *rectangle* is a parallelogram with right angles. The *square* is a parallelogram with right angles and all its sides equal. The *rhombus* is a parallelogram with all sides equal. A square, as you can see, is both a rectangle and a rhombus. A baseball diamond is a square.

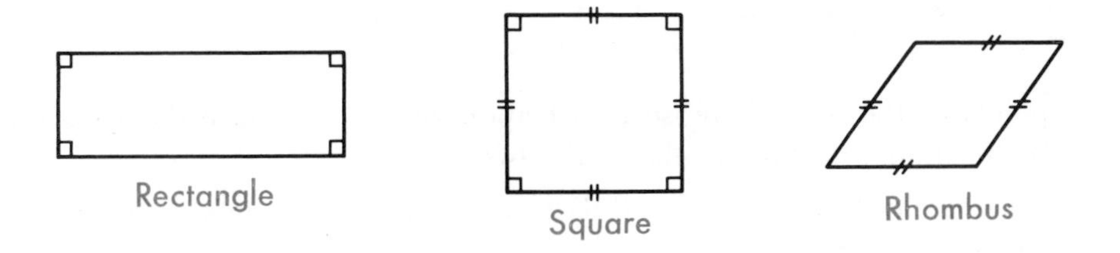

Fig. 8-5. Special types of rectangles.

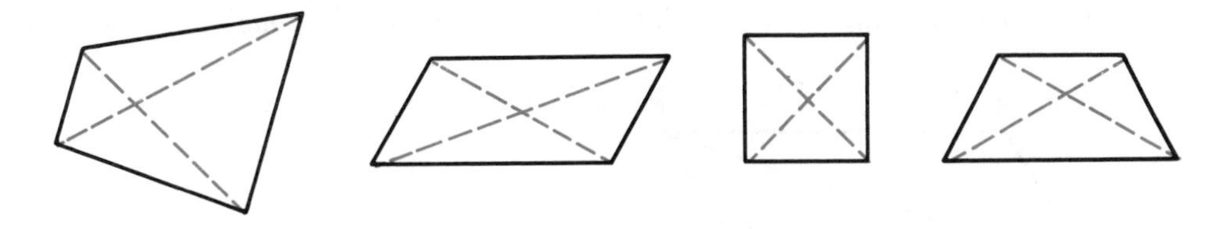

Fig. 8-6. Diagonals.

In our investigations, we shall also deal with the *diagonals* of quadrilaterals. Diagonals are the line segments shown by dashes in Fig. 8-6.

Test: Section 1

Part A. Verify the following facts about parallelograms.

1 The opposite sides of any parallelogram are equal.

2 The opposite angles of any parallelogram are equal.

3 The diagonals of any parallelogram bisect each other.

4 The diagonals of any rhombus are at right angles.

Part B. Investigate the following:

1 The median of a trapezoid (Fig. 8-7) is a line segment joining the mid-

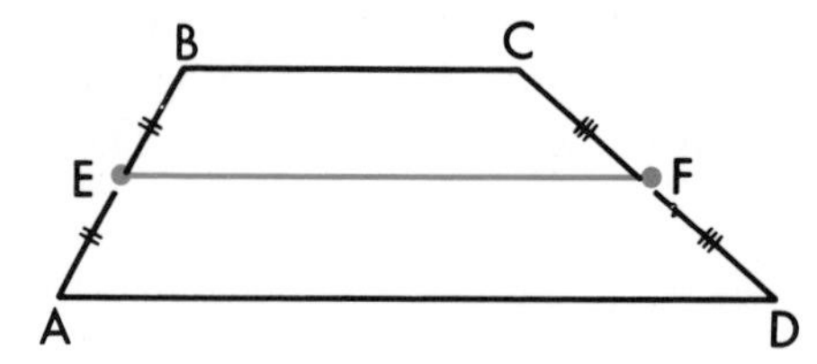

Fig. 8-7. The median of a trapezoid.

points of the legs. Draw several trapezoids and compare the length of the median with the lengths of the two bases.

2 An isosceles trapezoid (Fig. 8-8) is a trapezoid with equal legs. Investigate the *base angles.*

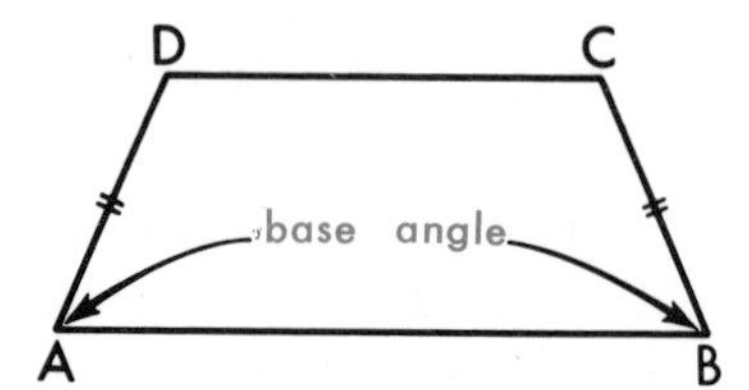

Fig. 8-8. Isosceles trapezoid.

3 Investigate the diagonals of an isosceles trapezoid.

4 Draw different kinds of parallelograms. Draw one diagonal (Fig. 8-9),

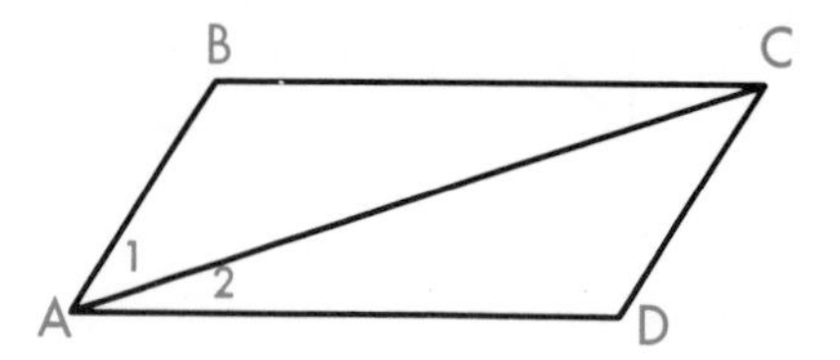

Fig. 8-9. Part B: Problem 4.

and investigate $\angle 1$ and $\angle 2$. For what special types of parallelograms is it true (within 2%) that $\angle 1 = \angle 2$?

2 OTHER POLYGONS

A five-sided polygon is called a *pentagon* (Fig. 8-10). A six-sided polygon is called a *hexagon* (Fig. 8-11). An eight-sided polygon is called an *octagon* (Fig. 8-12). For other kinds of polygons, a mathematician usually just

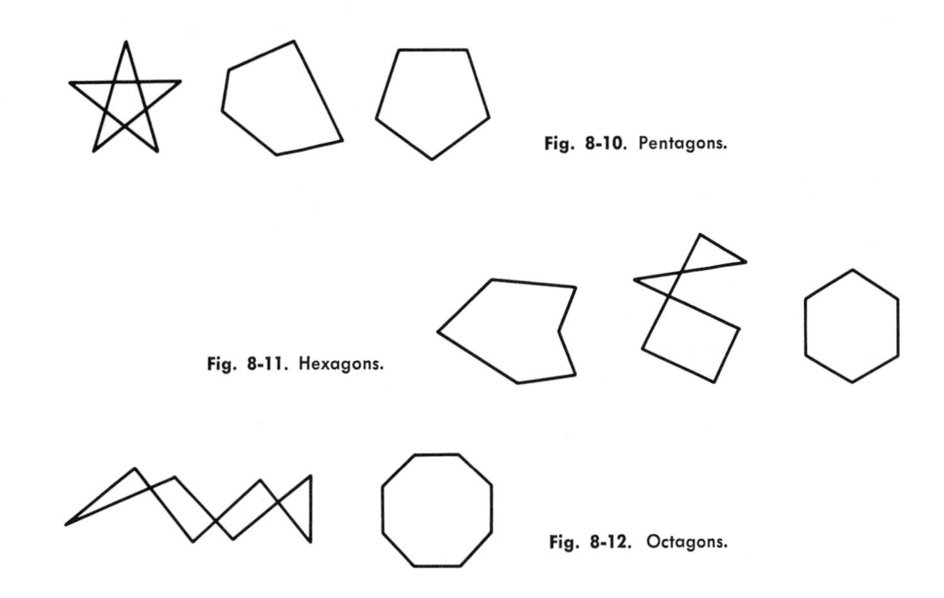

Fig. 8-10. Pentagons.

Fig. 8-11. Hexagons.

Fig. 8-12. Octagons.

identifies the number of sides; for example, "seven-sided polygon," or "nineteen-sided polygon."

By experimenting, we can show (within 2%) that the following rule holds for polygons with any number of sides:

Interior-Angle Rule. The sum of the interior angles of any polygon is found by (1) counting the number of sides; (2) subtracting 2; (3) multiplying the result by 180°.

Problem 1. Find the sum of the interior angles of a nine-sided polygon.

Solution: $9 - 2 = 7; 7 \times 180^\circ = 1260^\circ$.

If the polygon has all its sides equal, and all its angles equal, it is called a *regular polygon.* The equilateral triangle is the regular polygon with the smallest number of sides. Other regular polygons are shown in Fig. 8-13.

Using the interior-angle rule, we can easily find the size of any single interior angle of a regular polygon.

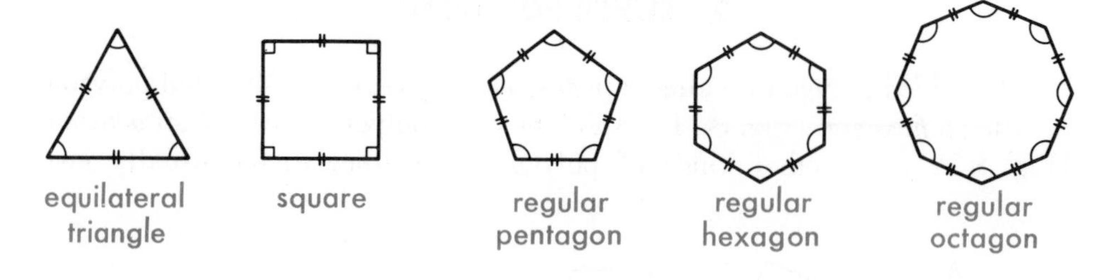

Fig. 8-13. Some regular polygons.

Problem 2. Find the size of each interior angle of a regular pentagon.

Solution: A pentagon has 5 sides.
Subtract 2, get a result of 3.
$3 \times 180^\circ = 540^\circ$
A regular pentagon has 5 equal angles.
Each of the angles must be $\frac{1}{5}$ of $540^\circ = 108^\circ$.

Problem 3. Find the size of each interior angle of a regular hexagon.

Solution: A hexagon has 6 sides.
$6 - 2 = 4$
$4 \times 180^\circ = 720^\circ$
A regular hexagon has 6 equal angles.
Each one must be $\frac{1}{6}$ of $720^\circ = 120^\circ$.

With this information, we can now draw any regular polygon.

Problem 4. Draw a regular polygon of 5 sides, with each side equal to 4 units.

Solution: (Fig. 8-14) First, find the size of each interior angle. According to Problem 2, each interior angle $= 108^\circ$. Then (*a*) rule a side of 4 units. (*b*) At both ends, draw angles of 108°. (*c*) Measure 4 units on each of these lines. (*d*) At *E* and *C*, make angles of 108°.

• Test: Section 2

Part A. Use the interior-angle rule to find the following:

1 The sum of the interior angles for any seven-sided polygon.
2 The sum of the interior angles for any eight-sided polygon.

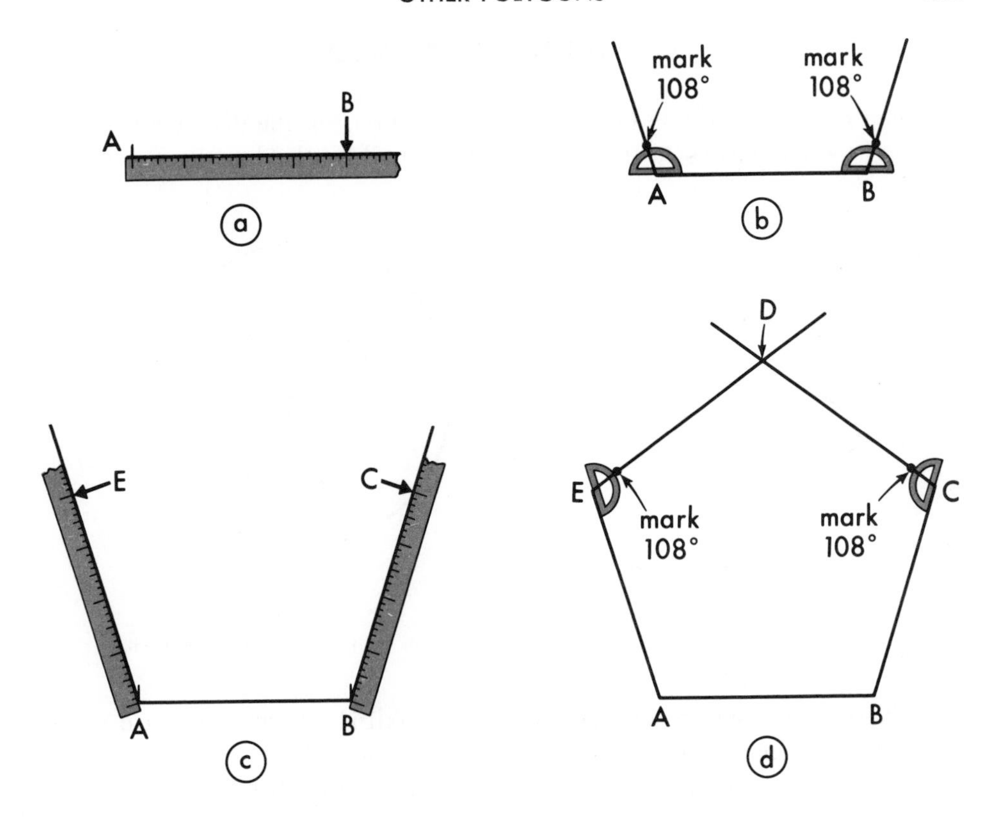

Fig. 8-14. Making a regular pentagon.

3 The sum of the interior angles for any nine-sided polygon.

4 The sum of the interior angles for any ten-sided polygon.

5 The size of each interior angle of a regular eight-sided polygon.

6 The size of each interior angle of a regular nine-sided polygon.

7 The size of each interior angle of a regular ten-sided polygon.

8 The size of each interior angle of a regular twelve-sided polygon.

Part B. Verify by experiment.

1 The interior-angle rule for any polygon.

2 The sum of the *exterior* angles of any polygon is 360°.

3 The diagonals of a regular pentagon are equal.

4 Make a regular hexagon. Draw line segments joining three alternate vertices. The resulting triangle is equilateral.

3 THE LINES OF A CIRCLE

When you draw a circle (Fig. 8-15) with compasses, the *distance* from the point of the compasses to the point of the pencil, is the length of a *radius*

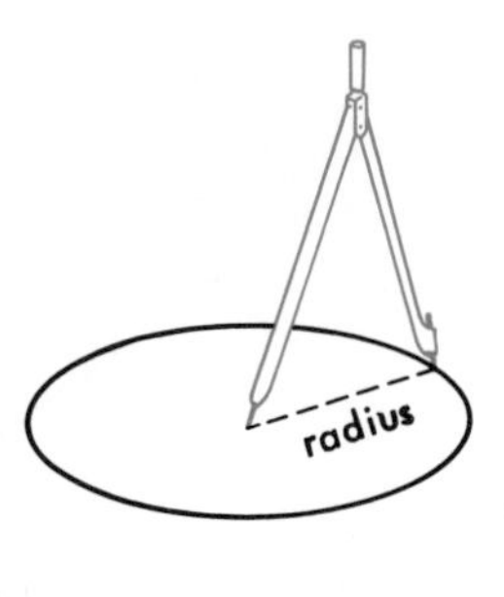

Fig. 8-15. Drawing a circle.

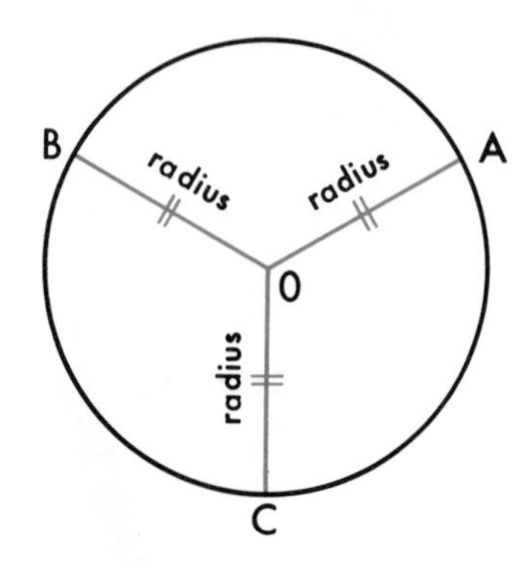

Fig. 8-16. The radii of a circle are equal.

(rā′dĭ·ŭs). It is easy to see that the *radii* (rā′dĭ·ī) of the circle are equal (Fig. 8-16), provided the compasses are held correctly.

A line segment across the center of the circle (Fig. 8-17) is double the radius. This is called the *diameter*. Any line segment joining two points on

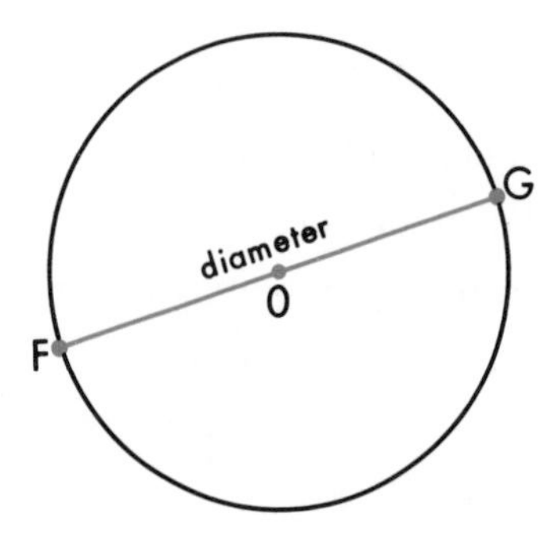

Fig. 8-17. Diameter of a circle.

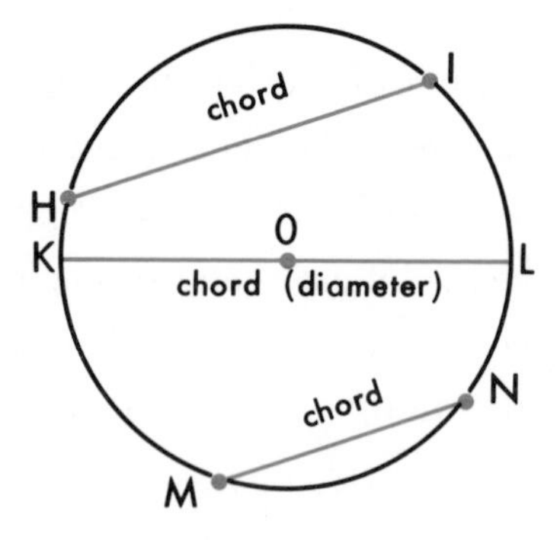

Fig. 8-18. Chords of a circle.

the circle (Fig. 8-18) is called a *chord* (kôrd). The diameter is just one of the chords of a circle.

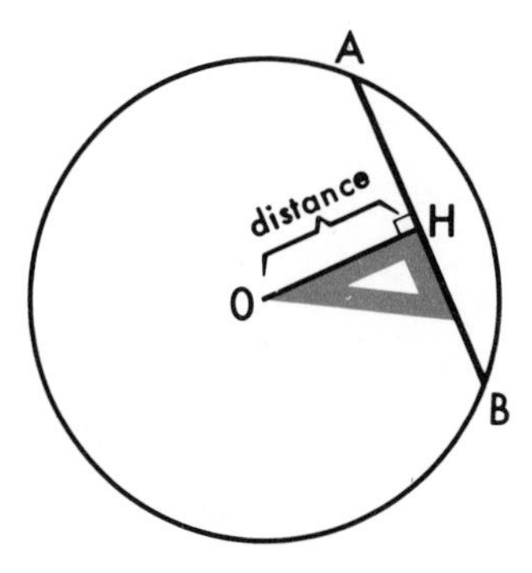

Fig. 8-19. Distance of a chord from the center of the circle.

The *distance* of a chord from the center is measured by the perpendicular line segment (Fig. 8-19).

If the chord is *extended* (made longer) so that it protrudes beyond the circle (Fig. 8-20), the whole line segment is called a *secant.* The part that

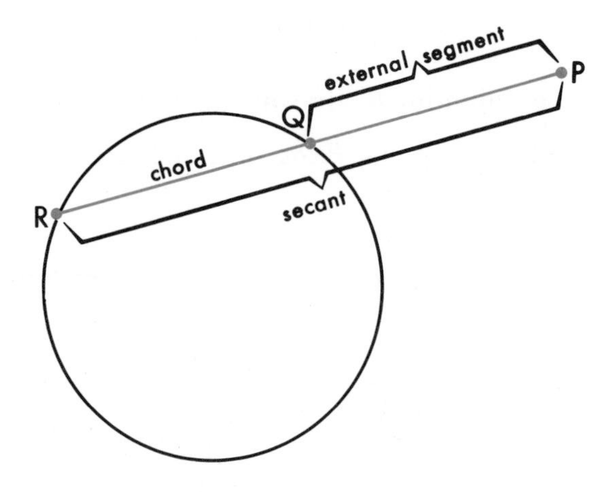

Fig. 8-20. Secant of a circle.

is *inside,* is a *chord*; the part that is *outside,* is called the *external segment of the secant.*

Now look at Fig. 8-21. In (a) the secant is being moved up so that the inside segment is becoming smaller and smaller. Points R and Q are getting closer to each other. Finally, in (b), the line segment just *touches* the circle *once,* at point T, instead of intersecting it *twice.* When this happens, PT is called a *tangent* to the circle. To draw it, you place a ruler, or draftsman's triangle, at P, and crossing the circle at two points, like R and Q. Then you

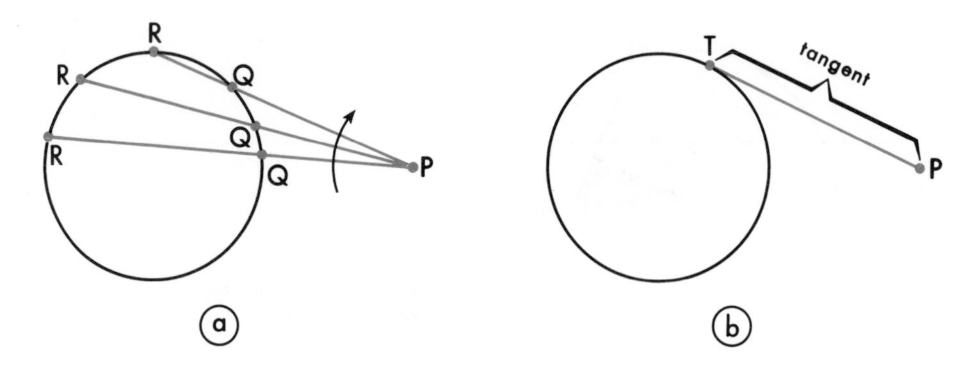

Fig. 8-21. Making the tangent to a circle from a fixed point outside the circle.

move the ruler or triangle carefully, so that it stays at P. You move it until it just touches the edge of the circle.

Test: Section 3

Part A. Verify the following by drawing different circles:

1 Draw a circle. Choose a point, P, outside, and draw *two* tangents (Fig. 8-22). Show that $PT = PV$.

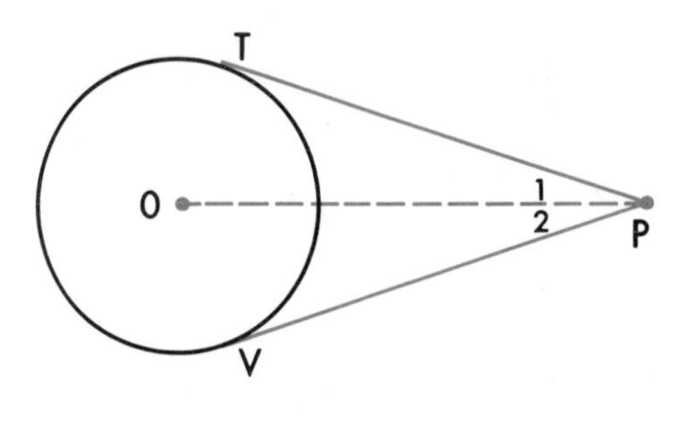

Fig. 8-22. Part A: Problems 1 and 2.

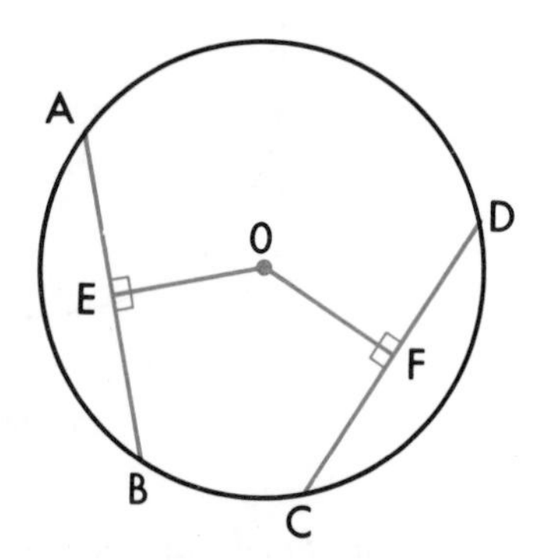

Fig. 8-23. Part A: Problem 3.

2 Using the same circle as in No. 1, draw PO and show that $\angle 1 = \angle 2$.

3 Draw a circle, and in it draw two equal chords (Fig. 8-23). Now measure the distances from the center to the chords. Show that $OE = OF$.

4 Draw a circle, and in it two chords that are unequal. Measure the distances from the center. Show that the distances are also unequal.

Part B. Investigate the following:

1 Draw a circle, a chord, and the perpendicular from the center (Fig. 8-24). Compare AC and CB.

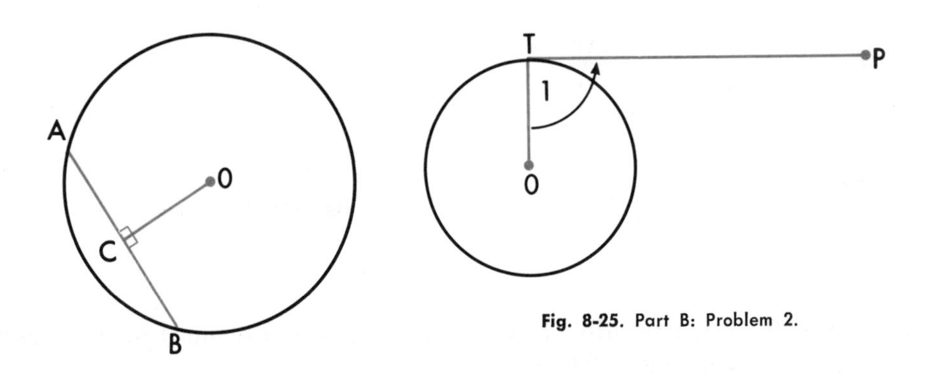

Fig. 8-25. Part B: Problem 2.

Fig. 8-24. Part B: Problem 1.

2 Draw a circle, a tangent, and a radius, as shown in Fig. 8-25. Measure $\angle 1$. What do you find? This gives you a method for drawing a tangent at any fixed point *on* a circle. The method discussed before, was for a tangent from a point *outside* the circle.

Part C. Verify the following:

1 Draw a circle, and in it any two intersecting chords (Fig. 8-26). Measure AE, EB, CE, and ED. Does $AE \times EB = CE \times ED$?

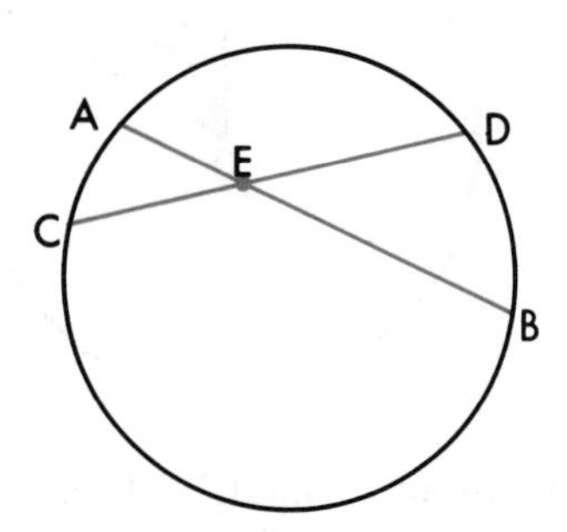

Fig. 8-26. Part C: Problem 1.

2 In No. 1 (Part C), if $AE = 2$, $CE = 8$, and $ED = 3$, how great is EB?

3 Draw a circle, a tangent, and a secant through the center (Fig. 8-27). Does $(PT)^2 = PA \times PB$? [$(PT)^2$ means $PT \times PT$.]

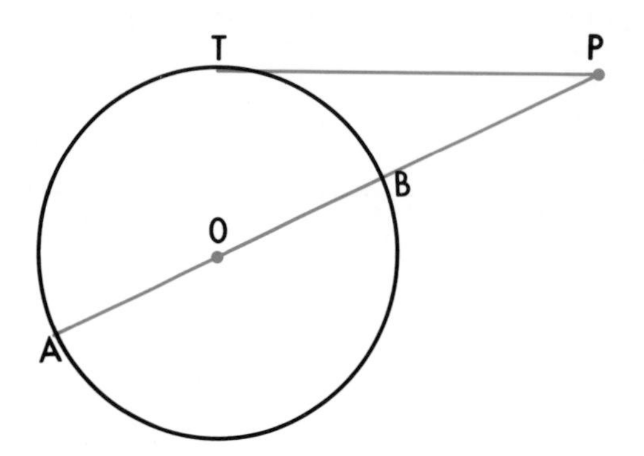

Fig. 8-27. Part C: Problem 3.

4 In Fig. 8-27, if the radius is 3 in. and the external segment of the secant is 2 in., how long will PT be?

4 ANGLES OF A CIRCLE

Any *part* of the circumference of a circle is called an *arc*. In Fig. 8-28, that portion of the circle between points A and B, is called *arc AB*. This is written: $\overset{\frown}{AB}$. If the endpoints of the arc are connected to the center of the

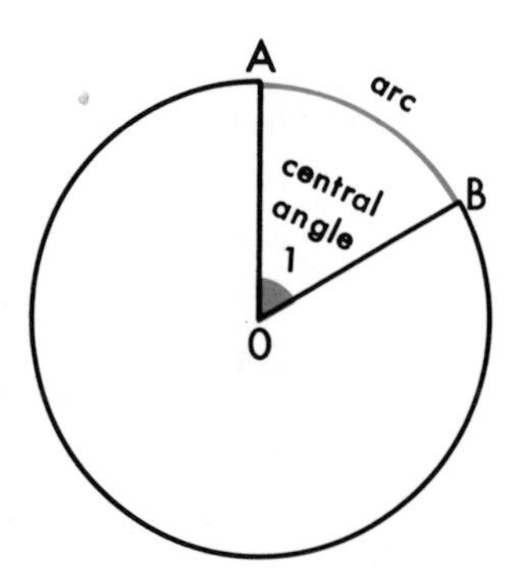

Fig. 8-28. Arcs and central angles.

circle, the angle formed, $\angle 1$, is called a *central angle*, because it is at the center of the circle. The *size of an arc* means the number of degrees in its central angle. If the central angle of an arc is $30°$, we say that the arc has a size of $30°$.

In Fig. 8-29, arcs AB, and $A'B'$ (A prime, B prime) have different lengths, but they have the same size because they have exactly the same central angle.

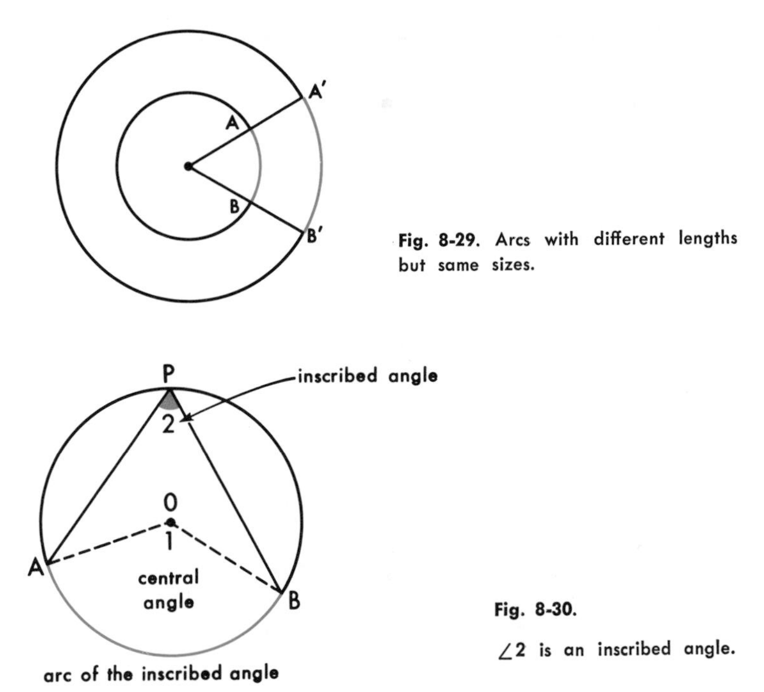

Fig. 8-29. Arcs with different lengths but same sizes.

Fig. 8-30. ∠2 is an inscribed angle.

A second kind of angle is called an *inscribed angle* (Fig. 8-30). The inscribed angle is formed by two chords meeting on the circle.

The procedure to be used in finding rules for the size of angles of a circle is shown in the following experiment:

Experiment on Inscribed Angles. Draw several circles. In them, draw inscribed angles, and the central angles of the arcs (Fig. 8-31). Measure the central angles. This gives you the size of the arcs. Now measure the inscribed angles. Compare the two. It seems that (within 2%) the inscribed

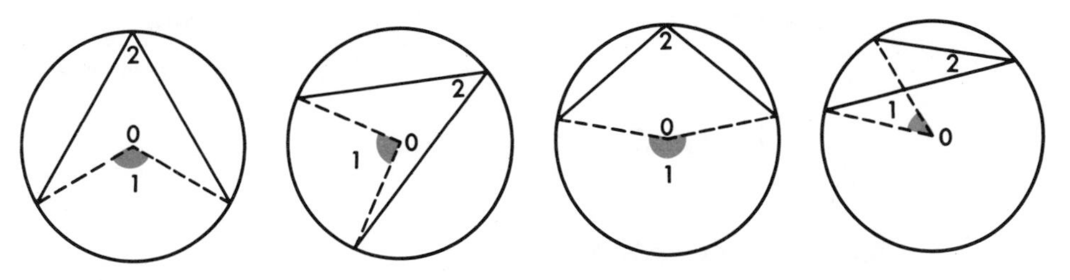

Fig. 8-31. Experiment on inscribed angles.

angle has one half as many degrees as the arc. The report form is shown in Fig. 8-32.

Experiment No. C-1

Testing: The inscribed angle equals half its arc.

Results:

	Inscribed Angle	Arc
1.	84°	170°
2.	52°	100°
3.	31°	60°
4.	107°	210°
5.		

Totals: 274° 540°

Average: 68.5° 135°

Per Cent Error:

$$\frac{(68.5-67.5)\times 100}{67.5} = \frac{100}{67.5} = 1.48\%$$

Conclusion: Within 2%, the inscribed angle equals half its arc.

Fig. 8-32.

Report on inscribed angles.

Problem. In Fig. 8-33, how large is $\angle 1$? $\angle 2$?

Solution: $\angle 1$ is a central angle. It has an arc of 75°. Therefore, $\angle 1 = 75^\circ$. $\angle 2$ is an inscribed angle. It has an arc of 75°. By our experiment, an

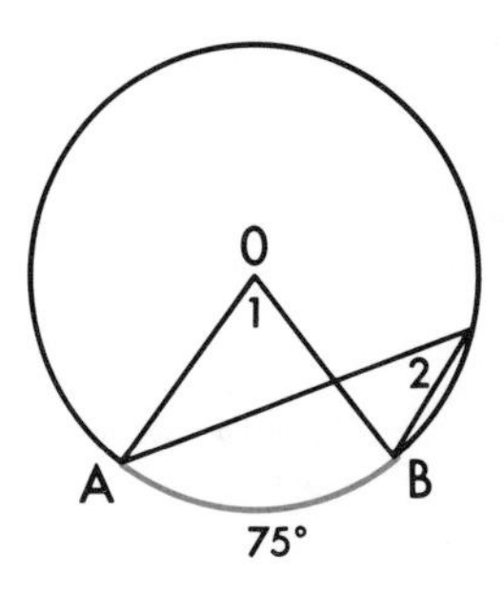

Fig. 8-33. Illustrative problem.

inscribed angle has half as many degrees as its arc. Therefore, $\angle 2 = \frac{1}{2} \times 75^\circ = 37\frac{1}{2}^\circ$.

Test: Section 4

Part A. Verify the following by making central angles to find the sizes of the arcs.

1 In Fig. 8-34, $\angle 3$ is an angle formed by a tangent, and a chord. We call this a *tan-chord angle*. Show that $\angle 3 = \frac{1}{2}\widehat{AB}$.

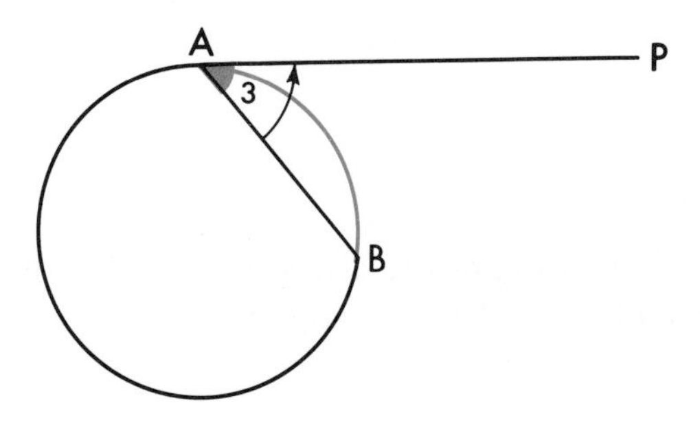

Fig. 8-34. Tan-chord angle.

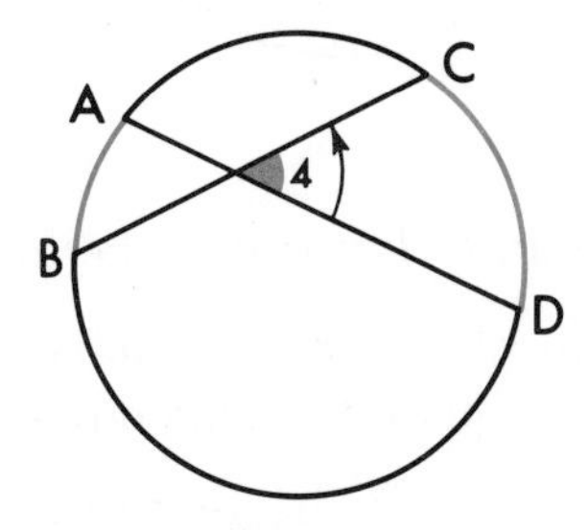

Fig. 8-35. Chord-chord angle.

2 In Fig. 8-35, $\angle 4$ is an angle formed by two chords meeting inside the circle. We call this a *chord-chord angle*. Show that $\angle 4$ is found by adding arcs AB and CD, then dividing by 2.

3 In Fig. 8-36, $\angle 5$ is formed by two secants. We call this a *secant-secant angle.* Show that $\angle 5$ is found by subtracting $\overset{\frown}{CD}$ from $\overset{\frown}{AB}$, then dividing by 2.

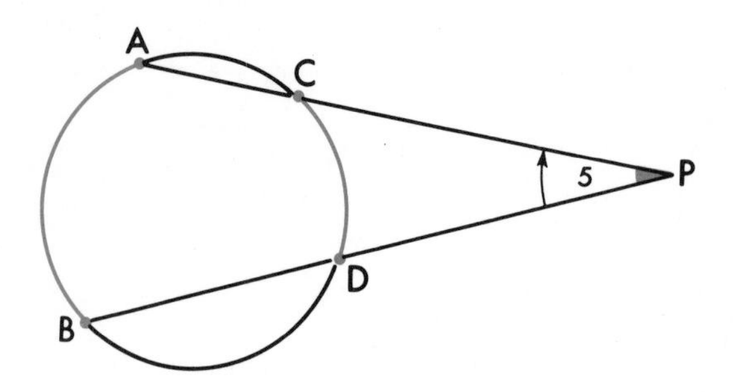

Fig. 8-36. Secant-secant angle.

4 In Fig. 8-37, $\angle 6$ is formed by a tangent, and a secant. We call this a *tangent-secant angle.* Show that $\angle 6$ can be found by subtracting $\overset{\frown}{TD}$ from $\overset{\frown}{TB}$, then dividing by 2.

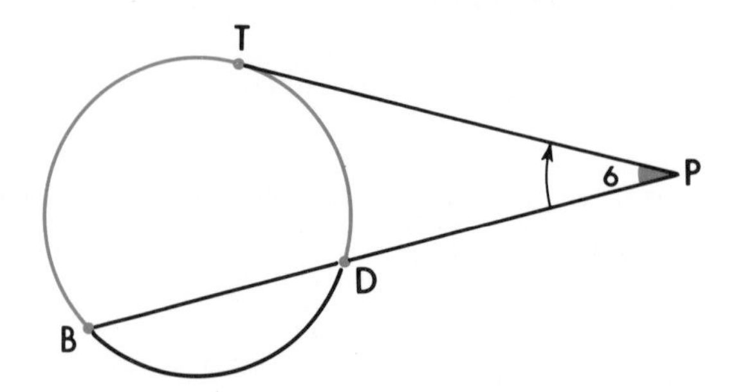

Fig. 8-37. Tangent-secant angle.

Part B. Investigate the following:

1 In Fig. 8-38, a circle is drawn. Then a diameter, *AB,* is drawn. Finally, any point *C* on the circle is joined to *A* and *B*. Investigate $\angle 1$.

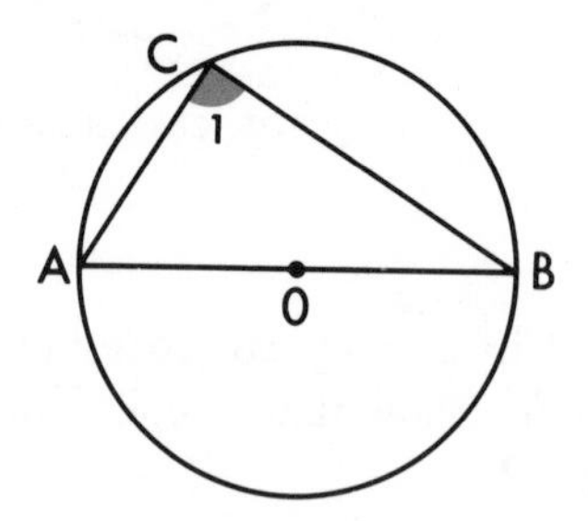

Fig. 8-38.

An angle inscribed in a semicircle.

2 In Fig. 8-39, a circle is drawn, and a quadrilateral is formed by drawing any four chords. A quadrilateral formed by chords is called an *inscribed quadrilateral.* Choose two opposite angles, such as $\angle 1$, and $\angle 2$, and

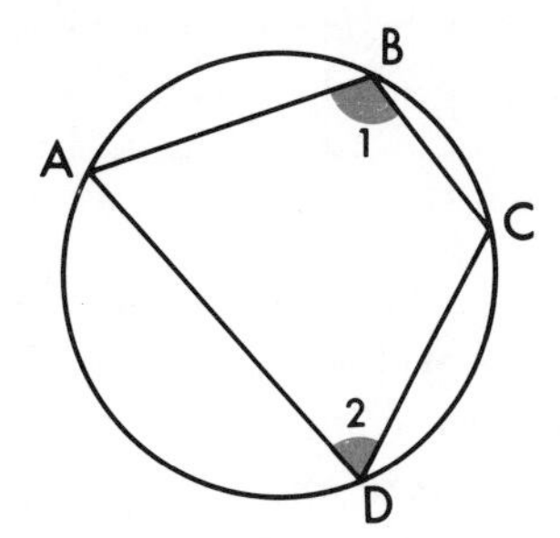

Fig. 8-39. Opposite angles of an inscribed quadrilateral.

measure them with a protractor. Now find their sum. What is your conclusion?

Part C. Using the laws found in this section, name each angle according to type (central angle, inscribed angle, and so on). Then try to tell the size of each angle *without* measurement.

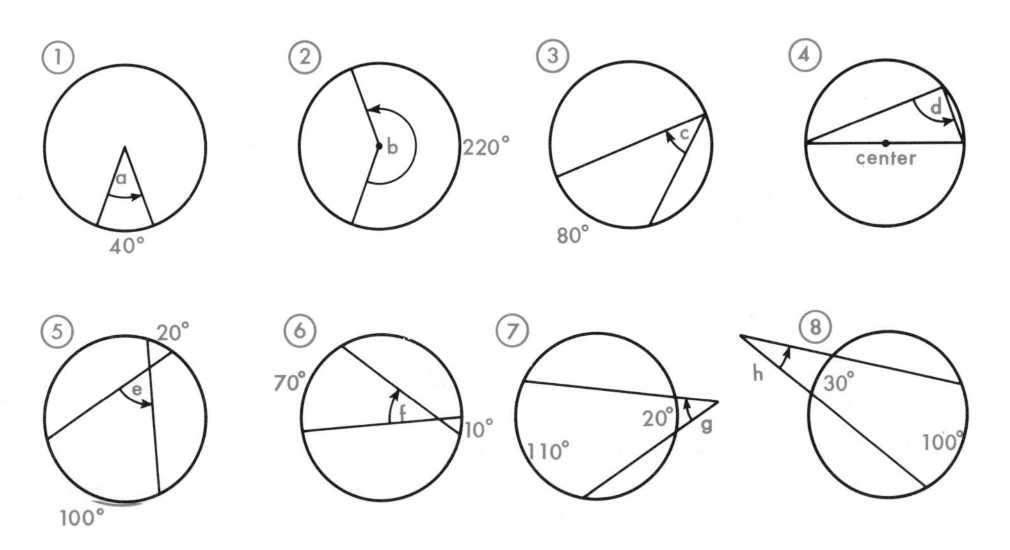

5 AREAS

Everyone has a rough idea as to what is meant by the word, "area." For example, in Fig. 8-40, it is obvious that part (b) has a larger area than part

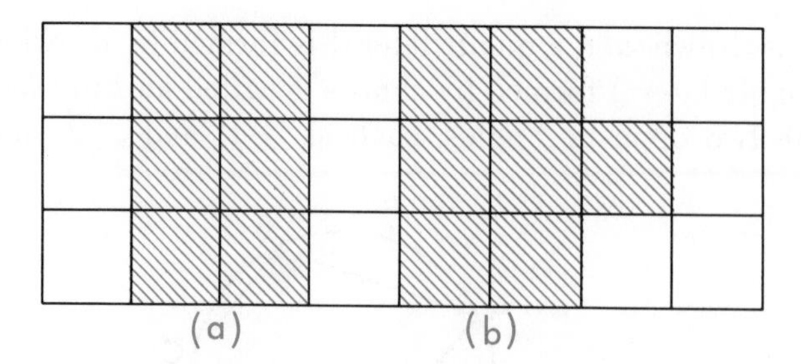

Fig. 8-40. Areas.

(a) because (b) has more square boxes than (a). In general, mathematicians measure area by the number of square boxes that a figure contains. For instance, just by counting, it is clear from Fig. 8-41, that the first area is $4 \times 4 = 16$ *square units,* and the second area is $7 \times 5 = 35$ *square units.*

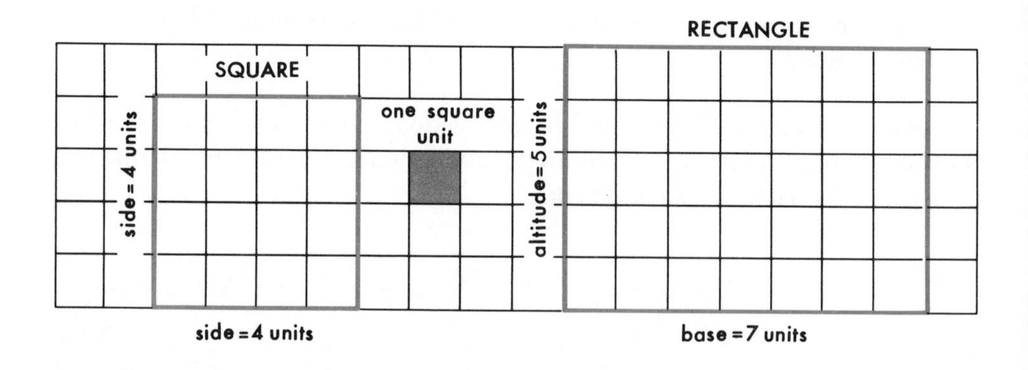

Fig. 8-41. Area of a rectangle.

So we already have two rules for area:

- *Area of a square* = *side* × *side.*
- *Area of a rectangle* = *base* × *altitude.*

Other figures are not so easy. Look at the parallelogram in Fig. 8-42. If we try to count the boxes, we see that some boxes are "split." Let us agree to count a whole box whenever *one half or more* of one is inside the parallelogram, and to ignore every box *less than half* of which is inside the parallelogram. In this case, the area comes out to 40 square units. This is very inconvenient. Perhaps there is a simpler rule. If we measure the *altitude,* it is 5 units. The base is 8 units. Now we have the rule!

- *Area of a parallelogram* = *base* × *altitude.*

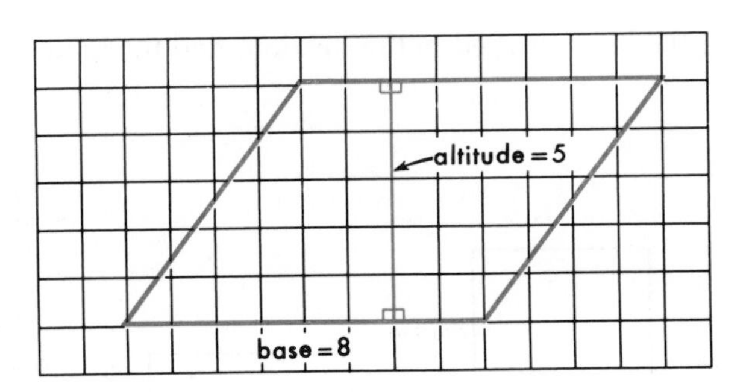

Fig. 8-42. Area of a parallelogram.

Problem. Find the area of the parallelogram in Fig. 8-43.

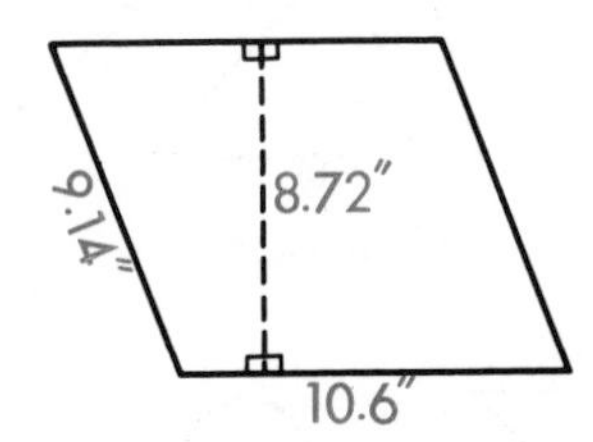

Fig. 8-43. Illustrative problem.

Solution: Area of parallelogram = base × altitude

$$= 10.6 \text{ in.} \times 8.72 \text{ in.}$$

$$= 92.432 \text{ sq. in.}$$

Rounding off to three significant figures:

$$\text{Area} = 92.4 \text{ sq. in.}$$

Test: Section 5

Part A. Verify the following:

1 The area of a triangle = $\frac{1}{2}$ base × altitude.

2 The area of a trapezoid is one half the altitude multiplied by the sum of the bases.

3 Area of a circle is approximately 3.142 times the square of the radius.

Part B. Using the laws verified in this section, find the areas of the following figures:

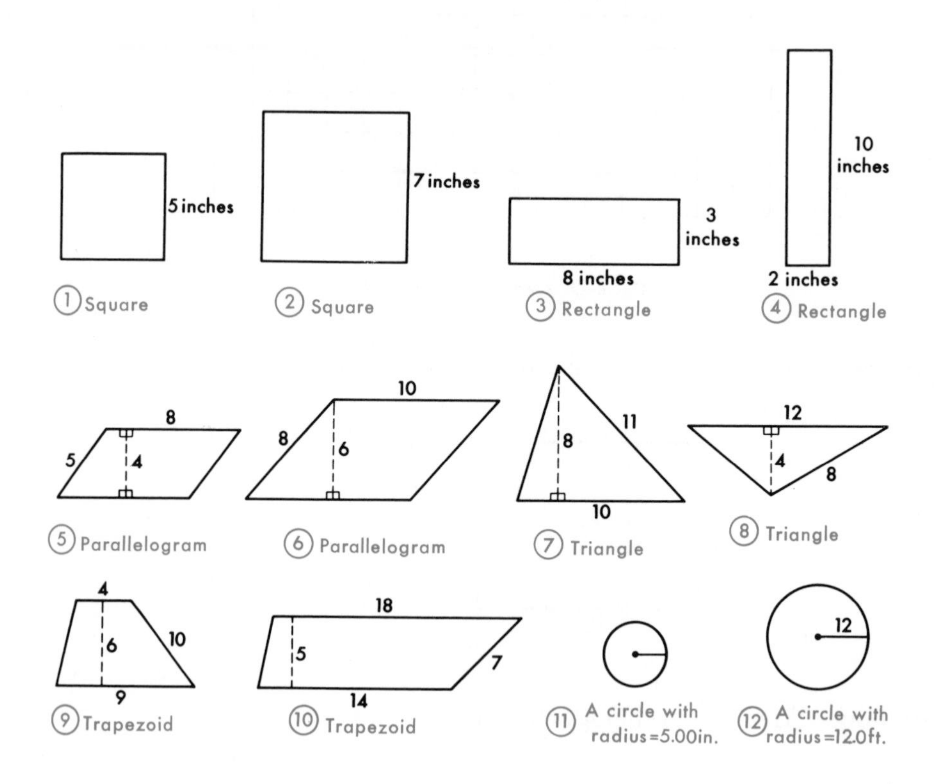

Part C. Using the laws verified in this section, find the areas of the following figures.

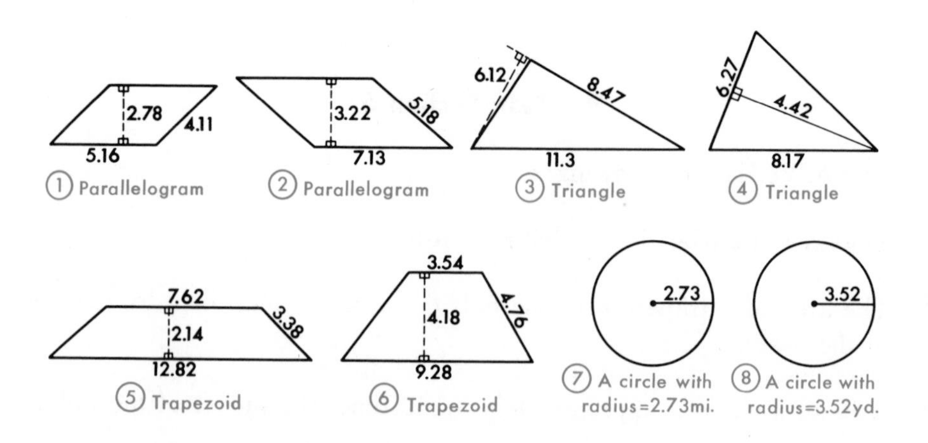

6 SIMILAR FIGURES

If two things are *exactly* alike, so that one can be made to fit on the other (Fig. 8-44) they are called *congruent* (kŏng′grōō•ĕnt) *figures.* If they *look alike,* but are not the same size (Fig. 8-45), they are called *similar figures.*

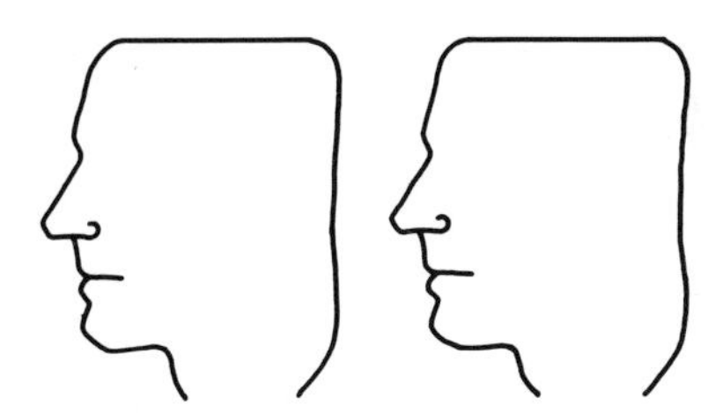

Fig. 8-44. Congruent figures.

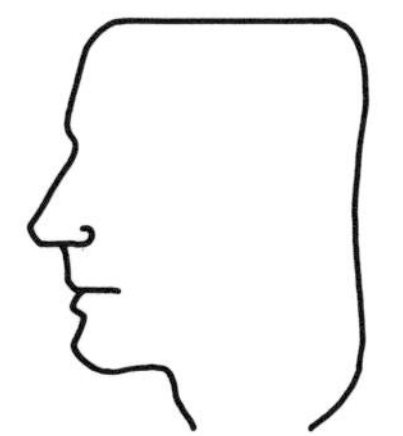

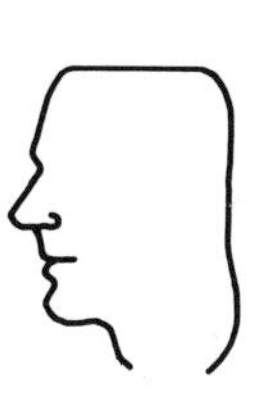

Fig. 8-45. Similar figures.

Similar figures are simply figures made to different scales, like two pictures of the same thing with one enlarged more than the other.

If we draw two similar triangles (Fig. 8-46) and actually measure the sides and angles, we find that $\angle A = \angle A'$ (angle A equals angle A prime),

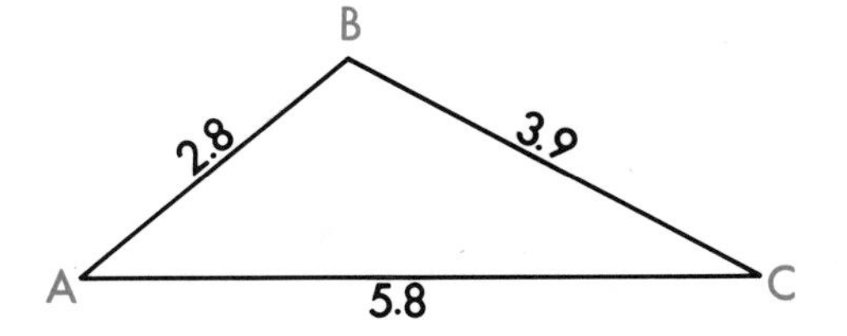

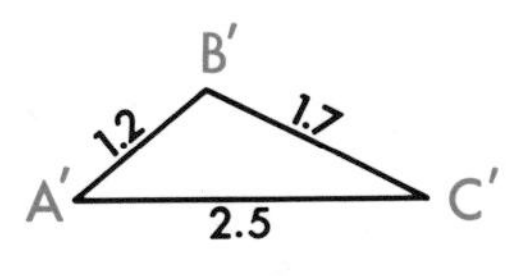

Fig. 8-46. Two similar triangles.

$\angle B = \angle B'$ (angle B equals angle B prime), and $\angle C = \angle C'$, within 2% error. This illustrates the *first property* of similar figures:

- *Angle Rule for Similar Figures:* Similar angles are equal.

The second rule is found by comparing the sides. Notice that

$$\frac{2.8}{1.2} = 2.33 \qquad \frac{3.9}{1.7} = 2.29 \qquad \frac{5.8}{2.5} = 2.32$$

Rounding off, we find that the *ratio,* or *fraction,* is 2.3 for all three pairs of sides. This is the *second property* of similar figures:

- *Side Rule for Similar Figures:* Similar sides have the same ratio.

These two properties can be used to draw something to scale.

Problem 1. The triangle in Fig. 8-47 has sides and angles as marked. If a similar triangle is made with a base of 3.0 instead of 4.7, what will be the sides and angles of the new triangle?

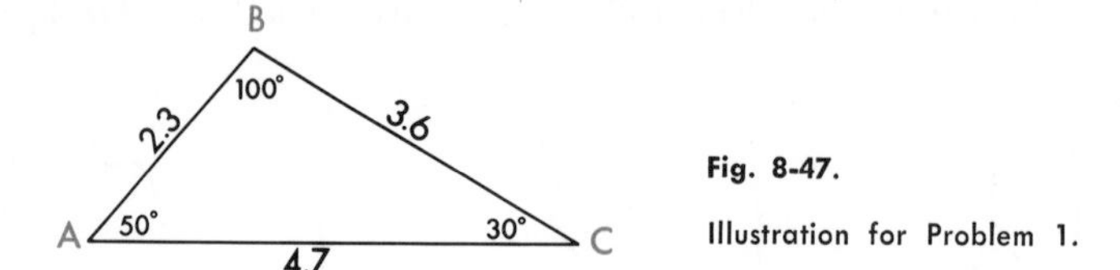

Fig. 8-47.

Illustration for Problem 1.

Solution: The similar angles will be equal, so $\angle A' = 50°$, $\angle C' = 30°$, and $\angle B' = 100°$. The similar sides will have to be in the same ratio. This ratio is $\dfrac{3.0}{4.7} = 0.638$. Notice that we keep an extra figure on the ratio, temporarily. This means that

$$B'C' = 0.638 \times 3.6 = 2.3$$
$$A'B' = 0.638 \times 2.3 = 1.5$$

The similar triangles are shown in Fig. 8-48.

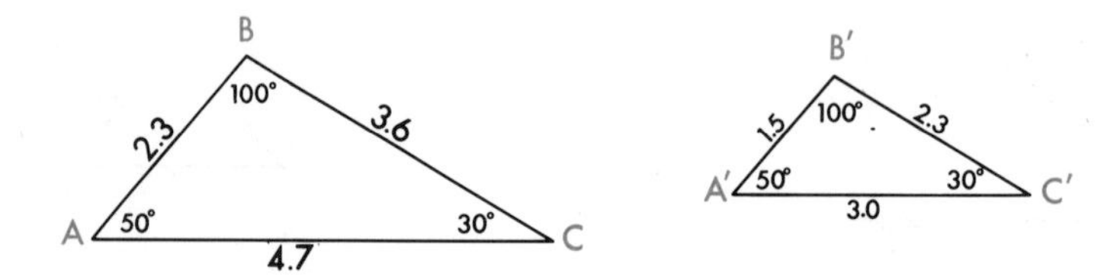

Fig. 8-48. The similar triangles.

Problem 2. The quadrilateral in Fig. 8-49 has sides and angles as shown. What will be the sides and angles of a similar quadrilateral with a side as marked?

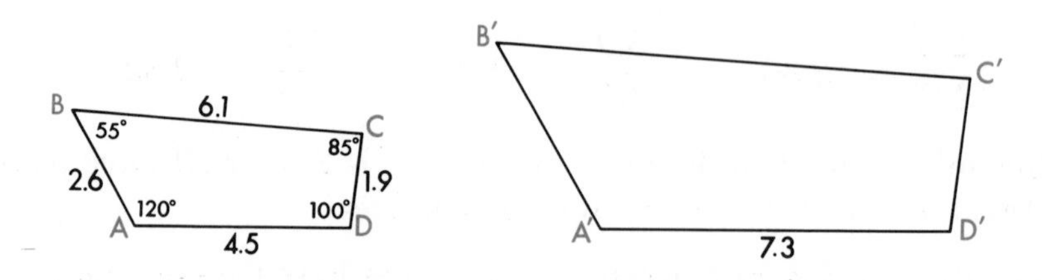

Fig. 8-49. Similar quadrilaterals.

Solution: The similar angles will be equal, so that $\angle A' = 120°$, $\angle B' = 55°$, $\angle C' = 85°$, and $\angle D' = 100°$. The similar sides must have the ratio $\frac{7.3}{4.5} = 1.62$. This means that

$$A'B' = 1.62 \times 2.6 = 4.2$$
$$B'C' = 1.62 \times 6.1 = 9.9$$
$$C'D' = 1.62 \times 1.9 = 3.1$$

If two squares are drawn (Fig. 8-50), one with sides three times greater than the other, it is easily found by counting squares that the area of the larger one is *nine* times the area of the smaller. If the experiment is continued to a square with sides *four times* as great, the resulting area (c) is *sixteen* times as large as the original. In each case, the *area ratio* is found by *squaring* the ratio of the sides.

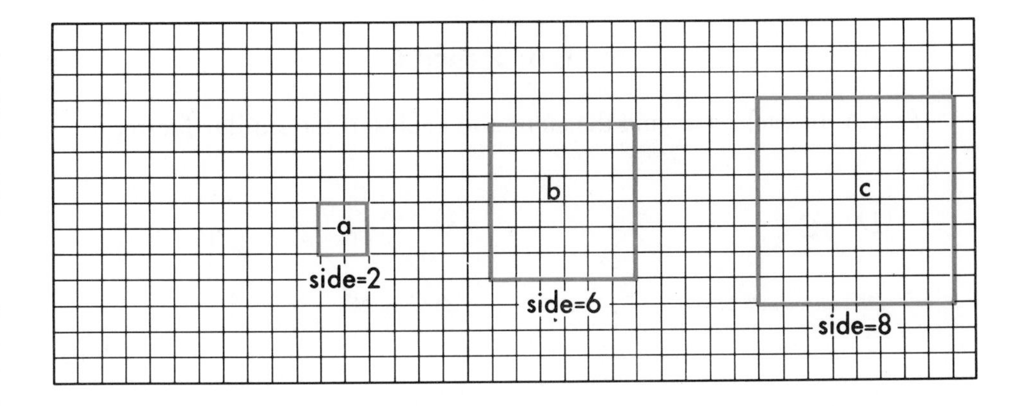

Fig. 8-50. Similar squares.

● *Area Rule for Similar Figures.* Similar areas have a ratio equal to the square of the side ratio.

Problem 3. In Fig. 8-51, the two triangles are similar, and the area of the larger one is 32.

a What is the ratio of sides?

b What is the ratio of areas?

c What is the area of the smaller figure?

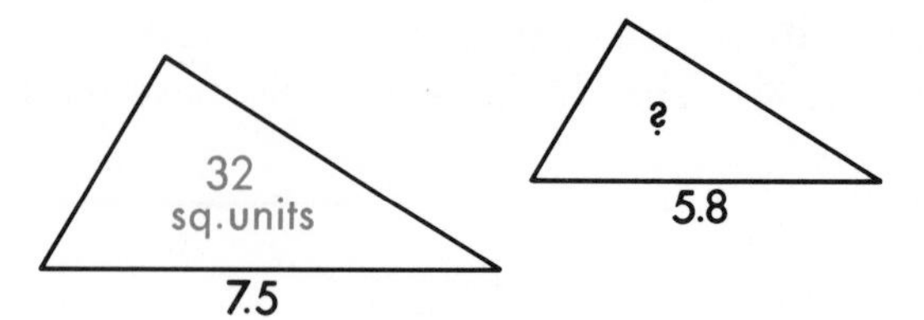

Fig. 8-51. Similar areas.

Solution:

a. The ratio of sides is $\frac{5.8}{7.5} = 0.773.$

b. The ratio of areas is $(0.773)^2 = 0.773 \times 0.773 = 0.598.$

c. The area of the smaller triangle is $0.598 \times 32 = 19$ square units.

Test: Section 6

Part A. In each case, find the sides and angles of the similar figure.

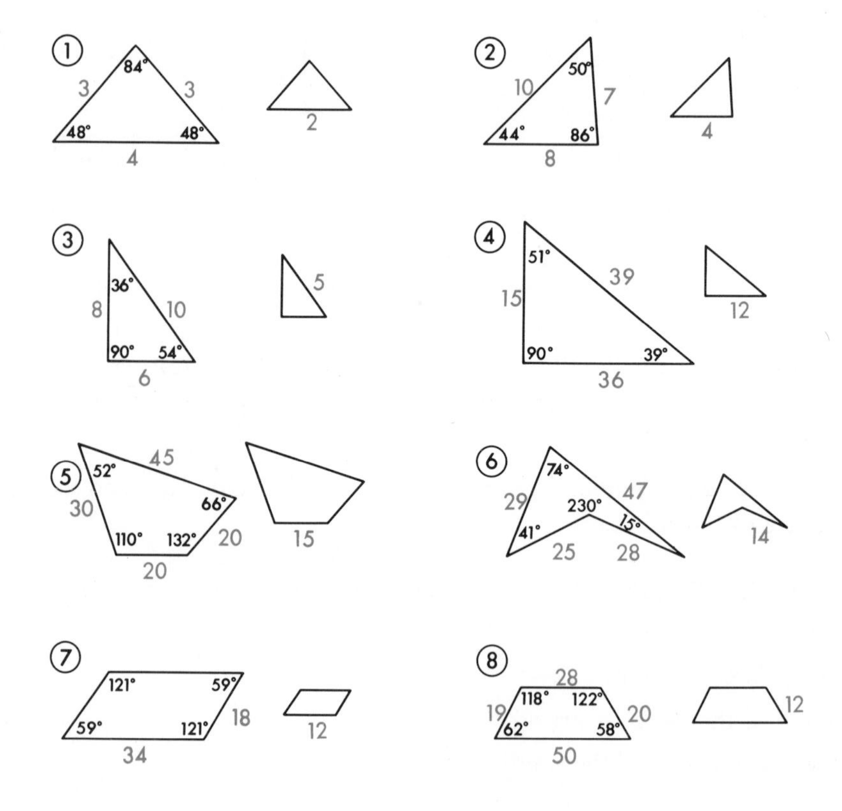

Part B. In each case, find the area of the similar figure. In Nos. 5 and 6, use the length of a *radius* instead of a *side.*

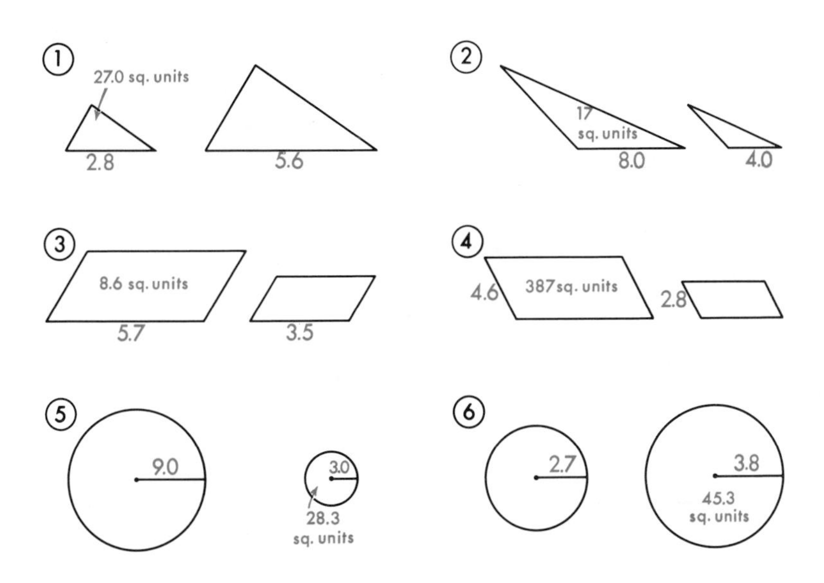

7 PRISMS AND CYLINDERS

Figures 8-52, 8-53, and 8-54 show three very common *solid* figures in our civilization. The *triangular prism* is found in binoculars and telescopes. The

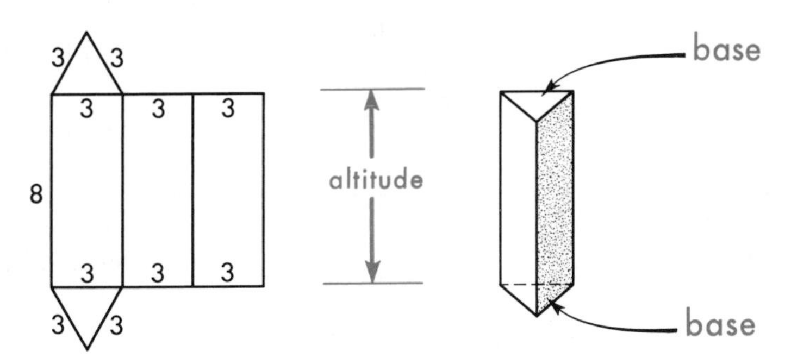

Fig. 8-52. Triangular prism.

square prism, is simply a box. The circular prism, or *cylinder,* has the shape of a cigarette.

The *volume* (vŏl′yŭm) of a solid body is the number of 1-in. *cubes* (boxes) that can be squeezed into it. Looking at Fig. 8-55, it is easy to see that there

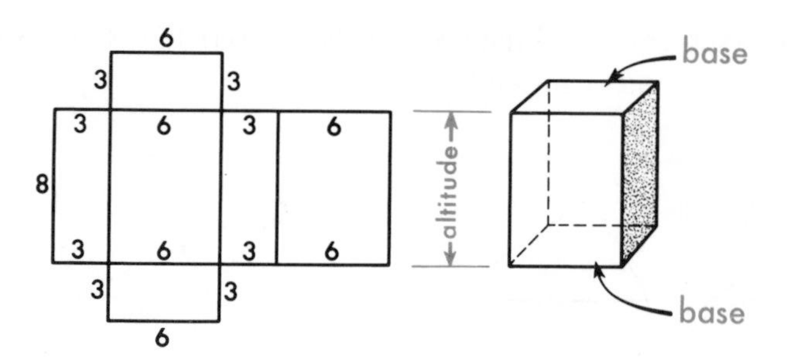

Fig. 8-53. Rectangular prism.

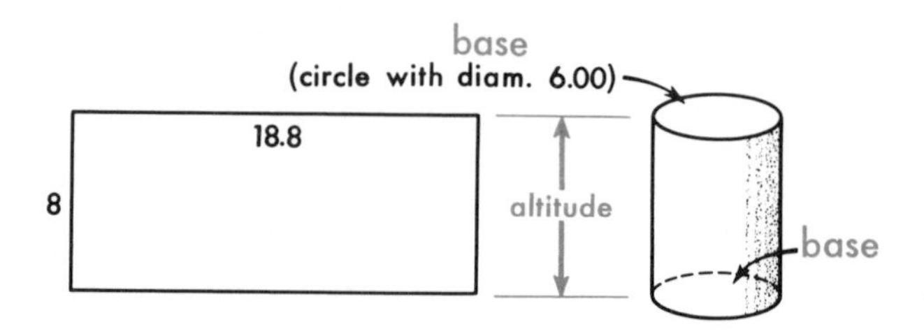

Fig. 8-54. Circular prism, or cylinder.

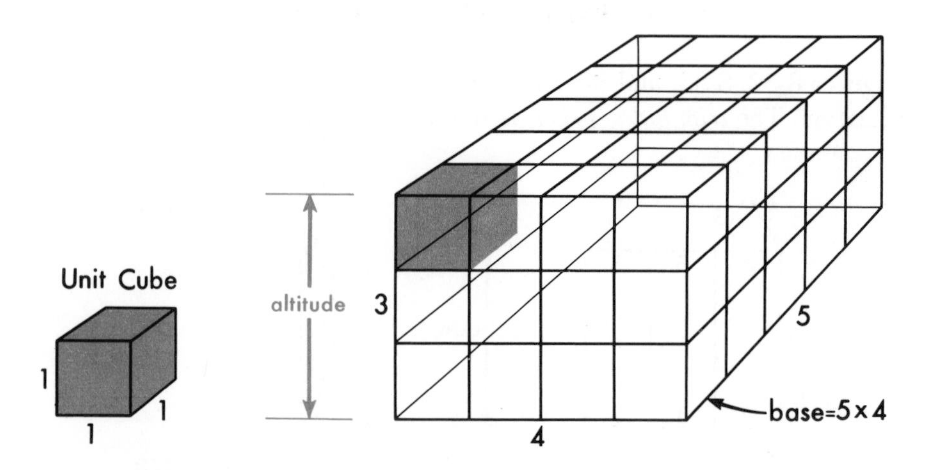

Fig. 8-55. Volume of a prism.

are 20 unit cubes resting on the base, since the area of the base is $4 \times 5 = 20$. These are stacked three deep because the altitude of the prism in this case, is 3. The number of boxes, or the volume, is therefore $3 \times 20 = 60$ *cubic units*. The general rule is:

● ***Prism or Cylinder: Volume*** = altitude × area of the base.

In Fig. 8-52, if the triangular base has an area of 3.9 sq. in., and the altitude = 8.0 in., the volume is 8.0 × 3.9 = 31 cu. in. In Fig. 8-53, if the rectangular base has an area of 18 sq. in., volume is 8.0 × 18 = 144 cu. in.

In Fig. 8-54, if the area of the circle is $3.142 \times (3.00)^2 = 28.3$ sq. in., then the volume of the cylinder is 8.0 × 28.3 = 226 cu. in.

● Test: Section 7

Part A. In each of the following, draw the figure, and find the volume. Assume that each measurement has three significant figures.

1 Triangular prism, altitude 6, area of the base is 25.
2 Triangular prism, altitude 8, base area = 16.
3 Square prism, altitude 15, base area = 25.
4 Square prism, altitude 20, base area = 49.
5 Rectangular prism, altitude 12, base area = 20.
6 Rectangular prism, altitude 14, base area = 32.
7 Cylinder, altitude 13, base area = 79.
8 Cylinder, altitude 7, base area = 113.

Part B. In each of the following, find the volume, and name the figure. Assume that each measurement has three significant figures.

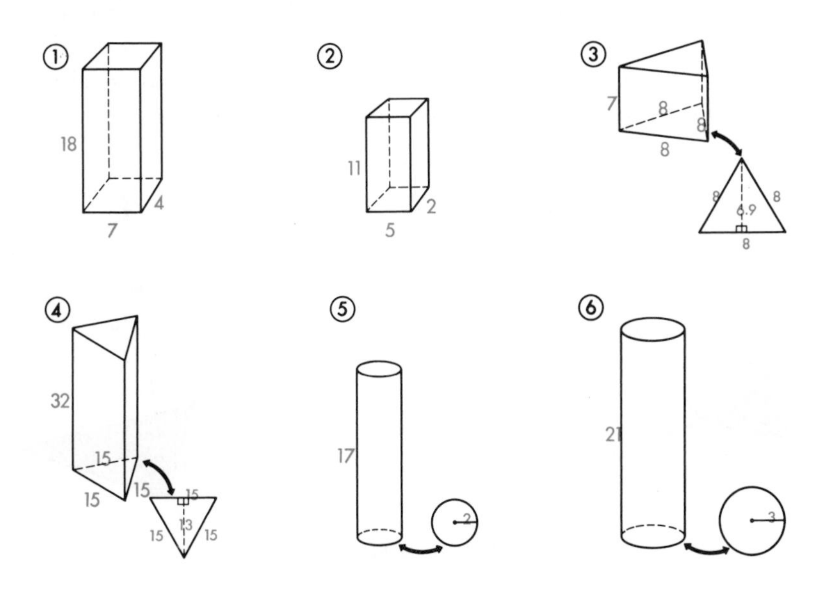

Fig. 8-56. The Step Pyramid at Saqqara, designed by Amhoteb, an Egyptian engineer and architect of the 3rd dynasty. *Courtesy United Arab Republic.*

8 PYRAMIDS AND CONES

In Chapter 1 we talked about and showed you the Great Pyramids of Giza built by Cheops or Khufu about 2900 B.C. The largest, Cheops (look back at the picture), is a square pyramid (a pyramid with a square base). Another famous Egyptian pyramid is the Step Pyramid at Saqqara (Fig. 8-56).

Other general types of pyramids are: the triangular pyramid (Fig. 8-57), the rectangular pyramid (Fig. 8-58) and the circular pyramid, or *cone* (Fig. 8-59).

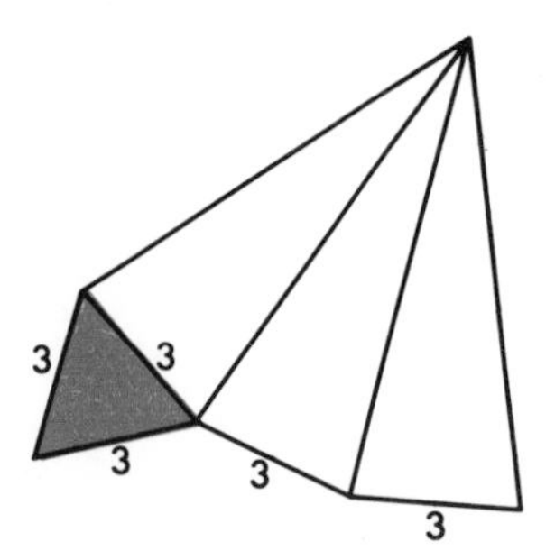

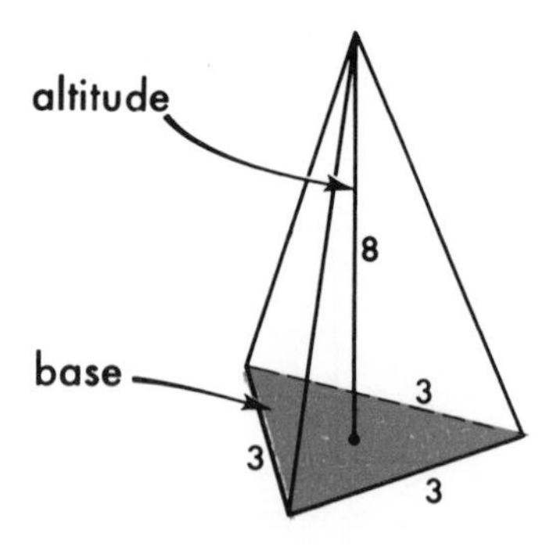

Fig. 8-57. Triangular pyramid.

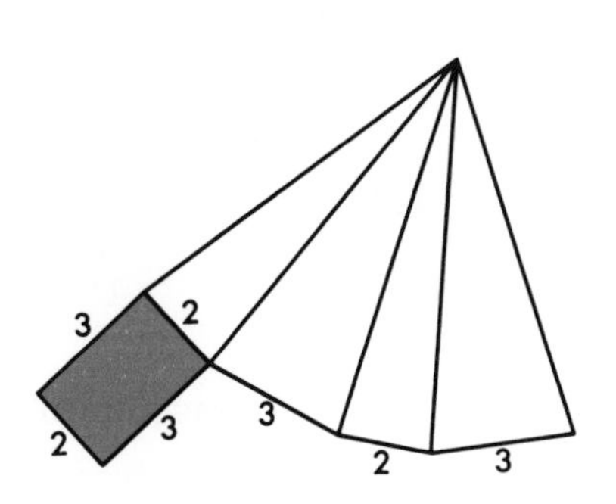

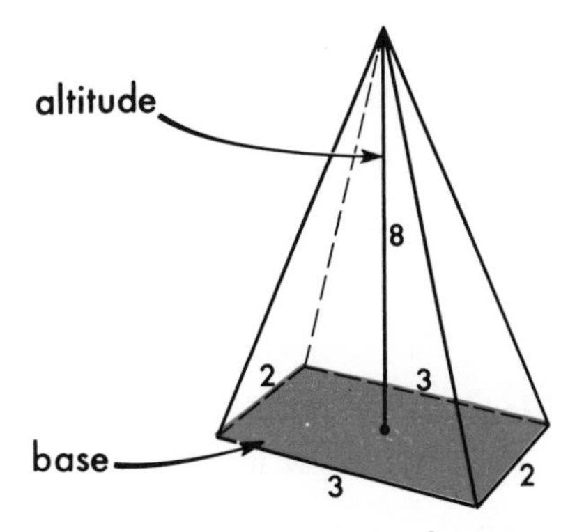

Fig. 8-58. Rectangular pyramid.

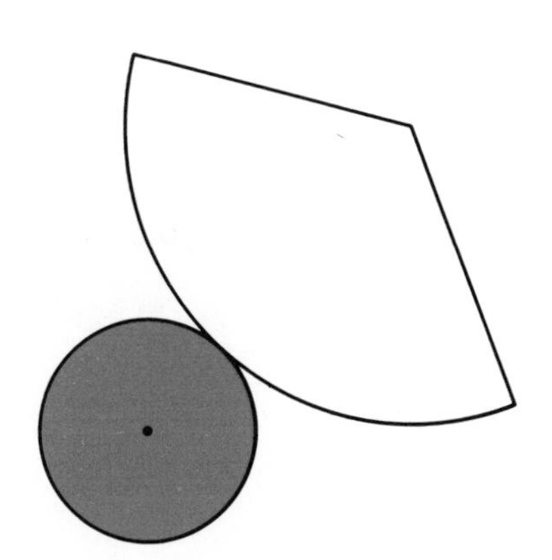

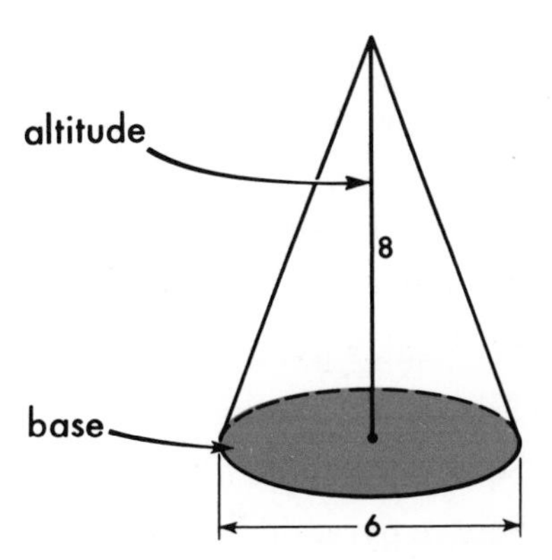

Fig. 8-59. Circular pyramid, or cone.

The volume of a pyramid is found in the same way as the volume of a prism, except that it turns out to be only one third as large, because it comes to a point:

- *Pyramid or Cone: Volume* $= \frac{1}{3} \times$ altitude $\times$ base area.

Problem 1. Find the volume of the triangular pyramid in Fig. 8-57, if the area of the base is 3.90 square units, and the altitude is 8.00 units.

Solution: Volume of pyramid $= \frac{1}{3} \times$ altitude $\times$ base area

$= \frac{1}{3} \times 8.00 \times 3.90$

$=$ 10.4 cubic units

Problem 2. Find the volume of the rectangular pyramid in Fig. 8-58, if the measurements have two significant figures.

Solution: The area of the rectangular base is $2.0 \times 3.0 = 6.0$ square units.

$$\text{Volume of pyramid} = \tfrac{1}{3} \times \text{altitude} \times \text{base area}$$
$$= \tfrac{1}{3} \times 8.0 \times 6.0$$
$$= 16 \text{ cubic units}$$

Problem 3. Find the volume of the cone in Fig. 8-59, if the measurements have two significant figures.

Solution: The area of the circular base is 28 square units.

$$\text{Volume of cone} = \tfrac{1}{3} \times \text{altitude} \times \text{base area}$$
$$= \tfrac{1}{3} \times 8.0 \times 28$$
$$= 75 \text{ cubic units}$$

Test: Section 8

Part A. In each of the following, draw the figure, and find the volume. Assume three significant figures for all measurements.

1 Triangular pyramid, altitude 15, base area = 25.
2 Triangular pyramid, altitude 6, base area = 16.
3 Square pyramid, altitude = 15, base area = 25.
4 Square pyramid, altitude = 20, base area = 49.
5 Rectangular pyramid, altitude = 12, base area = 20.
6 Rectangular pyramid, altitude = 14, base area = 32.
7 Cone, altitude = 13, base area = 79.
8 Cone, altitude = 7, base area = 113.

Part B. In each of the following, find the volume. Assume three significant figures for all measurements.

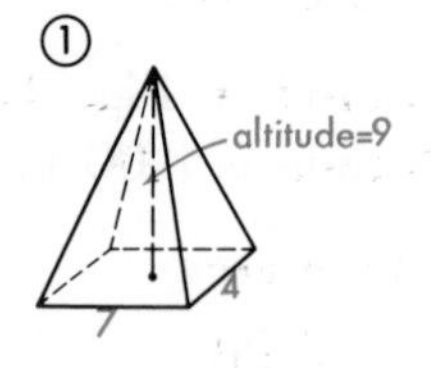

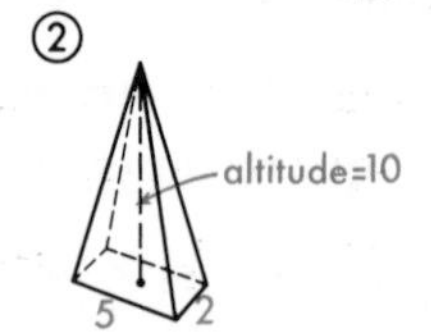

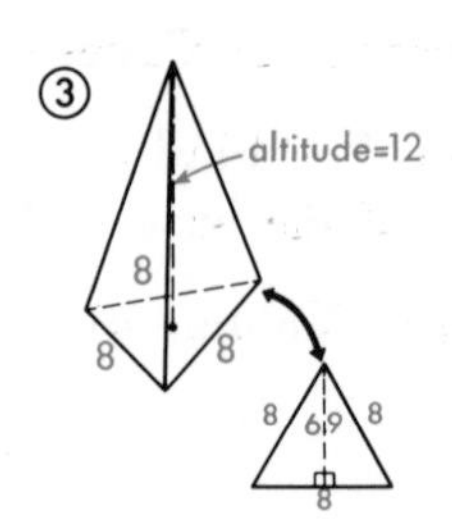

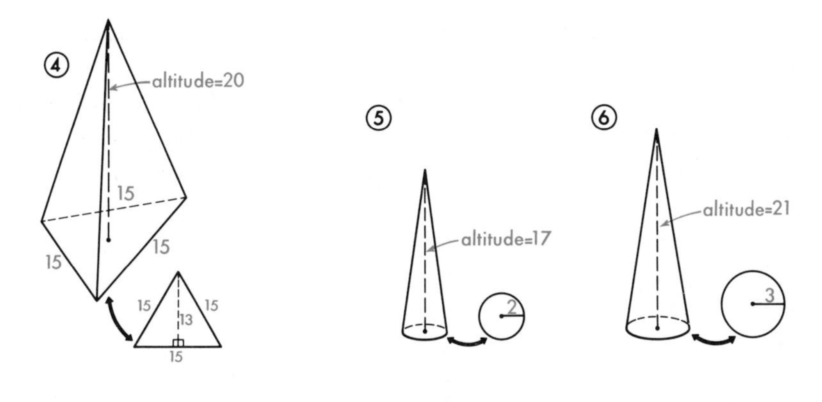

9 SPHERES

Everyone is familiar with a sphere. A tennis ball is a sphere, and so is the earth we live on. If a circle is drawn on a sphere, it may or may not have the same center as the center of the sphere. If it has the same center, it is called a *great circle* (Fig. 8-60). If it does not have the same center as the

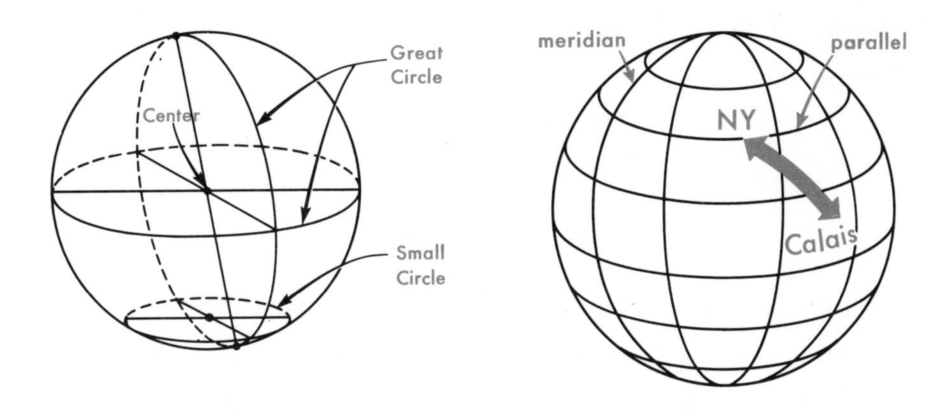

Fig. 8-60. Great circles and small circles.

Fig. 8-61. The earth.

sphere, it is called a *small circle.* In a globe of the earth (Fig. 8-61), the Equator, and all the meridians of longitude, are great circles. The parallels of latitude are small circles except for the Equator.

The *distance* (shortest path) between two points on the surface of the earth, such as New York and Calais, is an arc of a great circle. Thus, a plane or ship traveling by a great circle route is going by the shortest route. You can test this idea by marking two points on a rubber ball, and stretching a rubber band between the two points.

The volume of a sphere can be found by the *overflow method* shown in Fig. 8-62. Fill a jar with water, right to the brim. Carefully push a spherical object (say, a rubber ball) into it, and catch the overflow in a can. Now

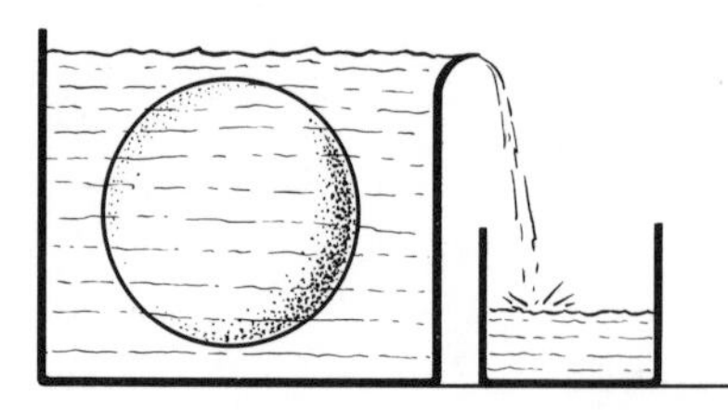

Fig. 8-62. The volume of a sphere.

measure the volume of overflow, by using the rule for the volume of a cylinder, if the can is cylindrical. This overflow must be the same as the volume of the ball. When this is done, you find that the rule is:

- *Volume of a Sphere:* $V = 0.5236 \times (\text{diameter})^3$.

Problem. Find the volume of a sphere with a diameter of 7.50 in.

Solution: $\text{Volume} = 0.5236 \times 7.50 \times 7.50 \times 7.50$

$= 221$ cu. in.

• Test: Section 9

Find the volume of spheres with the following diameters:

1 2.00 in. 2 3.00 in. 3 4.50 in. 4 5.50 in.
5 6.25 in. 6 7.25 in. 7 8.70 in. 8 9.30 in.
9 12.0 ft. 10 13.5 ft.

10 SIMILAR SOLIDS

You already know that when you have similar figures, the angles remain unchanged, the sides change according to a fixed ratio, and the area changes according to the squares of the side ratio.

Now, let us see what happens to the *volume* of similar figures (Fig. 8-63).

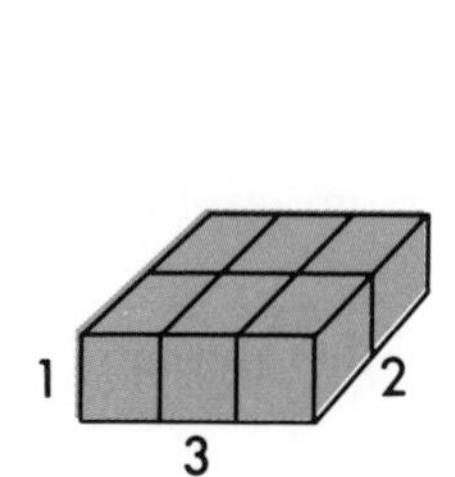

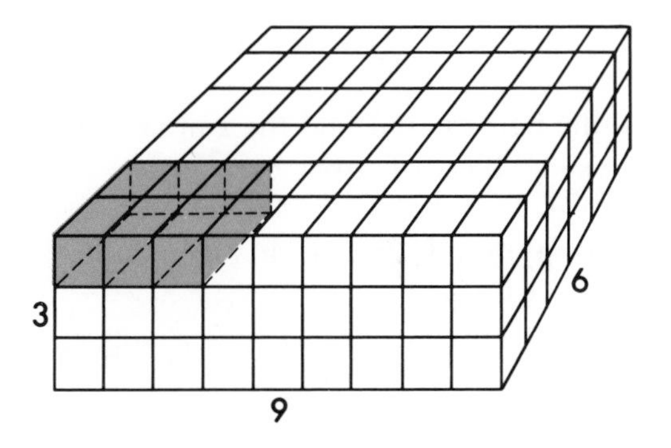

Fig. 8-63. Volumes of similar solids.

The sides have been tripled so that the side ratio is 3 : 1. The area of any two similar faces has been multiplied, as you can see, in the ratio 9 : 1. Now count unit cubes. The first figure has $1 \times 2 \times 3 = 6$ unit cubes. The second one has 162 unit cubes! The volume has been multiplied by 27, or $3 \times 3 \times 3$. This illustrates the rule:

- *Volume Rule for Similar Figures:* Similar volumes have a ratio equal to the cube of the side ratio.

For spheres, the radii or diameters may be used instead of sides.

Problem 1. A sphere with a diameter of 7.50 in. has a volume of 221 cu. in. What is the volume of a sphere with a diameter of 15.0 in.?

Solution: The side ratio is $\frac{15.0}{7.50} = 2.00 : 1$, and the volume ratio is the cube of this: 8.00 : 1.

The volume is therefore $8.00 \times 221 = 1770$ cu. in. (3 s.f.)

Problem 2. A cylinder with a radius of 3.70 in. has a volume of 830 cu. in. What is the volume of a similar cylinder with a radius of 2.40 in.?

Solution: The side ratio is $\frac{2.40}{3.70} = 0.649 : 1$. The volume ratio is therefore $(0.649)^3 = 0.649 \times 0.649 \times 0.649 = 0.273$, so the new volume is $0.273 \times 830 = 227$ cu. in.

Test: Section 10

Draw the figures, and find the similar volumes. Assume all measurements have three significant figures.

1 Square pyramid, 200 cu. in., 3-in. side. The similar pyramid has a similar side of 6 in.

2 Triangular pyramid, 300 cu. ft., 2-ft. side. The similar pyramid has a similar side of 8 ft.

3 Cylinder, 150 cu. m., 4.8 m. altitude. The similar cylinder has an altitude of 2.4 m.

4 Cone, 210 cu. mi., 18-mi. altitude. The similar cone has an altitude of 6 mi.

5 Square prism, 1000 cu. in., 36-in. side. The similar prism has a similar side of 9 in.

6 Triangular prism, 1500 cu. in., 48-in. altitude. The similar prism has an altitude of 12 in.

9

INDIRECT MEASUREMENT

"That's all very well," said Tom, as he entered the math class.

"What's all very well?" asked the teacher.

"Measuring things," replied Tom. "It's easy, if they're small enough to use a ruler or protractor on, but what do you do if things are too big, or too far away?"

"Like what?" queried the teacher.

"Like, say, how high a mountain is, or how wide a swamp is, or how far away a building is."

"That's not too difficult," the teacher said. "If a mathematician can't measure something *directly*, he figures out a way to measure it *indirectly*. The brain is a much better tool than a ruler or a protractor!"

1 FINDING ANGLES OF HEIGHT AND DEPTH

The easiest method for conveniently measuring a large object, makes use of *similar figures*. You remember that if two figures are similar, then their similar angles are *equal*, and their similar sides are *proportional*, as shown in Fig. 9-1.

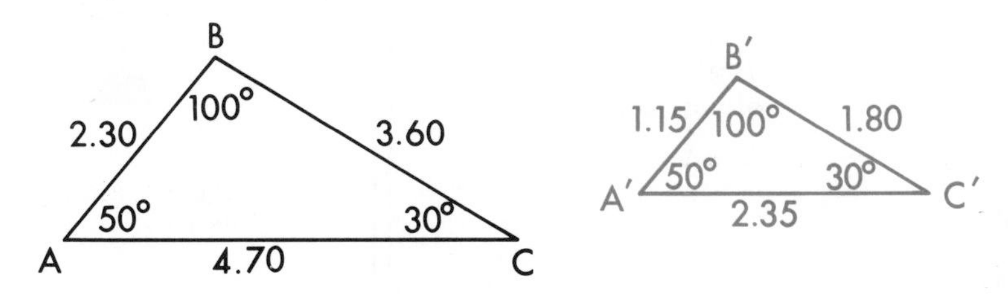

Fig. 9-1. Similar triangles.

Before doing anything else, we shall have to find a way to measure angles for large or distant objects. Surveyors who make this kind of measurement, use an instrument called a *transit* (Fig. 9-2). For a few cents, you can have a home-made transit (Fig. 9-3). Take an ordinary protractor, and fasten a

Fig. 9-2. Surveyor and transit.

vertex

string

protractor

weight

Fig. 9-3. Home-made transit.

string to the vertex mark. If you have a drill with a fine point, make a very small hole, and tie the string there. Now tie a weight to the end of the string, and you are ready!

Problem 1. Find the angle of elevation of the ceiling of a room. (Use a corner of the room.)

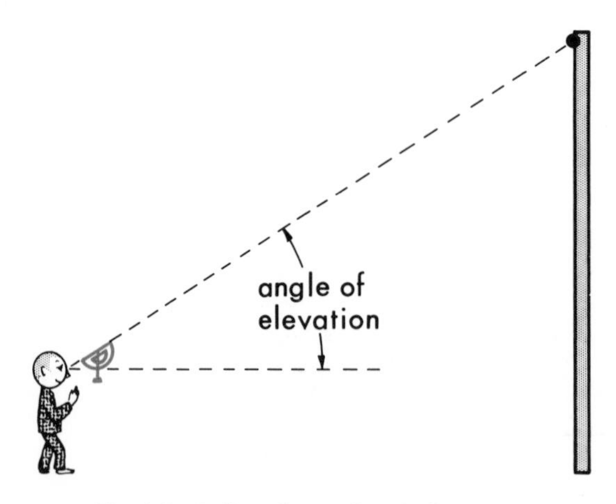

Fig. 9-4. Finding the angle of elevation.

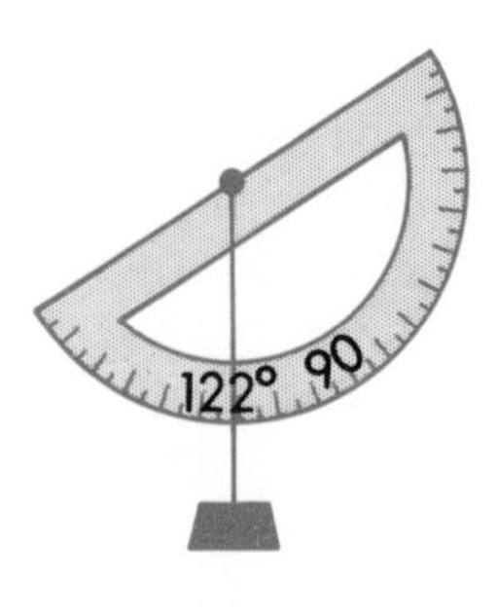

Fig. 9-5. Reading the transit.

Solution: See Figs. 9-4 and 9-5.

(*a*) Hold the protractor to your eye so that you sight the corner of the ceiling of the room along the straight edge of the protractor. (*b*) When the string has stopped swinging, grasp it carefully on the outer track of the protractor. (*c*) Now lift the protractor down without letting go of the end of the string, and read the angle on the outer track (Fig. 9-5). (*d*) The difference between the angle and 90°, is the angle of elevation. The answer, in this diagram, is $122° - 90° = 32°$. It is called the *angle of elevation* because you have to *elevate* (*lift*) *your eyes* to see the corner of the ceiling.

Problem 2. Find the angle of depression of the corner of the floor of the room.

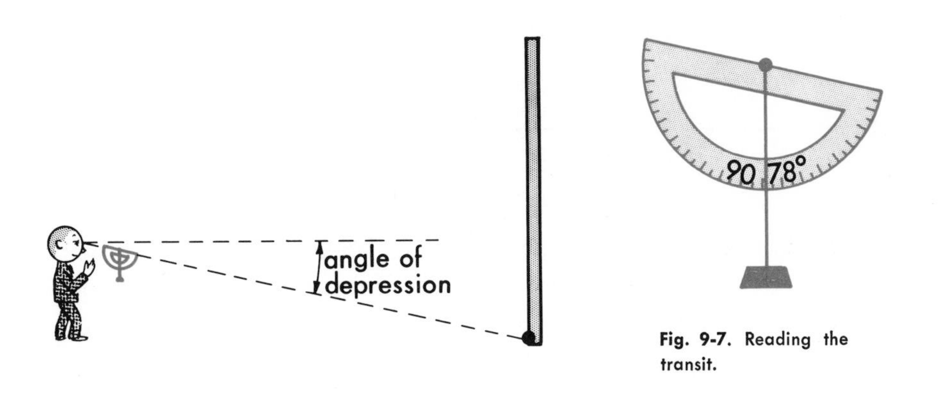

Fig. 9-6. Finding the angle of depression.

Fig. 9-7. Reading the transit.

Solution: See Figs. 9-6 and 9-7.

(*a*) Hold the protractor to your eye so that you sight the corner of the floor of the room along the straight edge. (*b*) When the string has stopped swinging, grasp it carefully on the outer track of the protractor. (*c*) Now lift the protractor down without letting go of the end of the string, and read the angle on the outer track (Fig. 9-7). (*d*) The difference between this angle and 90°, is the angle of depression. In the diagram, the answer is $90° - 78° = 12°$. It is called the *angle of depression* because you have to *depress* (*lower*) your eyes to see the corner of the floor.

Test: Section 1

Part A. In each of the following, tell whether the angle marked is an angle of elevation, or an angle of depression. Then make a diagram similar to the one in this book, and measure the angle. *DO NOT WRITE IN THIS BOOK.*

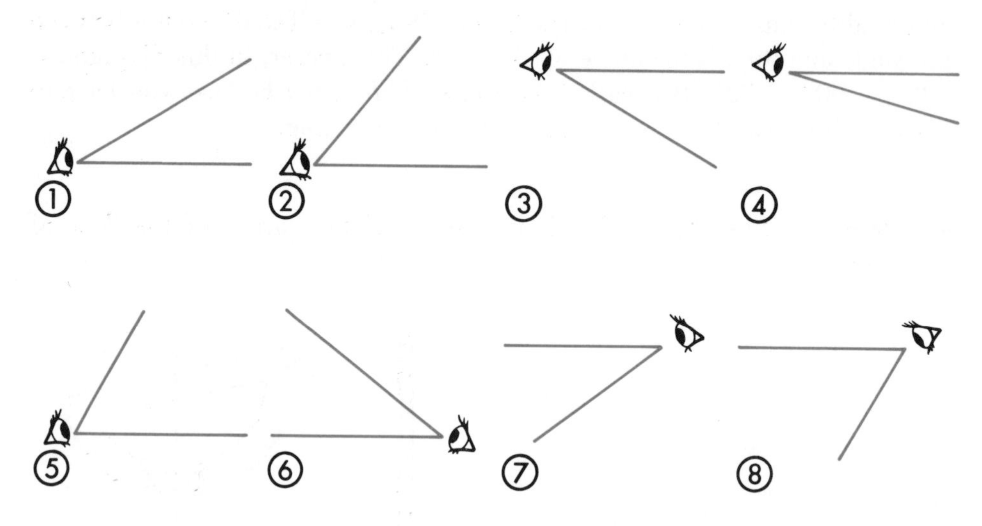

Part B. Find the angles of elevation and depression for each of the following. Check by doing each one at least four times, and then finding the average.

1 The corner of the ceiling of a room.

2 A spot on the top of a building.

3 The corner of the floor of a room.

4 A spot at the street level of a building.

2 FINDING THE HEIGHT OF AN OBJECT

To find the height of an object, we will have to find a way to measure *one* length. The surveyor uses a *surveyor's tape* (Fig. 9-8) which may be quite expensive. You can use a folding ruler, or a yardstick to measure distances.

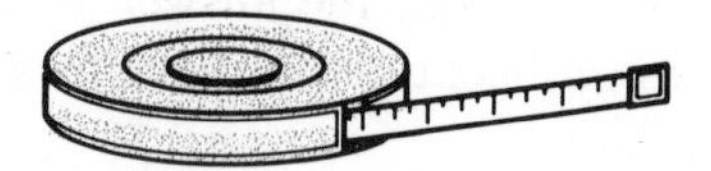

Fig. 9-8. Surveyor's tape.

Problem. Find the height of a room. The angles of elevation and depression have already been established as 32°, and 12°, in that order.

Solution: See Figs. 9-9, through 9-13.
(*a*) Mark the place where you measured the angles. Call this point *P*. (*b*) Measure the distance to the front of the room. This is the only length we need to complete the problem! (*c*) On a sheet of paper, draw a line, and mark a point *P* any place on the line (Fig. 9-9). (*d*) Using the protractor,

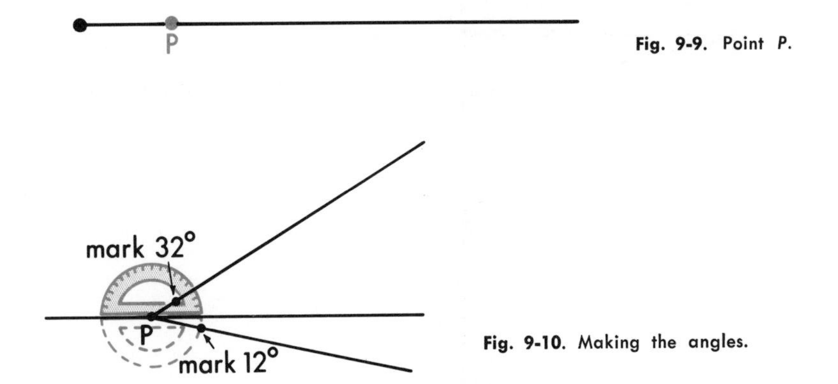

Fig. 9-9. Point *P*.

Fig. 9-10. Making the angles.

draw angles of 32°, and 12° as shown in Fig. 9-10. (*e*) Now, suppose the distance to the front of the room was 15 ft. 2 in. We make the following scale:

Scale: 10 millimeters (mm.) ⟷ 1 ft.

This means that 15 ft. 2 in., which is approximately 15.2 ft., is to be repre-

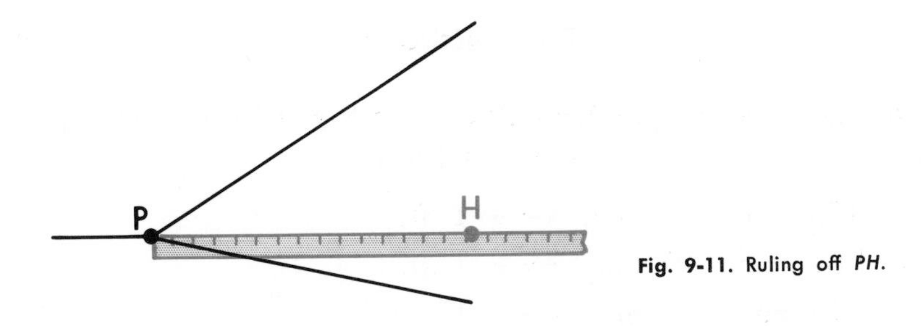

Fig. 9-11. Ruling off *PH*.

sented by a line segment 152 mm. long. Rule off 152 mm. from *P* (Fig. 9-11), and call the other end *H*. (*f*) At *H*, using your protractor or your draftsman's triangle, draw TB (Fig. 9-12) at right angles to PH. (g) Now measure TB. In this example, TB turns out to be 127 mm. But we agreed that 1 ft. $\longleftrightarrow$ 10 mm. on your scale. Therefore, the room is 12 ft. 8 in. high.

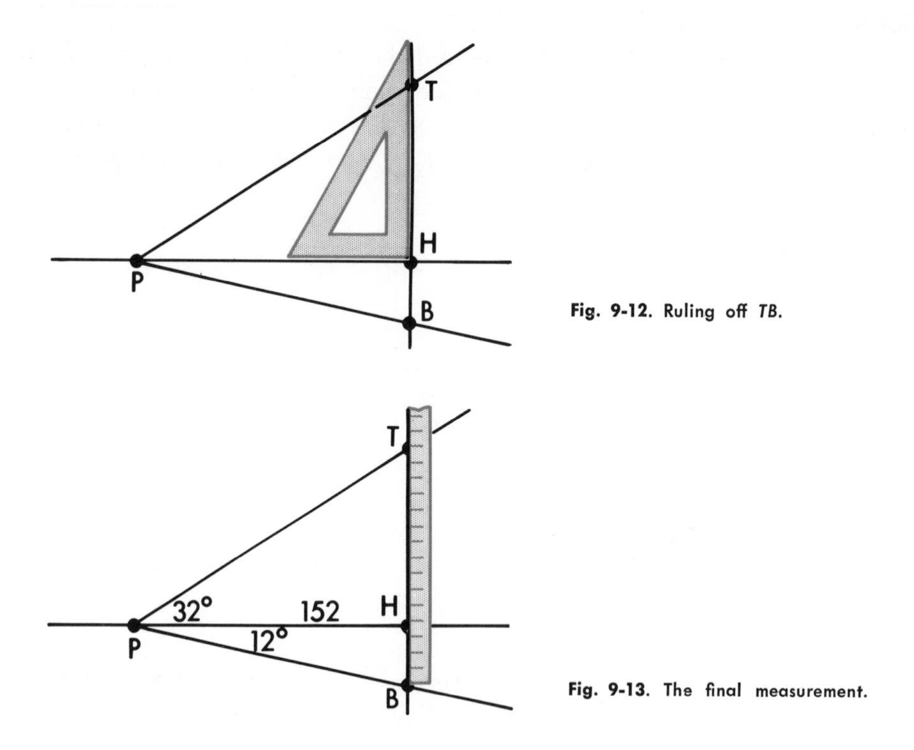

Fig. 9-12. Ruling off *TB*.

Fig. 9-13. The final measurement.

Figure 9-13 is called a *scale drawing*. It is a picture of the room, but much smaller.

• Test: Section 2

Part A. The following problems all refer to Fig. 9-14. In each case, find the height, represented by TB, in feet, and inches.

1 $TB = 173$ mm., 10 mm. $\longleftrightarrow$ 1 ft.
2 $TB = 87$ mm., 10 mm. $\longleftrightarrow$ 1 ft.
3 $TB = 75$ mm., 10 mm. $\longleftrightarrow$ $1\frac{1}{2}$ ft.
4 $TB = 64$ mm., 10 mm. $\longleftrightarrow$ $1\frac{1}{2}$ ft.
5 $TB = 58$ mm., 10 mm. $\longleftrightarrow$ 2 ft.
6 $TB = 49$ mm., 10 mm. $\longleftrightarrow$ 2 ft.

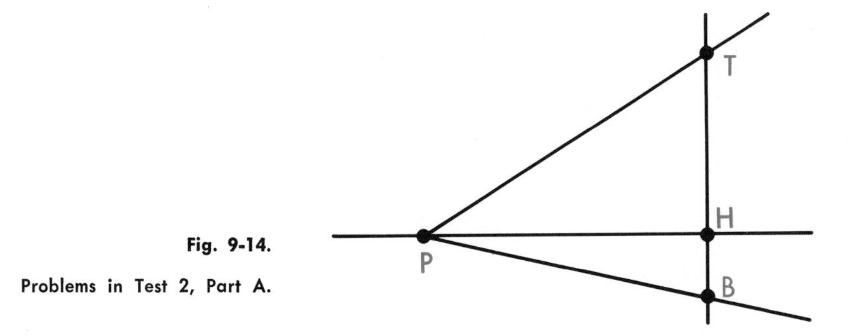

Fig. 9-14.
Problems in Test 2, Part A.

Part B. Projects.

1 Measure the height of your classroom. Check your result from different points in the room.

2 Measure the height of a building. Check your result from different positions.

3 FINDING AN ANGLE OF WIDTH

Before we can find the width of an object, we must first find an angle of width. All you need is a piece of paper, a flat surface to write on, and two pencils (or one stick and a pencil).

Problem. See Figs. 9-15 through 9-21.

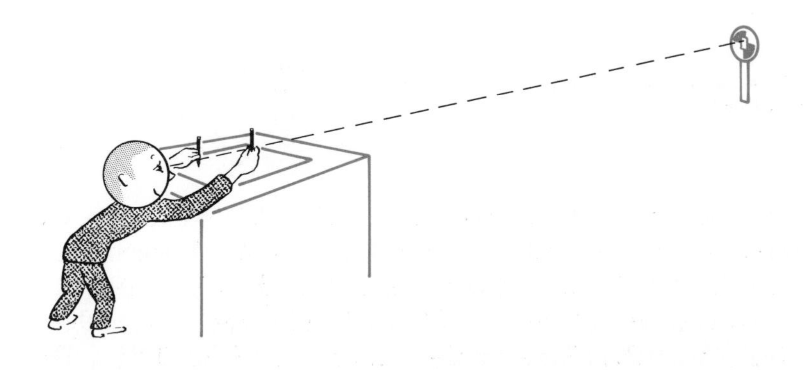

Fig. 9-15. Setting up the pencils.

Solution: (*a*) First, fasten a sheet of paper to a flat surface with *tape*—do not use thumb tacks (Fig. 9-16). (*b*) Make a mark on it, and call the mark *P*. (*c*) Place a pencil upright at *P*, holding it with your left hand. Bend over until your eye is in such a position that this pencil is in the line-of-sight of

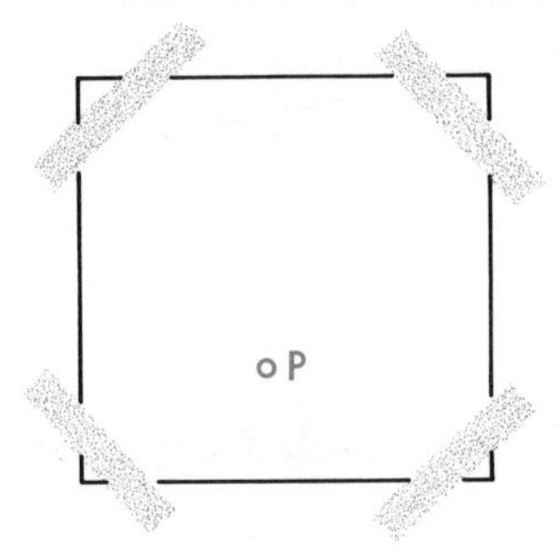

Fig. 9-16. Fastening the paper.

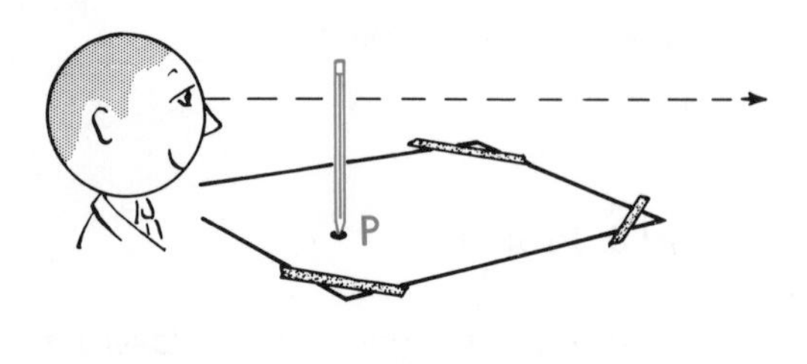

Fig. 9-17. Getting your eye in position.

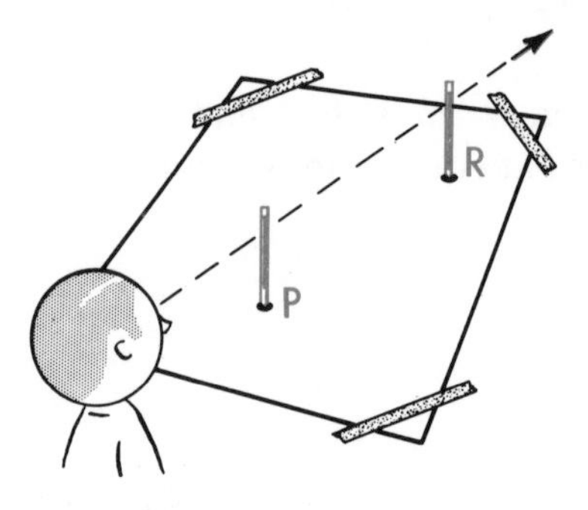

Fig. 9-18. Getting the second pencil into position.

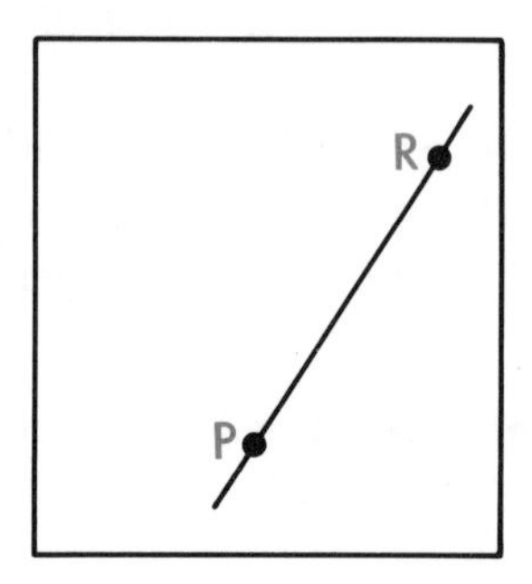

Fig. 9-19. The right line-of-bearing.

the right hand corner of the room (Fig. 9-17). (*d*) Now, take your right hand pencil, and move it until it is behind the left hand pencil (Fig. 9-18). Make a mark, *R*. (*e*) Draw a line through *P* and *R* (Fig. 9-19). This is the *right line-of-bearing*. (*f*) Now, switch hands, and repeat, to get the left line-of-bearing (Fig. 9-20). Measure the angle formed (Fig. 9-21). This is the *angle of width*.

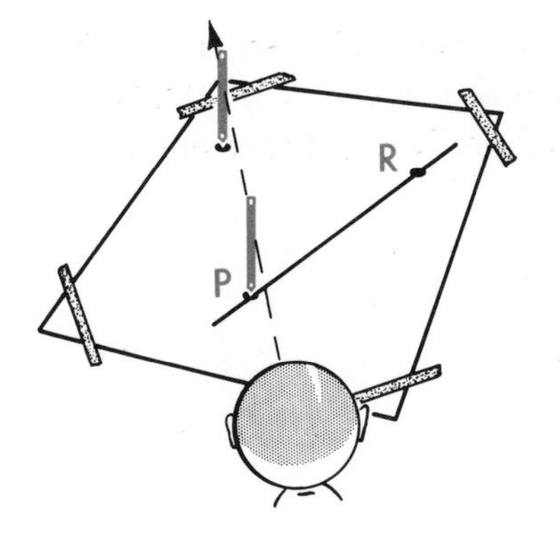

Fig. 9-20. Left line-of-bearing.

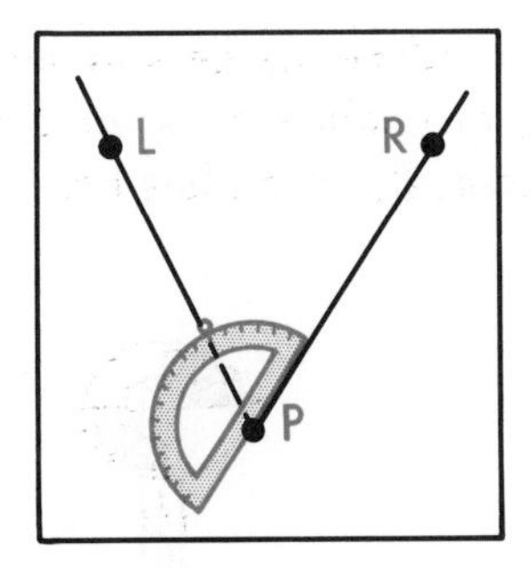

Fig. 9-21. Measuring the angle of width.

Test: Section 3

1 Find the angle of width of a room, from different points.

2 Find the angle of width of a building, from different points.

4 FINDING A WIDTH

The problem of finding a width arises when it is not practicable to measure the distance involved. In Fig. 9-22, if you wanted to find the distance from *L*

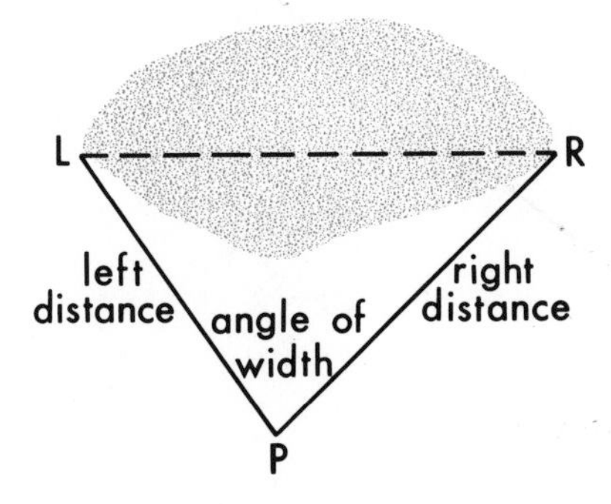

Fig. 9-22. The width of a swamp.

to *R* across a swamp, you could not very well take a tape across! However, with the help of a scale drawing, this is a fairly easy problem to solve.

First, we place markers of some sort at L and R. These may be branches, or rocks, or chalk marks, or a professional marker (Fig. 9-23). Then we pick a point, P, which has two "qualifications". (1) From point P we must

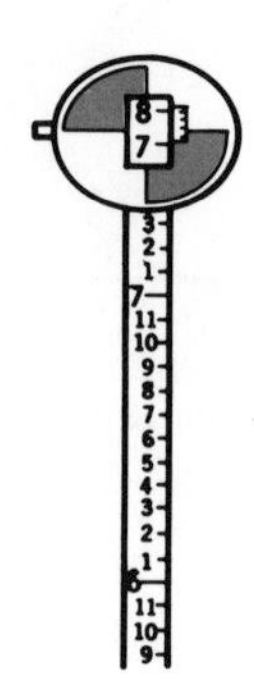

Fig. 9-23.

A surveyor's marker.

be able to see the markers at L and R; (2) the ground is such that we can measure the distances from P to L, and from P to R. Surveyors use tapes for this, but we may use folding rulers or yardsticks.

Now we choose a scale. Suppose the angle of width (Fig. 9-24) turns out to be 80°, and suppose the right distance is 72 ft., and the left distance is

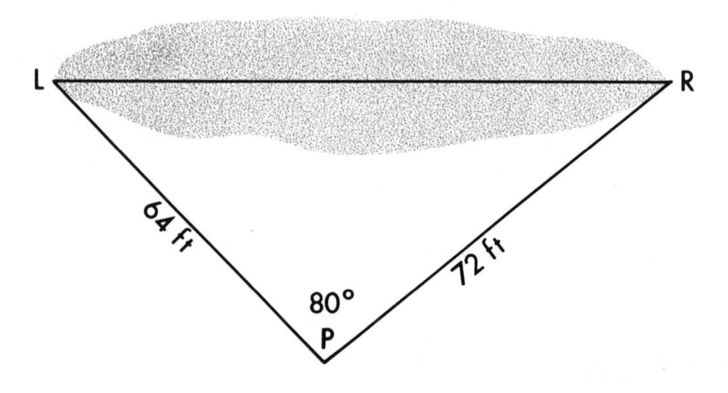

Fig. 9-24. Measuring the swamp.

64 ft. We may choose 1 mm. $\longleftrightarrow$ 1 ft., and make a scale drawing with RP = 72 mm., and LP = 64 mm. Now, when we measure LR, it comes out at approximately 86 mm., which means that the swamp is 86 ft. wide.

Test: Section 4

Part A. In the following, the measurement of LR, and the scale is given. Find the actual width.

1 38 mm., 1 mm $\longleftrightarrow$ 1 yd.
2 47 mm., 1 mm $\longleftrightarrow$ 1 yd.
3 102 mm., 10 mm $\longleftrightarrow$ 1 ft.
4 134 mm., 10 mm $\longleftrightarrow$ 1 ft.
5 28.8 mm., 1 mm $\longleftrightarrow$ 1 ft.
6 29.6 mm., 1 mm $\longleftrightarrow$ 1 ft.
7 85.9 mm., 1 mm $\longleftrightarrow$ 2 ft.
8 76.3 mm., 1 mm $\longleftrightarrow$ 2 ft.

Part B. Reproduce the following diagrams accurately, and measure the width, LR. In each case, 1 mm. $\longleftrightarrow$ 1 ft.

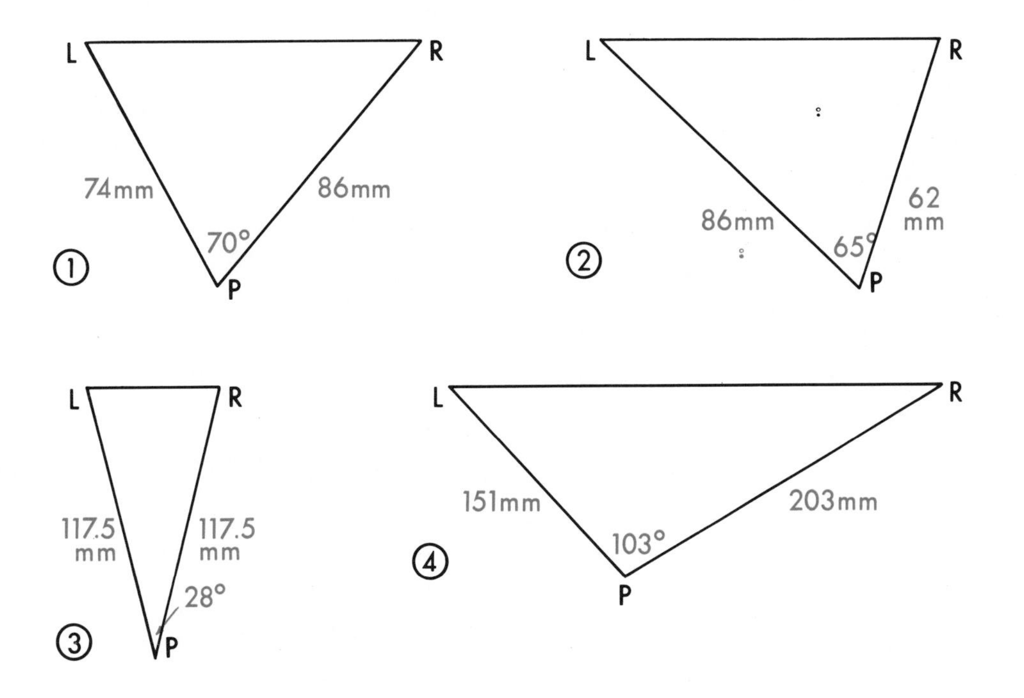

Part C. Projects.

1 Measure the width of your classroom, and check by direct measurement.
2 Measure the width of a building, and check by direct measurement.

5 THE PYTHAGOREAN THEOREM

Several thousand years ago, it was discovered that a right triangle with *legs* of 3 and 4 (Fig. 9-25), always had a *hypotenuse* of 5. Then it was found

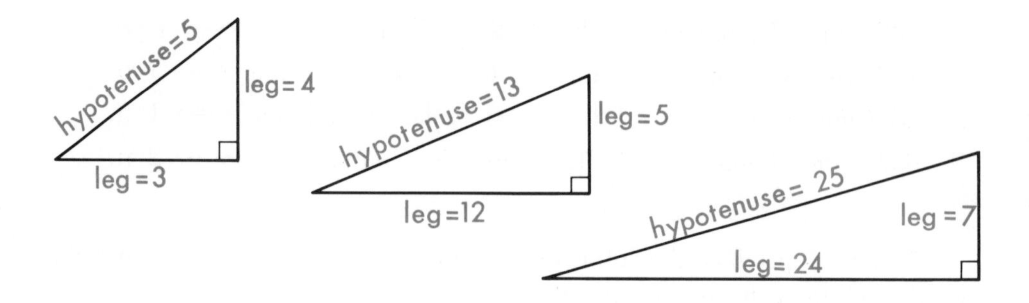

Fig. 9-25. Right triangles.

that a right triangle with legs 5 and 12, always had a hypotenuse of 13, and a right triangle with legs 7 and 24, always had a hypotenuse of 25.

Further study showed the following:

3, 4, 5 Triangle	
Leg 1 = 3	Leg^2 = 9
Leg 2 = 4	Leg^2 = 16
Hy = 5	Hy^2 = 25

5, 12, 13 Triangle	
Leg 1 = 5	Leg^2 = 25
Leg 2 = 12	Leg^2 = 144
Hy = 13	Hy^2 = 169

7, 24, 25 Triangle	
Leg 1 = 7	Leg^2 = 49
Leg 2 = 24	Leg^2 = 576
Hy = 25	Hy^2 = 625

Notice that $9 + 16 = 25$, $25 + 144 = 169$, and $49 + 576 = 625$. Will this always work? Let us try one more.

Problem 1. Draw any right triangle, measure the sides, *square the lengths* (multiply each number by itself), and compare.

Solution: See Fig. 9-26. In the figure:

leg 1 = 5.6, $\text{leg}^2 = 5.6 \times 5.6 = 31.36$
leg 2 = 7.3, $\text{leg}^2 = 7.3 \times 7.3 = 53.29$
hy = 9.2, $\text{hy}^2 = 9.2 \times 9.2 = 84.64$

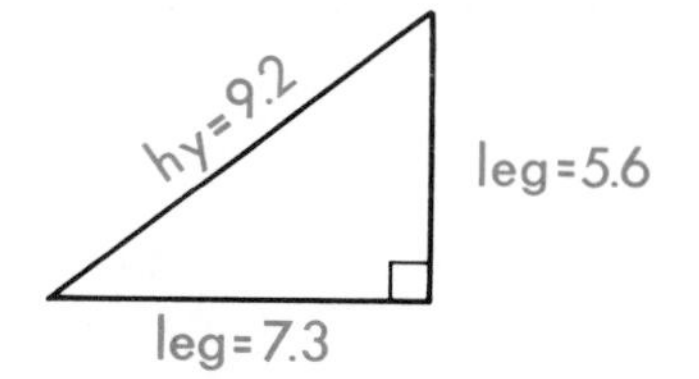

Fig. 9-26. Problem 1.

But 31.36 + 53.29 = 84.65, so the result agrees within 2% with the square of the hypotenuse.

It was *proved* by Greek mathematicians in the School of Pythagoras (pĭ•thăg′o•răs) that this rule *always* holds for a right triangle. It is called the *Pythagorean* (pĭ•thăg′ô•rē′ăn) *Theorem,* a theorem being a statement that has been *proved* by mathematicians.

- *Pythagorean Theorem (PT):* $\text{hy}^2 = \text{leg}^2 + \text{leg}^2$.

Because this rule holds only for *right* triangles, it is possible to find out whether a triangle is a right triangle by trying the rule.

Problem 2. Is the figure in Fig. 9-27 a right triangle?

Solution:

side 1 = 3.7 $\quad \text{side}^2 = 3.7 \times 3.7 = 13.69$
side 2 = 4.5 $\quad \text{side}^2 = 4.5 \times 4.5 = 20.25$
$\text{side}^2 + \text{side}^2 = 33.94$
side 3 = 5.8 $\quad \text{side}^2 = 5.8 \times 5.8 = 33.64$

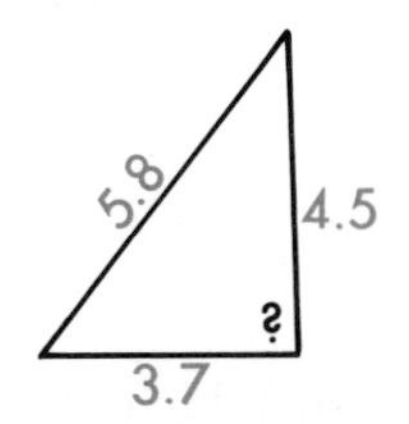

Fig. 9-27. Problem 2.

The error is 33.94 − 33.64 = 0.30. The per cent error is found in the usual way:

$$\text{Per cent error} = \frac{0.30 \times 100}{34} = \frac{30}{34} = 0.9\%$$

Answer: Yes, this is a right triangle within 2% error.

Problem 3. Is the triangle in Fig. 9-28 a right triangle?

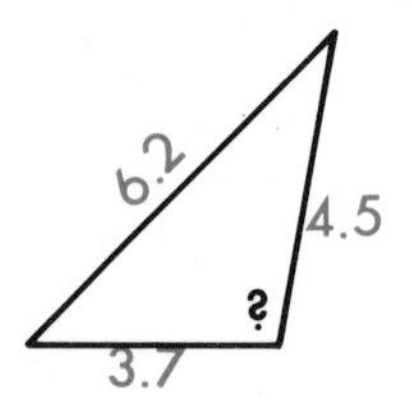

Fig. 9-28. Problem 3.

Solution: The first and second sides are the same as those in Problem 2, so that

$$\text{side}^2 + \text{side}^2 = 33.94$$

$$\text{side } 3 = 6.2, \ \text{side}^2 = 6.2 \times 6.2 = 38.44$$

The error is $38.44 - 33.94 = 4.50$. In finding the per cent error, we use in the denominator the average of 38.44, and 33.94, rounded off to two places:

$$\text{Per cent error} = \frac{4.50 \times 100}{36} = 12.5\%$$

Answer: No, this is not a right triangle. The per cent error is too large.

Test: Section 5

Part A. Which of the following are right triangles?

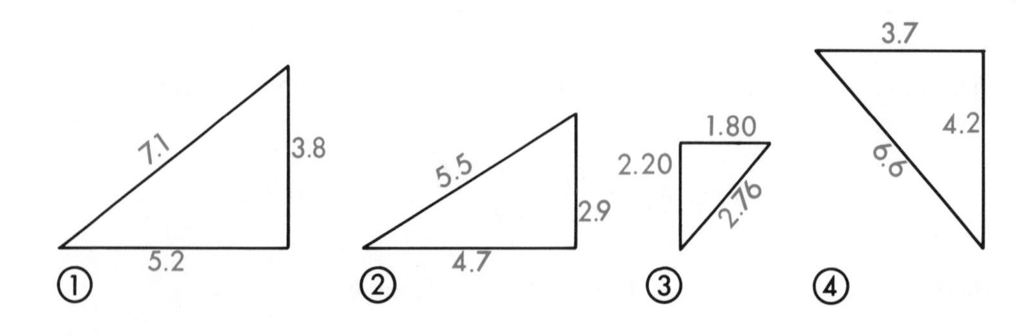

Part B. Verify the PT for each of the following right triangles:

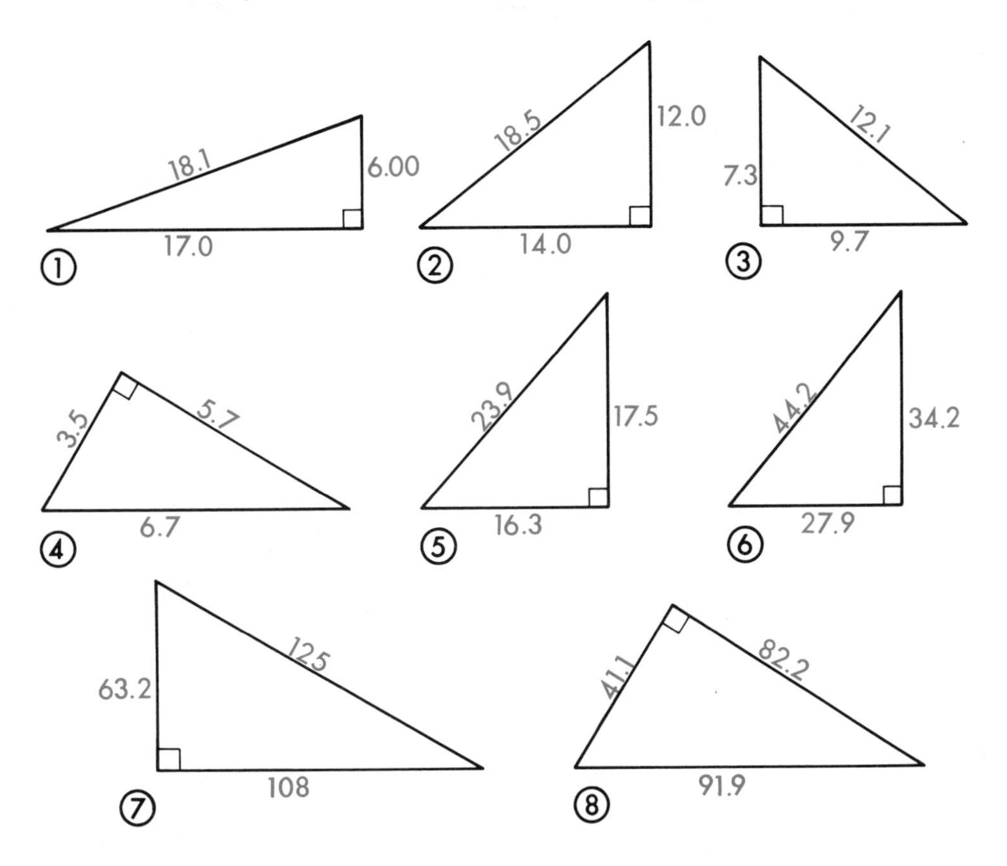

6 MEASURING WITH THE PYTHAGOREAN THEOREM

The PT discussed in the previous section can be used for indirect measurement if there are right triangles, and if you do not wish to measure angles and make scale drawings. Before showing you how this is done, let us investigate a couple of puzzle problems which will lead into the practical end of the work.

Problem 1. The following are part of the calculations for a PT problem. Find the missing numbers marked x and y:

$$\begin{aligned} \text{leg 1} &= 2.5 & \text{leg}^2 &= 6.25 \\ \text{leg 2} &= 3.4 & \text{leg}^2 &= 11.56 \\ \text{hy} &= x & \text{hy}^2 &= y \end{aligned}$$

Solution: Using the PT, we know that $leg^2 + leg^2 = hy^2$. So

$$y = 6.25 + 11.56$$
$$y = 17.81$$

But y is just x multiplied by itself, or x^2. To put it another way, x is the *square root of* y:

$$x = \sqrt{17.81}$$

We may find this square root by the *method of estimating.*

$$\text{Guess: } \sqrt{17.81} = \text{approximately } 4.00$$

$$\text{Divide: } \frac{17.81}{4.00} = 4.45$$

$$\text{Average: } \frac{4.00 + 4.45}{2} = 4.23$$

$$\text{Divide: } \frac{17.81}{4.23} = 4.21$$

$$\text{Average: } \frac{4.23 + 4.21}{2} = 4.22$$

Answer: Rounding off, the answer to the problem is: hy = 4.2.

Problem 2. The following are part of the calculations for a PT problem. Find the missing numbers marked x and x^2.

$$\text{leg } 1 = 3.5 \qquad \text{leg}^2 = 12.25$$
$$\text{leg } 2 = x \qquad \text{leg}^2 = x^2$$
$$\text{hy} = 7.1 \qquad \text{hy}^2 = 50.41$$

Solution: Using the PT, we know that $leg^2 + leg^2 = hy^2$, so x^2 has to be $50.41 - 12.25 = 38.16$.

$$x^2 = 38.16$$
$$x = \sqrt{38.16}$$

Answer: Using the method of estimating, x (or the second leg) = 6.2.

The following problems show how the PT can be used for indirect measurement.

Problem 3. A pole, BC, is 15 ft. high. A stake is placed in the ground 10 ft. from the foot of the pole. How long is the guy wire from B to A (Fig. 9-29).

Solution:

$$\text{leg } 1 = 15 \qquad \text{leg}^2 = 225$$
$$\text{leg } 2 = 10 \qquad \text{leg}^2 = 100$$
$$\text{hy} = x \qquad \text{hy}^2 = x^2$$
$$\text{leg}^2 + \text{leg}^2 = \text{hy}^2$$
$$325 = x^2$$
$$x = \sqrt{325}$$
$$x = 18$$

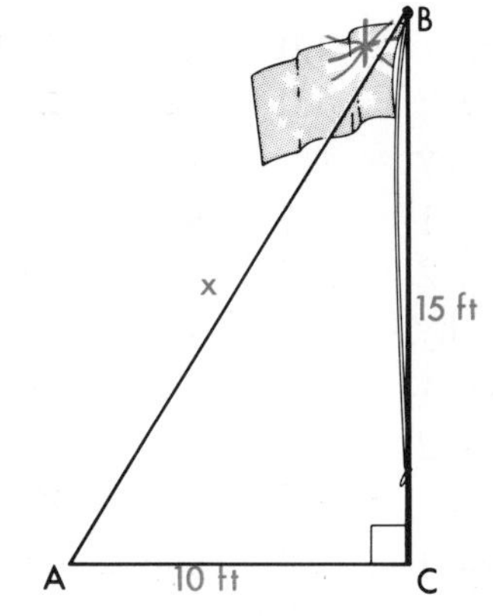

Fig. 9-29. Problem 3.

Answer: The guy wire will be about 18 ft. long.

Problem 4. A plank 12 ft. long is placed across a narrow gorge, the ends resting on points A and B (Fig. 9-30). If the distance from A to C is 10 ft., how much higher is B than A?

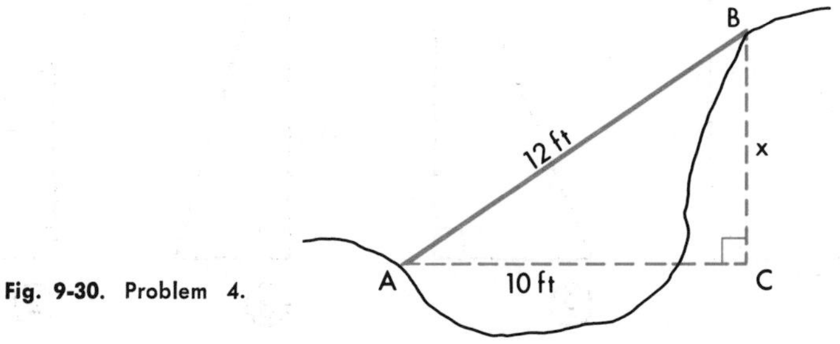

Fig. 9-30. Problem 4.

Solution:

$$\text{leg } 1 = 10 \qquad \text{leg}^2 = 100$$
$$\text{leg } 2 = x \qquad \text{leg}^2 = x^2$$
$$\text{hy} = 12 \qquad \text{hy}^2 = 144$$
$$\text{Therefore, } x^2 = 44$$
$$x = \sqrt{44}$$
$$x = 6.7 \text{ approximately}$$

Answer: B is 6.7 ft. (approximately 6 ft. 8 in.) higher than A.

Test: Section 6

Part A. Fill in the value of of x in each case.

1
leg 1 = 4.0 leg^2 = 16.00
leg 2 = 5.0 leg^2 = 25.00
hy = x hy^2 = x^2

2
leg 1 = 3.0 leg^2 = 9.00
leg 2 = 3.5 leg^2 = 12.25
hy = x hy^2 = x^2

3
leg 1 = 7.5 leg^2 = 56.25
leg 2 = 8.5 leg^2 = 72.25
hy = x hy^2 = x^2

4
leg 1 = 3.2 leg^2 = 10.24
leg 2 = 4.1 leg^2 = 16.81
hy = x hy^2 = x^2

5
leg 1 = 7.5 leg^2 = 56.25
leg 2 = x leg^2 = x^2
hy = 9.3 hy^2 = 86.49

6
leg 1 = 8.1 leg^2 = 65.61
leg 2 = x leg^2 = x^2
hy = 12.4 hy^2 = 153.76

7
leg 1 = x leg^2 = x^2
leg 2 = 23.4 leg^2 = 547.56
hy = 37.5 hy^2 = 1406.25

8
leg 1 = x leg^2 = x^2
leg 2 = 18.6 leg^2 = 345.96
hy = 23.3 hy^2 = 542.89

Part B. Find the value of x in each figure.

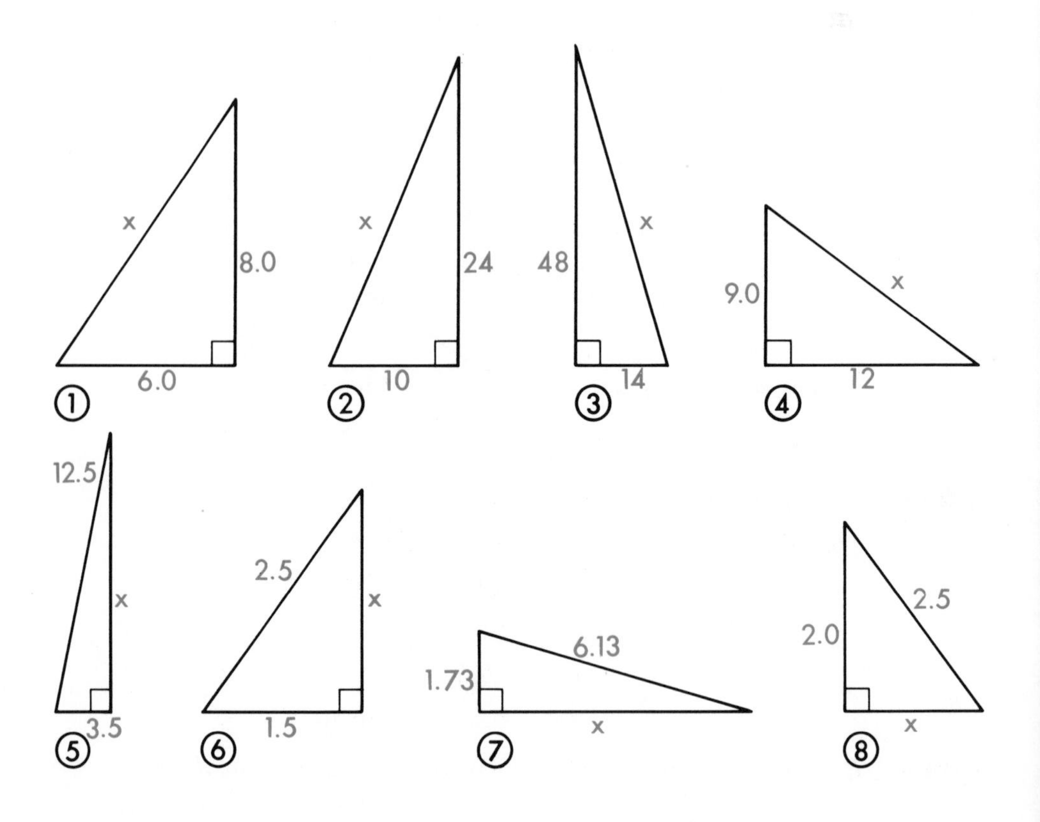

Part C. Read carefully, draw a diagram, and answer the question.

1. A ladder 14 ft. long rests against a wall. If the foot of the ladder is 3.0 ft. from the bottom of the wall, how far up the wall does the ladder reach?
2. A door is 3.5 ft. × 8.0 ft. high. Will a round table with diameter 10 ft. fit through the door?
3. The screen of a TV set has sides of 16 in. and 22 in. How long is the diagonal? (The size of a TV "big tube" is given in terms of the diagonal across the face.)
4. A tent in the shape of a cone is supported by a 10 ft. pole, with wires to the base of the tent. If the distance from the bottom of the pole to the edge of the tent is 7 ft. 6 in., how long must each guy wire be?

7 ANOTHER EXPERIMENT ON RIGHT TRIANGLES

If you know any two sides of a right triangle, you can find the third side without using a scale drawing. All you have to do is learn the Pythagorean theorem discussed in the last section.

But suppose you want to find an angle. Can it be done without a scale drawing?

Yes, a branch of mathematics called *trigonometry* can be used for this. Before learning this, you will have to learn two very important names for the legs of right triangles.

Look at Fig. 9-31 carefully. Each triangle is a right triangle, and the

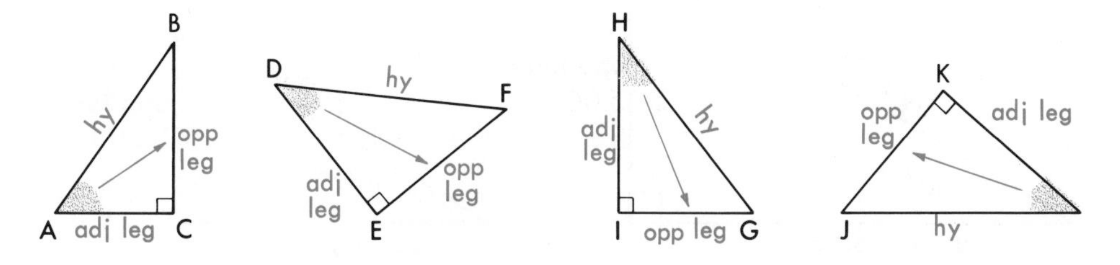

Fig. 9-31. Naming the legs of a right triangle.

longest side (facing the right angle) is called the *hypotenuse,* as you already know. Now, in each triangle there are two *acute angles.* You found, some time back, that these two acute angles are *complements* (they add up to

$90°$). If you know that one of the acute angles is $40°$, you can subtract, and say right away that the other angle is $50°$. So it does not matter which of the two you use. This is merely a matter of convenience.

Once you have decided on the angle to use, the legs are named *with reference to this angle.*

- The *opposite leg* (opp. leg) faces the angle you are working with.
- The *adjacent leg* (adj. leg) is part of the angle you are working with.

Go over Fig. 9-31 to make sure you understand how to name the legs. If you are working with $\angle A$, BC is the opposite leg, and AC is the adjacent

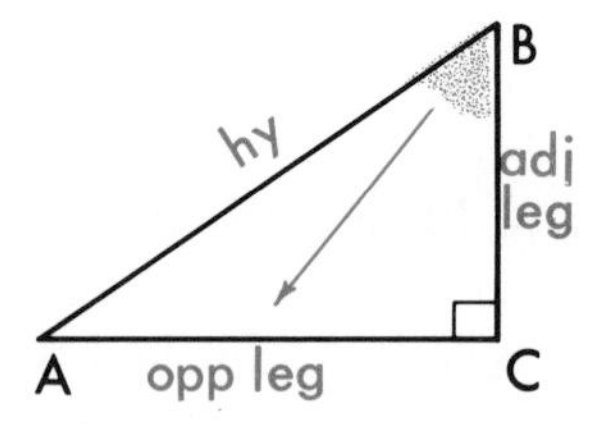

Fig. 9-32. Working with $\angle B$.

leg. Of course, if you are working with $\angle B$ (Fig. 9-32), then AC becomes the opposite leg, and BC becomes the adjacent leg.

Now we are ready to work with these angles. Look at the two triangles in Fig. 9-33.

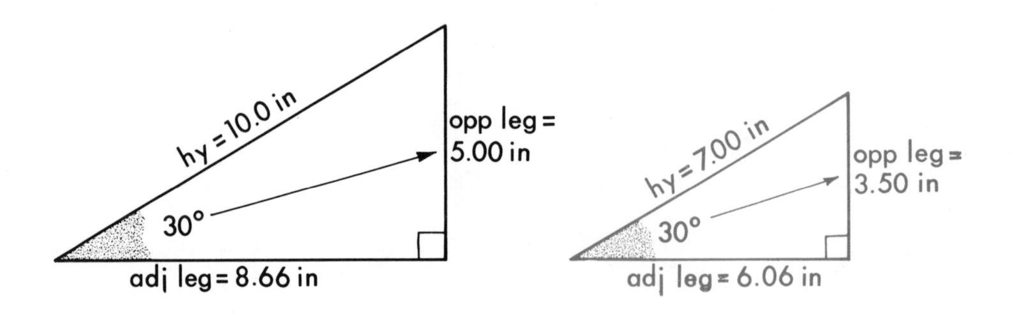

Fig. 9-33. An experiment with 30° right triangles.

The triangles are not the same size, but there is something the same about them. Notice that:

Ratio	For the First Triangle	For the Second Triangle
$\frac{\text{opp. leg}}{\text{adj. leg}}$	$\frac{5.00}{8.66} = 0.577$	$\frac{3.50}{6.06} = 0.577$
$\frac{\text{opp. leg}}{\text{hy}}$	$\frac{5.00}{10.0} = 0.500$	$\frac{3.50}{7.00} = 0.500$

Let us try another angle (Fig. 9-34).

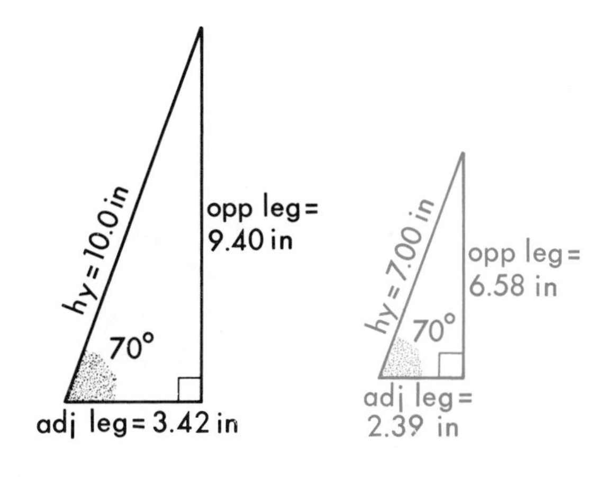

Fig. 9-34. An experiment with 70° right triangles.

Ratio	For the First Triangle	For the Second Triangle
$\frac{\text{opp. leg}}{\text{adj. leg}}$	$\frac{9.40}{3.42} = 2.75$	$\frac{6.58}{2.39} = 2.75$
$\frac{\text{opp. leg}}{\text{hy}}$	$\frac{9.40}{10.0} = 0.940$	$\frac{6.58}{7.00} = 0.940$

In other words, these *ratios* (fractions) are the same for all right triangles having the same angle. For convenience, mathematicians have figured them out once and for all, so that people do not have to work them out every time they want them. They have been given special names:

Definition. The ratio, $\frac{\text{opp. leg}}{\text{adj. leg}}$, is called the *tangent* of the angle.

In Fig. 9-34, the tangent of 70° is $\frac{9.40}{3.42}$. We write this in mathematical shorthand as:

$$\tan 70^\circ = 2.75$$

Definition. The ratio, $\frac{\text{opp. leg}}{\text{hy}}$, is called the *sine* of the angle.

In Fig. 9-34, the sine of 70° is $\frac{9.40}{10.0}$. We write this in mathematical shorthand as:

$$\sin 70^\circ = 0.940 \quad \text{(pronounced “sine”)}$$

Problem 1. In Fig. 9-35, find tan M, and sin M.

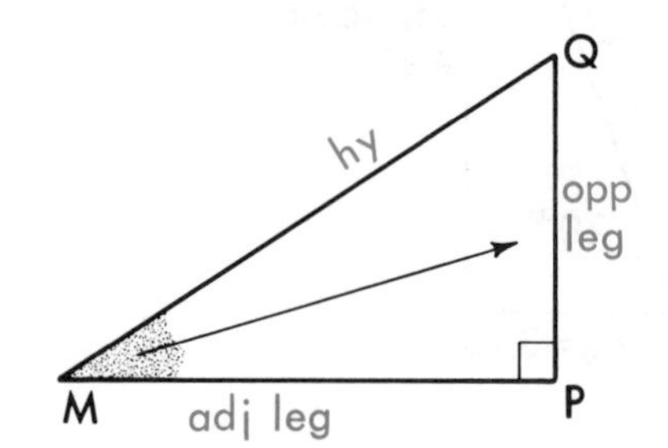

Fig. 9-35. Problem 1.

Solution: The first step is always to mark the legs clearly so that you do not make a mistake. Here, this has been done for you. Now

$$\tan M = \frac{PQ}{MP} \quad ; \quad \sin M = \frac{PQ}{MQ}$$

Problem 2. In Fig. 9-36, what is tan S, and sin S?

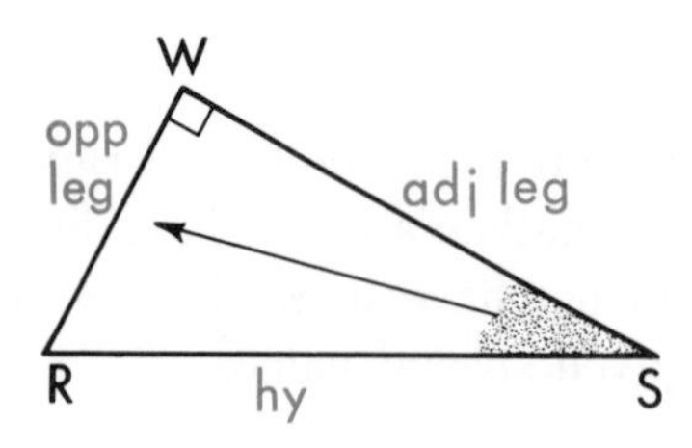

Fig. 9-36. Problem 2.

Solution: $\tan S = \dfrac{RW}{WS}$; $\sin S = \dfrac{WR}{RS}$

Problem 3. Find sin 25°, and tan 25°.

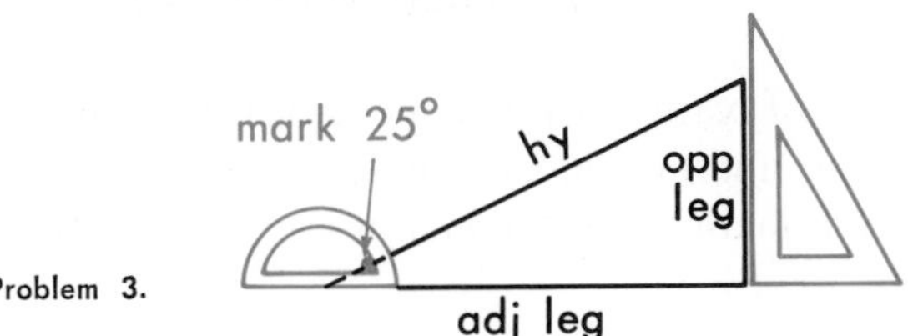

Fig. 9-37. Problem 3.

Solution: Make *any* right triangle with an acute angle of 25° (Fig. 9-37). Label the sides carefully. Then

$$\sin 25^\circ = \frac{\text{length of opp. leg}}{\text{length of hy}}$$

$$\tan 25^\circ = \frac{\text{length of opp. leg}}{\text{length of adj. leg}}$$

If you measure carefully, the answers will be:

$$\sin 25^\circ = 0.423 \quad ; \quad \tan 25^\circ = 0.466$$

Test: Section 7

Part A. Copy the following right triangles. In each case, $\angle C$ is a right angle. Label the sides with reference to $\angle x$ in each case.

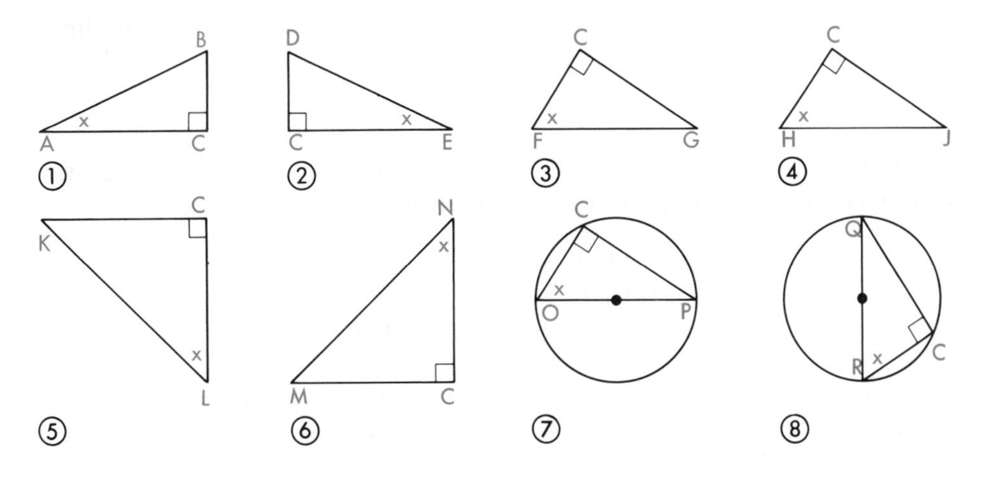

Part B. Find the sine and the tangent for each of the following angles:

1 10°   2 20°   3 40°   4 50°   5 60°   6 80°

8 FINDING AN ANGLE

The table of values of trigonometric functions on the opposite page, gives the sines and tangents of angles from 0° to 90°. They were calculated by advanced mathematics much more accurately than would have been possible by drawings.

Problem 1. Find sin 57°.

Solution: Using the table given, under "Angle" find "57°." Under "Sin" read .8387. The answer is written: sin 57° = 0.8387.

Problem 2. Find tan 37°.

Solution: Under "Angle" find "37°." Under "Tan" read .7536. The answer is written: tan 37° = 0.7536.

Problem 3. Find the angle whose sine is 0.9816.

Solution: Look in the "Sin" column until you get to .9816. Then the angle is 79°.

Problem 4. Find the angle whose tangent is 2.2460.

Solution: Look in the "Tan" column until you get to 2.2460. Then the angle is 66°.

Problem 5. Find the angle whose tangent is 0.5824.

Solution: Look in the "Tan" column. There is no 0.5824! But you *can* find:

30° .5774
31° .6009

so the angle is between 30°, and 31°. For our purposes, we will say the answer is 30°, because it is closer to the true angle:

$$\begin{array}{r} .5824 \\ -.5774 \\ \hline .0050 \end{array} \qquad \begin{array}{r} .6009 \\ -.5824 \\ \hline .0185 \end{array}$$

If the value you want is exactly between two angles in the table, you take the *higher* of the two, just as you did with approximate numbers.

VALUES OF TRIGONOMETRIC FUNCTIONS

Angle	*Sin*	*Tan*	*Angle*	*Sin*	*Tan*
1°	.0175	.0175	**46°**	.7193	1.0355
2°	.0349	.0349	**47°**	.7314	1.0724
3°	.0523	.0524	**48°**	.7431	1.1106
4°	.0698	.0699	**49°**	.7547	1.1504
5°	.0872	.0875	**50°**	.7660	1.1918
6°	.1045	.1051	**51°**	.7771	1.2349
7°	.1219	.1228	**52°**	.7880	1.2799
8°	.1392	.1405	**53°**	.7986	1.3270
9°	.1564	.1584	**54°**	.8090	1.3764
10°	.1736	.1763	**55°**	.8192	1.4281
11°	.1908	.1944	**56°**	.8290	1.4826
12°	.2079	.2126	**57°**	.8387	1.5399
13°	.2250	.2309	**58°**	.8480	1.6003
14°	.2419	.2493	**59°**	.8572	1.6643
15°	.2588	.2679	**60°**	.8660	1.7321
16°	.2756	.2867	**61°**	.8746	1.8040
17°	.2924	.3057	**62°**	.8829	1.8807
18°	.3090	.3249	**63°**	.8910	1.9626
19°	.3256	.3443	**64°**	.8988	2.0503
20°	.3420	.3640	**65°**	.9063	2.1445
21°	.3584	.3839	**66°**	.9135	2.2460
22°	.3746	.4040	**67°**	.9205	2.3559
23°	.3907	.4245	**68°**	.9272	2.4751
24°	.4067	.4452	**69°**	.9336	2.6051
25°	.4226	.4663	**70°**	.9397	2.7475
26°	.4384	.4877	**71°**	.9455	2.9042
27°	.4540	.5095	**72°**	.9511	3.0777
28°	.4695	.5317	**73°**	.9563	3.2709
29°	.4848	.5543	**74°**	.9613	3.4874
30°	.5000	.5774	**75°**	.9659	3.7321
31°	.5150	.6009	**76°**	.9703	4.0108
32°	.5299	.6249	**77°**	.9744	4.3315
33°	.5446	.6494	**78°**	.9781	4.7046
34°	.5592	.6745	**79°**	.9816	5.1446
35°	.5736	.7002	**80°**	.9848	5.6713
36°	.5878	.7265	**81°**	.9877	6.3138
37°	.6018	.7536	**82°**	.9903	7.1154
38°	.6157	.7813	**83°**	.9925	8.1443
39°	.6293	.8098	**84°**	.9945	9.5144
40°	.6428	.8391	**85°**	.9962	11.4301
41°	.6561	.8693	**86°**	.9976	14.3007
42°	.6691	.9004	**87°**	.9986	19.0811
43°	.6820	.9325	**88°**	.9994	28.6363
44°	.6947	.9657	**89°**	.9998	57.2900
45°	.7071	1.0000	**90°**	1.0000	∞

The usefulness of the trigonometric table is shown in the following problems:

Problem 6. A plank 6.00 ft. long leads up to a tailgate 4 ft. 3 in. high (Fig. 9-38). What is the *angle of inclination* ($\angle A$)?

Solution: The opp. leg = 4.25, and the hy = 6.00 ft. Therefore:

$$\sin A = \frac{\text{opp. leg}}{\text{hy}}$$

$$\sin A = \frac{4.25}{6.00}$$

$$\sin A = 0.7083$$

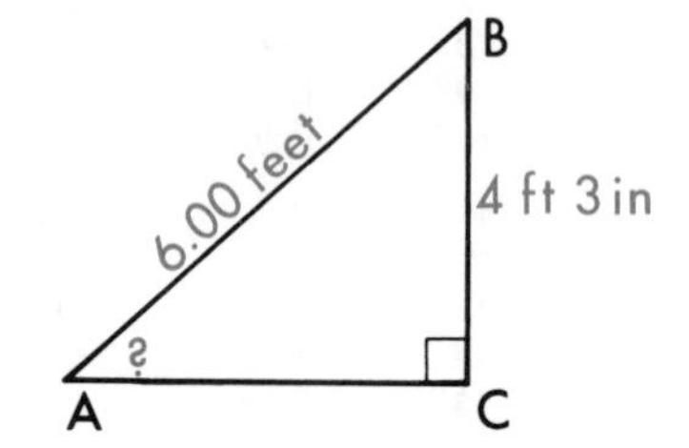

Fig. 9-38. Problem 6.

Looking in the sine table, the nearest value is: $A = 45°$.

Problem 7. A pole 12 ft. 5 in. high, is anchored by a stake 5 ft. 2 in. from its base (Fig. 9-39). Find the angle of inclination ($\angle B$).

Solution: The opp. leg = 12 ft. 5 in. = 12.42 ft. The adj. leg = 5 ft. 2 in. = 5.167 ft. Therefore:

$$\tan B = \frac{\text{opp. leg}}{\text{adj. leg}}$$

$$\tan B = \frac{12.42}{5.167}$$

$$\tan B = 2.404$$

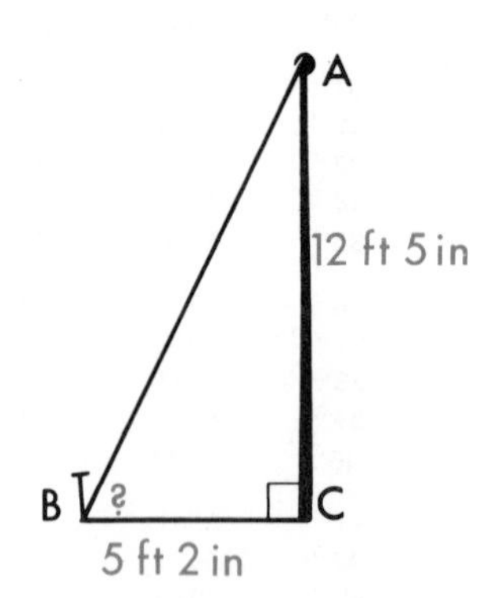

Fig. 9-39. Problem 7.

Looking in the tan table, the closest value is $B = 67°$.

Problem 8. In Fig. 9-40, find $\angle P$.

Solution: We cannot find $\angle P$ directly, because we do not know its opposite side. However, we *do* know the opposite leg for $\angle R$, so we can find this instead; we can worry about $\angle P$ later.

With reference to $\angle R$:

$$\text{opp leg.} = 39.8$$
$$\text{hy} = 41.8$$
$$\sin R = \frac{\text{opp. leg}}{\text{hy}}$$
$$\sin R = \frac{39.8}{41.8}$$
$$\sin R = 0.952$$

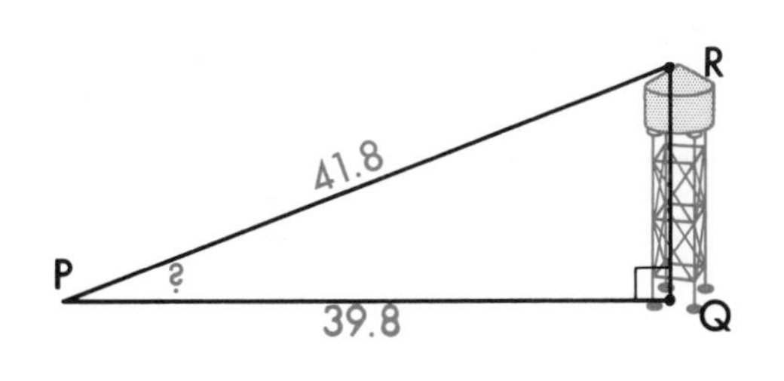

Fig. 9-40. Problem 8.

Looking in the sine table, the closest value is: $\angle R = 72°$. To find $\angle P$, subtract from 90°:

$$\angle P = 90° - 72°$$
$$\angle P = 18°$$

Test: Section 8

Part A. Look up the sine, and the tangent, of each of the following:

1 15°	2 27°	3 31°	4 37°	5 52°
6 62°	7 73°	8 81°	9 21°	10 7°

Part B. Find the angle that meets the following requirements:

1 $\sin A = 0.3090$	2 $\sin B = 0.9272$	3 $\tan C = 0.1763$
4 $\tan D = 0.6745$	5 $\sin E = 0.0872$	6 $\sin F = 0.3907$
7 $\tan G = 1.4826$	8 $\tan H = 4.7046$	9 $\sin I = 0.2700$
10 $\sin J = 0.5902$	11 $\tan K = 5.9027$	12 $\tan L = 1.4103$

Part C. Divide and find the angle in each of the following by using the table of sines and tangents.

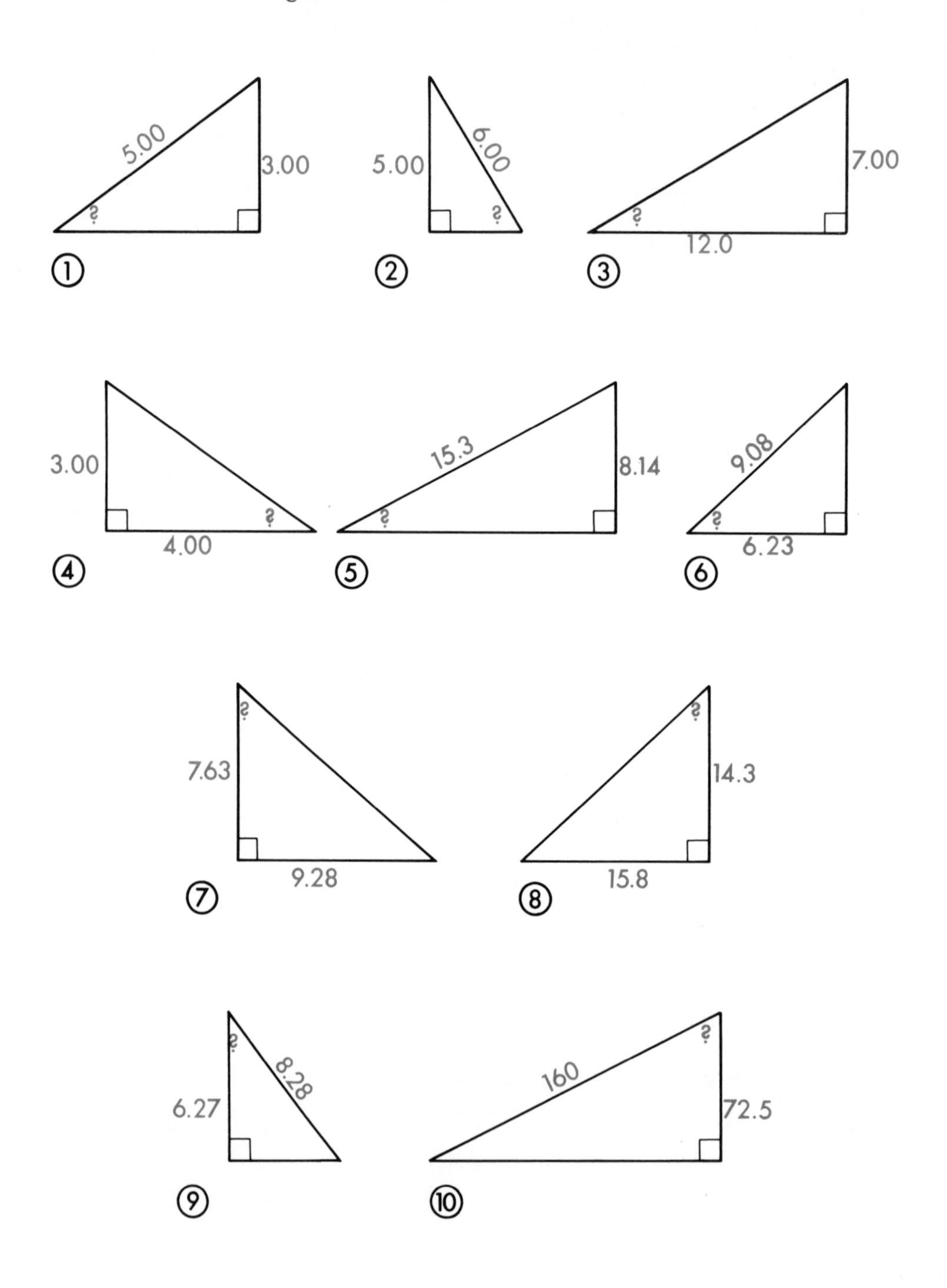

9 USING THE TANGENT RATIO

If you know one leg and one acute angle of a triangle, you can use trigonometry to find the other leg. Before showing you how this is done, let us review *proportions* for a moment.

You know that

$$\begin{matrix} \text{end} \longrightarrow \\ \text{middle} \longrightarrow \end{matrix} \frac{3}{4} = \frac{6}{8} \begin{matrix} \longleftarrow \text{middle} \\ \longleftarrow \text{end} \end{matrix}$$

is a proportion (two equal fractions). Recall that a true statement can be made by interchanging the ends:

$$\begin{matrix} \text{end} \longrightarrow \\ \text{middle} \longrightarrow \end{matrix} \frac{8}{4} = \frac{6}{3} \begin{matrix} \longleftarrow \text{middle} \\ \longleftarrow \text{end} \end{matrix}$$

In other words, if you find it convenient, you can always interchange the ends in a proportion, and get another proportion which is true.

Problem. A tower (Fig. 9-41) is known to be 700 ft. high. From point A, the angle of elevation of the top of the tower is 27°. How far away is the tower?

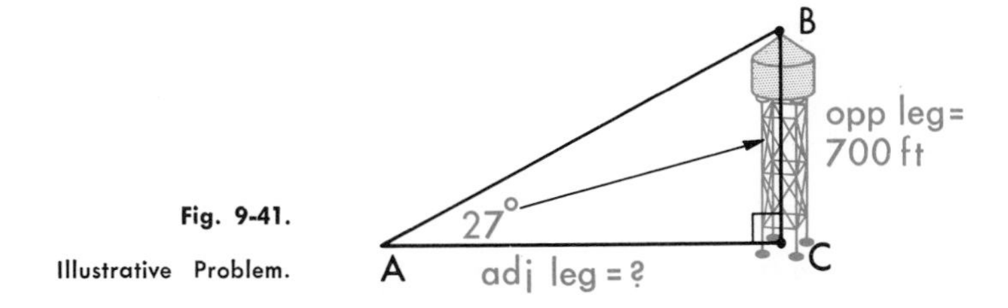

Fig. 9-41.
Illustrative Problem.

Solution (1): With respect to $\angle A$, opp. leg = 700 ft., and adj. leg = AC.

$$\tan 27^\circ = \frac{\text{opp. leg}}{\text{adj. leg}}$$

$$0.5095 = \frac{700}{AC}$$

This can be rewritten as a proportion:

$$\frac{0.5095}{1} = \frac{700}{AC}$$

Interchanging the ends, we get:

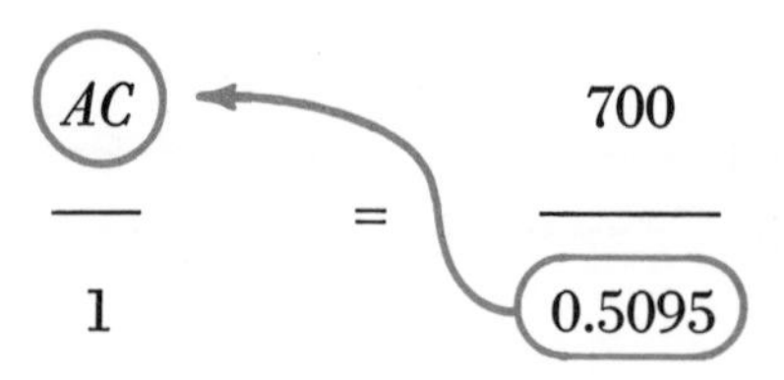

Doing the division, we get

$$AC = 1370 \text{ ft. (rounded to 3 s.f.)}$$

Solution (2): If we work with $\angle B$, the arithmetic is a little bit easier. Subtracting $90^\circ - 27^\circ$, we get $\angle B = 63^\circ$. Now the diagram looks like Fig. 9-42.

$$\tan 63^\circ = \frac{\text{opp. leg}}{\text{adj. leg}}$$

$$1.9626 = \frac{AC}{700}$$

Fig. 9-42. Solution 2.

Multiplying both members by 700, we get

$$700 \times 1.9626 = AC$$
$$AC = 1373.8200$$
$$AC = 1370 \text{ ft. (3 s.f.)}$$

- *REMEMBER*: Because it is easier to multiply than to divide, we always use the angle opposite the *unknown* leg in working with tangent ratios.

Test: Section 9

In each case, find the other acute angle, and use whichever angle is more convenient, to find the side marked.

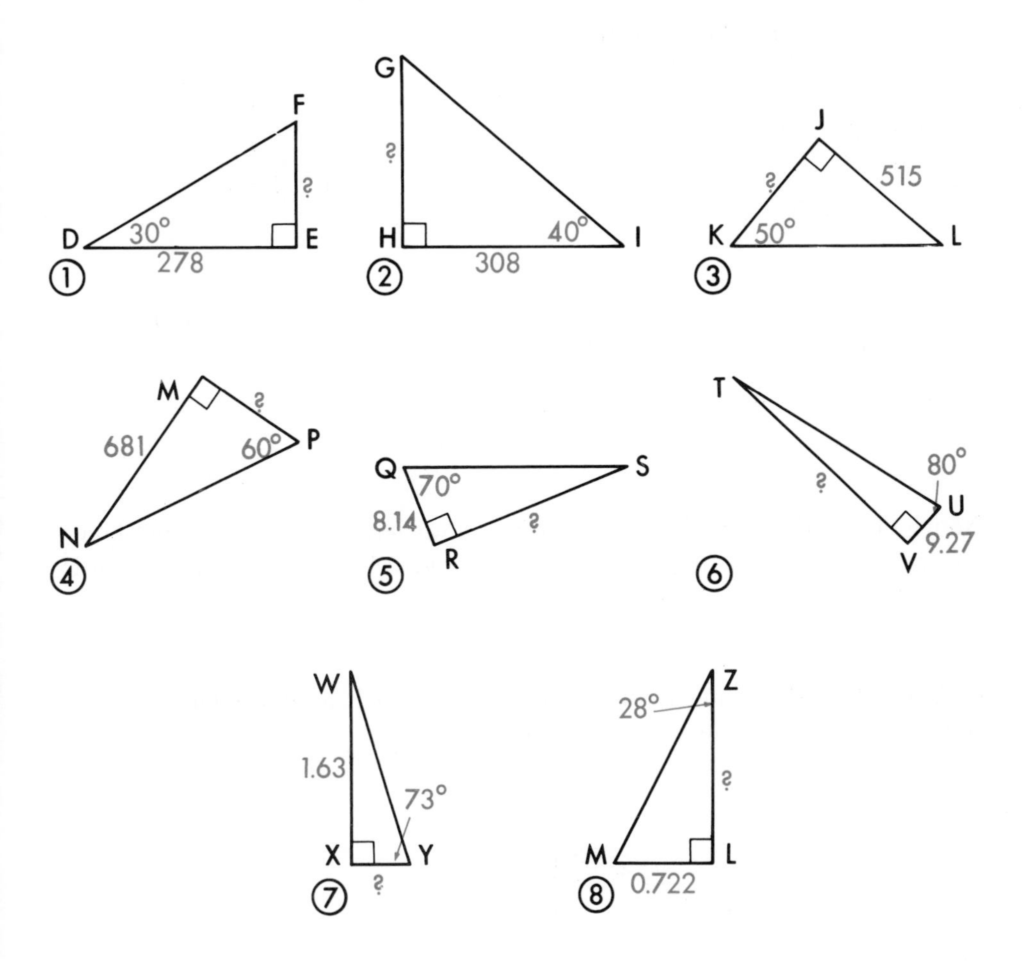

The *sine ratio* is the fraction: $\frac{\text{opp. leg}}{\text{hy}}$. In other words, if you know either the *opposite leg* or the *hypotenuse*, you can find the unknown—provided you have the proper acute angle.

Problem 1. If a 150-ft. mast is fastened with a rope as shown in Fig. 9-43, how long will the rope be?

Solution:

$$\sin\ 72^\circ = \frac{\text{opp. leg}}{\text{hy}}$$

$$\frac{0.9511}{1} = \frac{150}{AB}$$

Interchanging the ends:

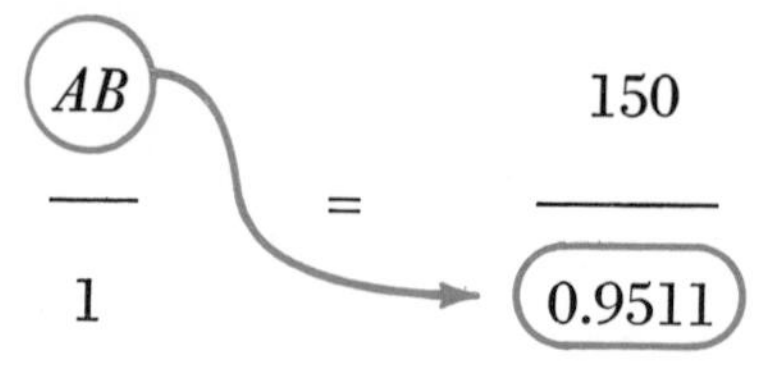

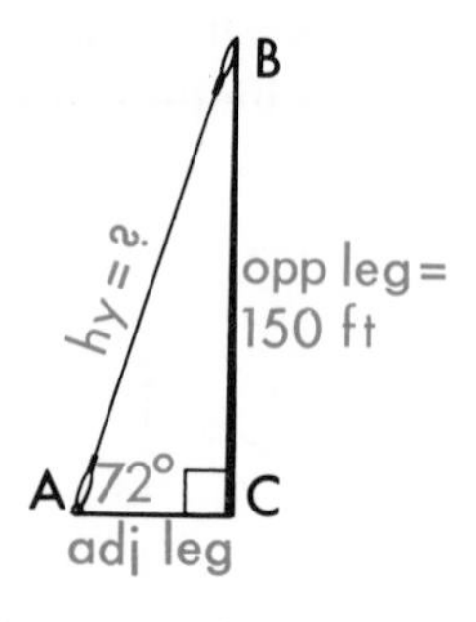

Fig. 9-43. Problem 1.

Dividing and rounding off:

$$AB = 158 \text{ ft.}$$

Notice that $\angle B = 18^\circ$. We cannot use it, however, because we do not know the opposite leg, or the hypotenuse, for this angle. As a matter of fact, even if we could use it, we would have to divide.

Problem 2. How long must a ladder be to reach across a hole 17.2 ft. wide, if the angle of elevation is 22° (Fig. 9-44)?

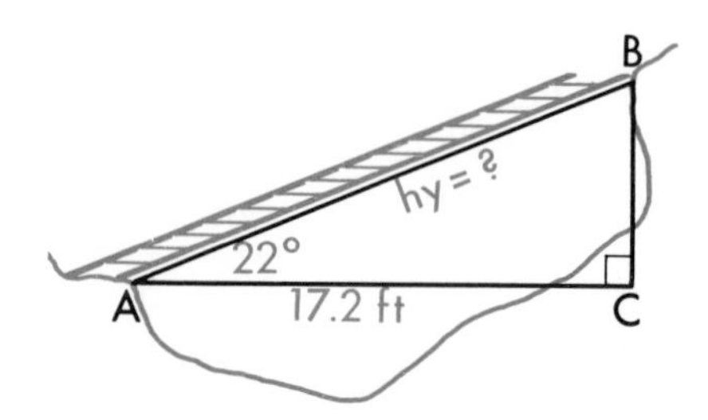

Fig. 9-44. Problem 2.

Solution: Solution: In this problem, we cannot use the 22° angle, because we know neither the opposite leg nor the hypotenuse! However, it is easy to calculate that $\angle B = 90^\circ - 22^\circ = 68^\circ$ (Fig. 9-45), and we *do* know the opposite leg for this angle.

$$\sin 68^\circ = \frac{\text{opp. leg}}{\text{hy}}$$

$$\frac{0.9272}{1} = \frac{17.2}{AB}$$

$$\frac{AB}{1} = \frac{17.2}{0.9272}$$

$$AB = 18.6 \text{ ft. or, } 18 \text{ ft. } 7 \text{ in.}$$

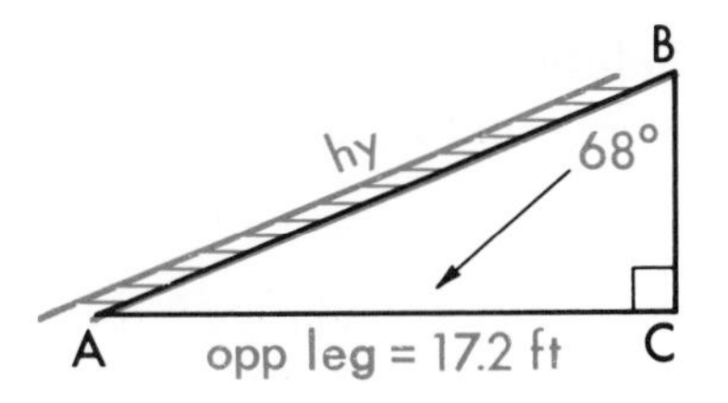

Fig. 9-45. Using the other angle.

Problem 3. How high up a wall does a 10.0 ft. ladder reach, if it is at an angle of 63° (Fig. 9-46)?

Solution:

$$\sin 63^\circ = \frac{\text{opp. leg}}{\text{hy}}$$

$$\frac{0.8910}{1} = \frac{BC}{10.0}$$

$$0.8910 \times 10.0 = BC$$

$$BC = 8.91 \text{ ft.}$$

$$\text{or } BC = 8 \text{ ft. } 11 \text{ in.}$$

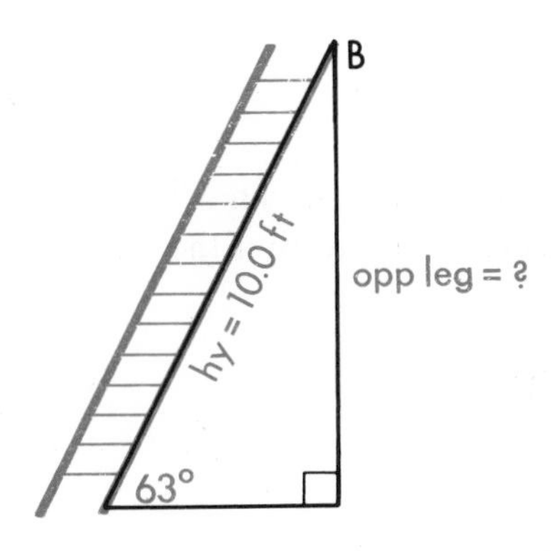

Fig. 9-46. Problem 3.

Problem 4. Assuming the sun is directly overhead, find the shadow cast by a 12.0 ft. log of wood resting at an angle of 63° (Fig. 9-47).

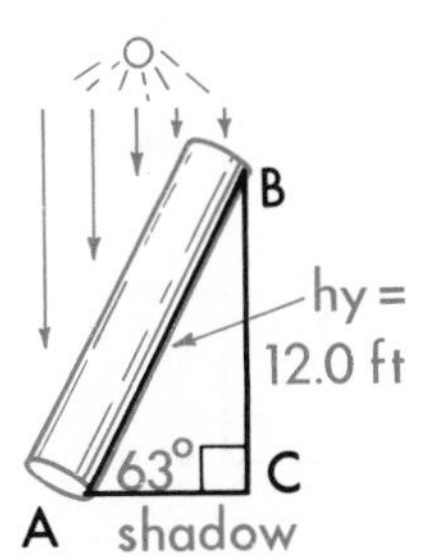

Fig. 9-47. Problem 4.

Solution: Here again, the angle of 63° is useless, because the opposite side would be BC, and we want AC. We can use $\angle B = 27°$ (Fig. 9-48).

$$\sin 27° = \frac{\text{opp. leg}}{\text{hy}}$$

$$\frac{0.4540}{1} = \frac{AC}{12.0}$$

$$0.4540 \times 12.0 = AC$$

$$AC = 5.45 \text{ ft.,}$$

or $$AC = 5 \text{ ft. } 5 \text{ in.}$$

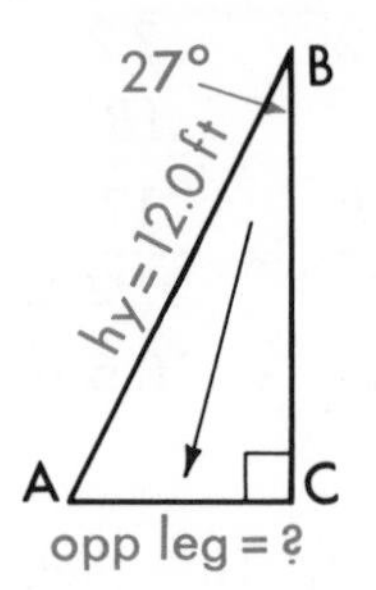

Fig. 9-48. Using the other angle.

Test: Section 10

In each case, find the other acute angle, and use whichever angle is more convenient, to find the side marked.

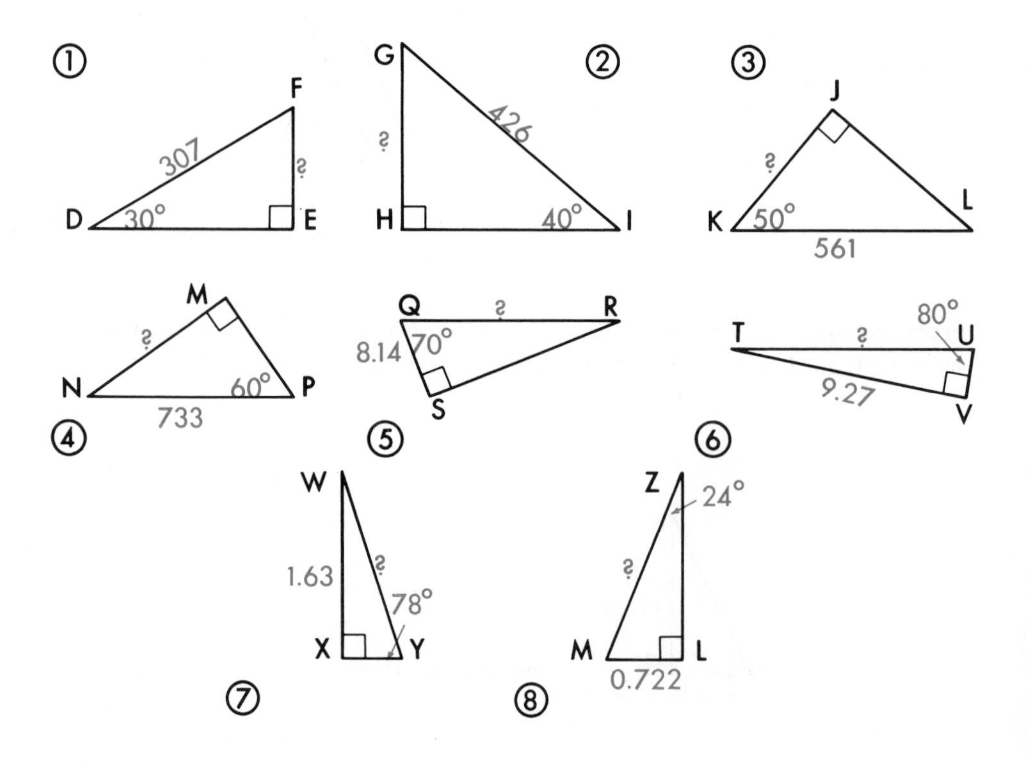

10

ADVERTISING, EDITORIALS and LOGICAL THINKING

Hundreds of times each day you must make a decision about what to do. To persuade you to make your decision in a certain way, there are signs ("Vote for Freem!"), advertisements ("Buy Now!"), and arguments ('Support your school Prom!").

Of all the abilities that human beings have, the one they prize most is the ability to think clearly, and logically. In this chapter, we shall explore some of the ways of detecting errors in reasoning, and some of the ways to make a good argument.

1 TALKING ABOUT THE SAME THING

A farmer once saw a sign which informed him that all dogs must be given "shots" to protect them against rabies. When he returned to the farm, he told the handyman to take the dog to the veterinarian to be shot.

You can guess what happened.

This is an example of the kind of misunderstanding that can take place when two people think they are talking about the same thing, but actually are not. The English language is a very rich one, there are so many different words. The same word, however, may mean different things to different people.

Here is another example. "The animal *runs fast,*" means that it moves quickly. "The animal is *made fast*," means that it is tied up so that movement is restricted, or even that it cannot move at all.

Now look at the following three sentences:

1. The ship took seven *days* to cross the ocean.
2. The man worked for seven *days*.
3. Students have about seven more *days* of mathematics this term.

In the first sentence, we mean that it took about 168 hours. In the second sentence, we mean that the man worked 30 to 60, hours. In the last sentence, we mean there are seven school periods, or about four to five hours.

In any argument or discussion, it is important that the people involved be sure that they are talking about the same thing. This is accomplished by *defining* the key words.

Problem 1. Discuss the following: Johnny walked into class just as the bell rang. The teacher marked him down for lateness. Johnny said that he was not late, because he did not come *after* the bell.

Discussion. The teacher and the class must agree on the exact meaning of the word "late." They probably agree that "after the bell" is "late," and "before the bell" is "on time," but it still remains to be defined as to what is meant by "*at* the bell."

Problem 2. Discuss the sentence, "Green blackberries are red."

Discussion. The words, "green," "black," and "red," are normally the names of colors. In this case, if the statement is to make sense, we must define "green" as "unripe," and "blackberry" as the name of a fruit which may or may not be black. In other words, the meaning of the sentence is, "The fruit called 'blackberry' is of the color 'red' when it is unripe."

In a formal course in mathematics, the first step is always for all mathematicians to agree upon the exact definitions of words like "addition," "triangle," and "graph." People trained in mathematics are always very critical about advertisements, editorials, and arguments, unless they define their words clearly.

• Test: Section 1

Part A. In each of the following, point out the word or words that need definition. *DO NOT WRITE IN THIS BOOK.*

1 Buy Super-Detergent. It is 99% pure.

2 Vote against government interference.

3 He is a self-made man.
4 Work for Associated. They pay a good wage.
5 A man is entitled to a living wage.
6 To be graduated from a high school, a student must have a satisfactory average.
7 Mrs. Rich said, "This hat was not expensive."
8 Jim was badly hurt in the accident.

Part B. Discuss the following:

1 The Civil War was fought partly because the phrase "all men" was not defined, in "All men are created equal." Explain.
2 What is a "foul" in basketball, baseball, wrestling, boxing?
3 On certain parkways, it is against the law to drive a business car. If a man owns his own taxi, and drives his family around on Sunday, is this a business vehicle in your state?
4 What is the difference between petty larceny, grand larceny, theft, and burglary? Would "stealing" not cover all of them?

Part C. Projects.

1 Read an editorial in your daily newspaper, and find all the words that are not clearly defined.
2 Read an advertisement, and find all the words that are not clearly defined.

2 TAKING THINGS FOR GRANTED

You would be surprised to know how much is taken for granted in an ordinary advertisement. For example, a picture of a movie star, *M*, holding a bar of *X*, is expected to persuade *you* to buy *X*, also.

If the whole thing were written out, the argument might run something like this:

1. Movie star *M* can afford to buy any brand.
2. Movie star *M* buys *X*.
3. He buys *X* because he prefers it to other brands.
4. He prefers brand *X* to other brands because it is better.
5. You should prefer what *M* prefers.
6. You should buy the brand you prefer.

• *Conclusion*: You should buy *X*, also.

Perhaps this is not quite so convincing when it is all exposed! If you accept statements 1 through 6, however, you must accept the conclusion.

The trouble is that most arguments are full of underlying meanings that are taken for granted. These are called *hidden assumptions.* They may, or may not, be true.

As mathematicians, we are not at the moment concerned with the truth or falsity of the conclusion of the argument. We *are* concerned, however, with the fact that we want to hear the *whole* argument before making up our minds!

Problem. Discuss the statement, "Don't let him get the job. He's an immigrant!"

Discussion. The whole argument runs as follows:

1. Any person who is an immigrant is undesirable for the job.
2. He is an immigrant.

● *Conclusion*: Therefore, he is undesirable for the job.

The *hidden assumption* in the original statement is sentence 1.

Notice that the presence of a hidden assumption does not necessarily make the argument false. For example, if the job were "working with the atomic bomb project," Einstein, who was an immigrant, was very well qualified, so that the hidden assumption was unjustified. If the job were "becoming President of the United States," the same immigrant could not hold it.

The point is, that assumptions should not be hidden. They should be brought out into the open. In mathematics, *all* assumptions are brought out. For example, mathematicians *assume* that it is possible to draw a straight line, and they state, at the beginning of a course in geometry, that they are making this assumption. It is not *hidden.*

● Test: Section 2

Part A. In each of the following, find the hidden assumption, or assumptions:

1 Sam Shady is the local bad boy. Mrs. Standing, a member of the community, has warned her son not to associate with Mary Shady, Sam's sister.

2 In an argument about doing the dishes, Leon said to Alice, "You should do the dishes, Alice. After all, you're a girl."

3 Muriel doesn't like me, Jane thought. I was the only girl in our club she didn't ask to her party.

4 Since Australia has an elected legislative body, it is a democracy.

5 Henry cannot be trusted. He lied about his age.

6 The sale of fire-crackers should be prohibited by law.

7 "This ought to be a good place to open a store," said Mr. E. "Thousands of people pass this location every day."

8 You cannot expect to get a contribution from him. He is a Scot.

Part B. Projects.

1 Analyze an advertisement, and list the hidden assumptions. Is it still a convincing argument when everything is brought into the open?

2 Analyze an editorial, and list the hidden assumptions. Is it still a convincing argument when everything is brought into the open?

3 THE WORLD OF "IF"

When a mathematician wants to analyze an argument completely he changes each statement into the "if-then" form first, to find out exactly what reasoning has been used. Here are some examples to show you how to do it, too.

Problem 1. Rewrite the statement, "All citizens of Chicago, are citizens of Illinois."

Solution: (Fig. 10-1) It always helps to draw a diagram to make clear which set of conditions fits *inside* the other. Notice that A is a citizen of

Fig. 10-1. Problem 1.

Illinois. This is what the original statement said. B is a citizen of Illinois, but not a citizen of Chicago.

Definition. When one "circle of conditions" fits inside another "circle of

conditions," we call the *smaller* one the *sufficient condition,* and the *larger* one the *necessary condition.*

The "if-then" form of the original statement is: "If X is a citizen of Chicago, then X is a citizen of Illinois." The rule for making "if-then" statements is:

If-Then Rule: The statement following "if" is the *sufficient* condition—the smaller circle of condition (Fig. 10-2).

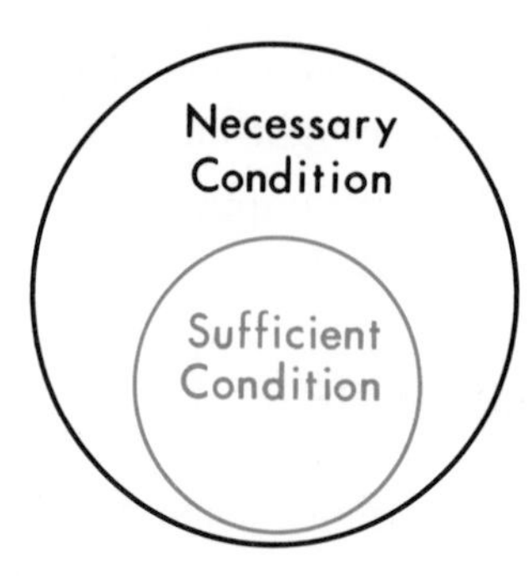

Fig. 10-2. Necessary and sufficient conditions.

Problem 2. Draw a diagram, and rewrite: All squares are rectangles.

Solution: (Fig. 10-3) From the diagram, it is clear that the smaller circle of condition refers to squares. The *sufficient* condition is: X is a square. The

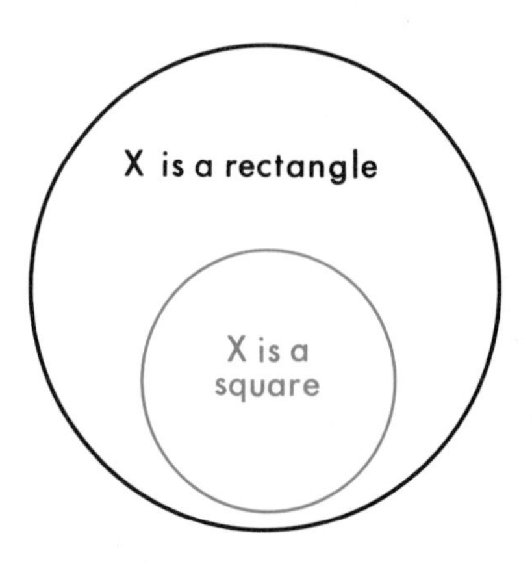

Fig. 10-3. Problem 2.

necessary condition is: X is a rectangle. The if-then statement is: "If X is a square, then X is a rectangle."

We must be very careful about the following situations:

Problem 3. Draw a diagram for, "Some animals have four legs."

Solution: (Fig. 10-4) Notice that A is not an animal at all. It may be a table with four legs! C is an animal, but does not have four legs. It may have two legs, like a bird; or six legs, like an insect; or eight legs, like a spider,

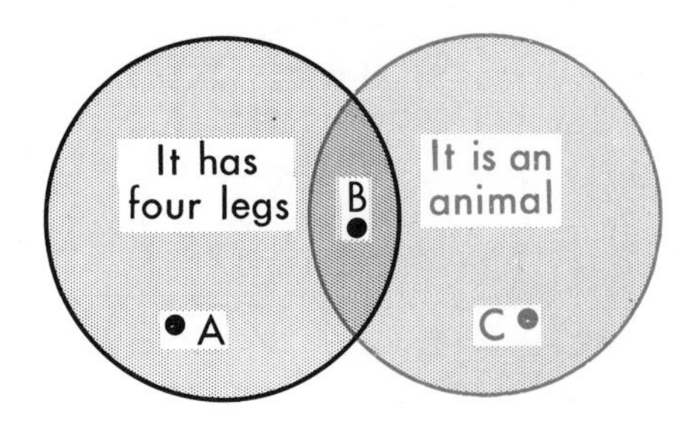

Fig. 10-4. Some animals have four legs.

etc. B is an animal with four legs. The small region common to the circles, is called the *intersection* of the two circles of condition. If we wanted to write an "if-then" statement for this diagram, the best we could do would be, "If X is an animal, it may or may not have four legs." As you can see, this is not very convincing. (If the original statement had been, "Most animals have four legs," the "if-then" statement would have been exactly the same.)

Problem 4. Draw a diagram, and write an "if-then" statement for "Some pianists are not girls."

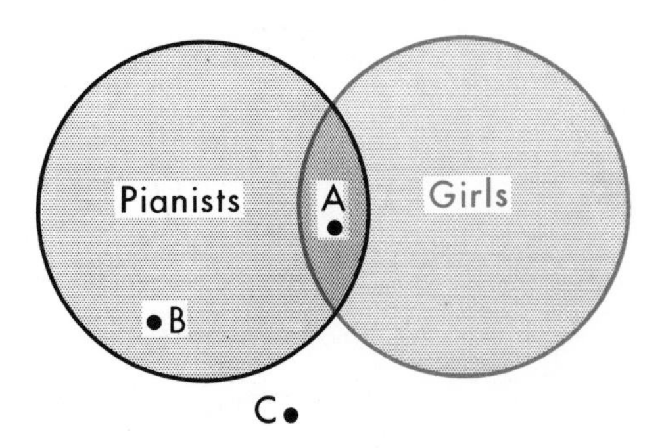

Fig. 10-5. Some pianists are not girls.

Solution: (Fig. 10-5) Notice that A is a pianist, and *is* a girl. C is not a girl, but is not a pianist, either. B is a pianist, and not a girl. The best we can do is, "If X is a pianist, X may or may not be a girl."

Test: Section 3

Part A. In each of the following, tell what is true about the "points" indicated (such as, *A*, *B*, and *C*); write an "All' or "Some" statement, and convert this to the "if-then" form.

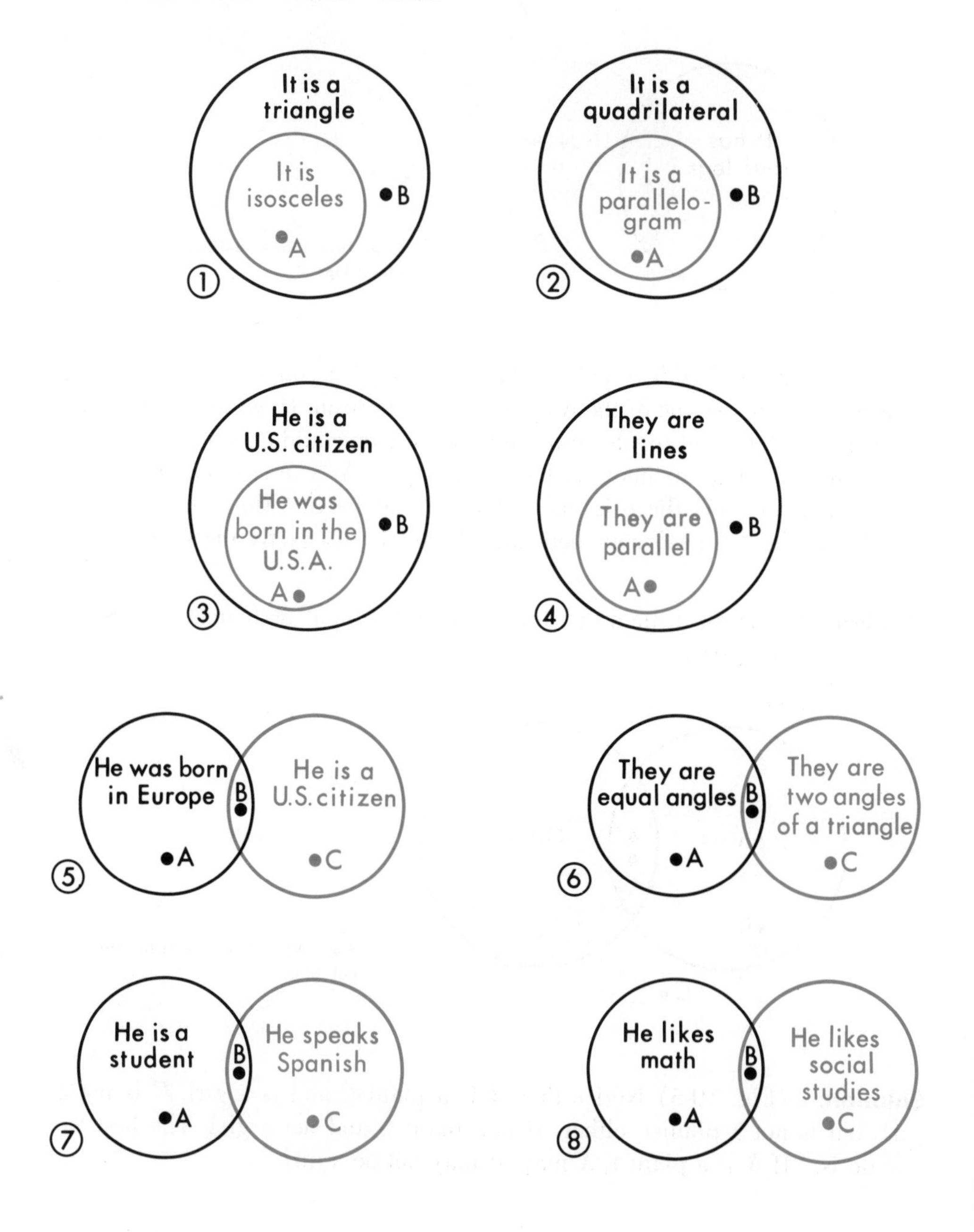

Part B. Draw diagrams for each of the following:

1 If you live in Oshkosh, then you live in Wisconsin.
2 If X is in Boston, then X is in Massachusetts.
3 If X is a man, then X is a human being.
4 If X is a rose, then X is a plant..
5 If X is a froom, then X is a gleeb.
6 If X is a skree, then X is a zilch.

Part C. Draw diagrams for the following and translate into the "if-then" form.

1 All pieces of iron are metal.
2 All trees are wood.
3 All teachers were once students.
4 All schools are good.
5 Some birds fly.
6 Some students are smart.
7 Some girls are pretty.
8 Some men are strong.
9 Some mushrooms are inedible.
10 Some ice-cream is not vanilla.

4 THE CONVERSE ERROR

"If you practice hard," said the camp counselor, "you will be a good swimmer."

"Oh," said the camper, "Pete is a great swimmer. He must have practiced hard."

Let us examine this conclusion more carefully. The first sentence can be diagrammed as shown in Fig. 10-6. Notice that anyone in A position practiced hard, *and* is a good swimmer. But then there are people in B position who did not practice hard, and are good swimmers, anyhow! In other words, you can guarantee both things *in the A position only.*

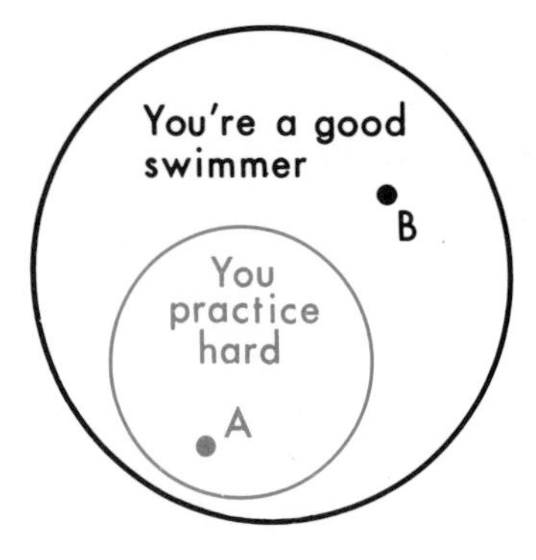

Fig. 10-6. Practice and swimming.

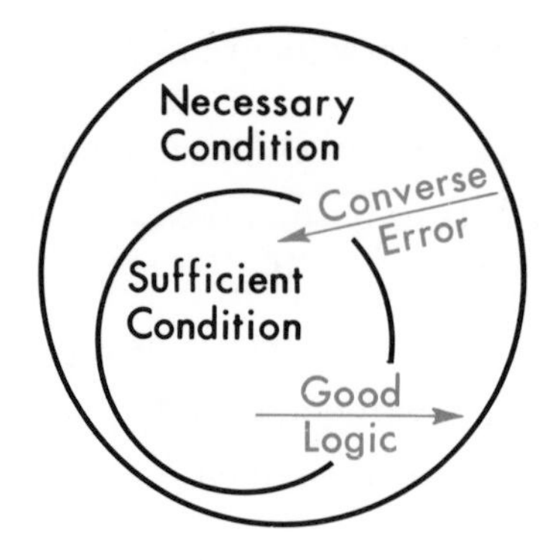

Fig. 10-7. The rule of good logic.

Rule of Good Logic. Always go from the sufficient condition to the necessary condition (Fig. 10-7).

The two statements:

1. If you practice hard, then you will be a good swimmer
2. If you are a good swimmer, then you practiced hard

are called *converses.*

Definition. Converses are formed by interchanging the sufficient and necessary conditions.

Problem 1. "All right angles are equal." Draw the diagram. Write in the if-then form. What is the converse? Is it true?

Solution: (Fig. 10-8) In if-then form, the statement becomes "If X, and Y, are right angles, then X, and Y, are equal." The converse is, "If X, and Y, are equal, then X, and Y are right angles." This is obviously not true. For example two 60° angles are equal, but they are not right angles.

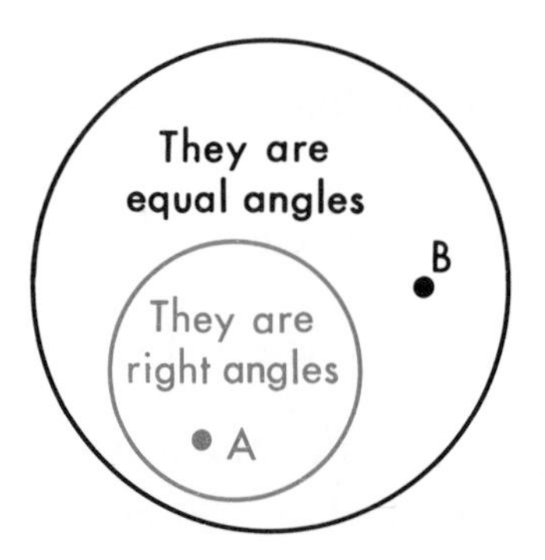

Fig. 10-8. Problem 1.

This illustrates the *converse error*. The fact that a statement is true does not mean that its converse is true!

Converse Rule. The converse of a true statement may, or may not, be true.

Problem 2. "All right angles have 90°." Draw the diagram. Write in the if-then form. What is the converse? Is it true?

Solution: If we draw the diagram in the usual way (Fig. 10-9), there appears to be two situations: the A situation, where you have a right angle

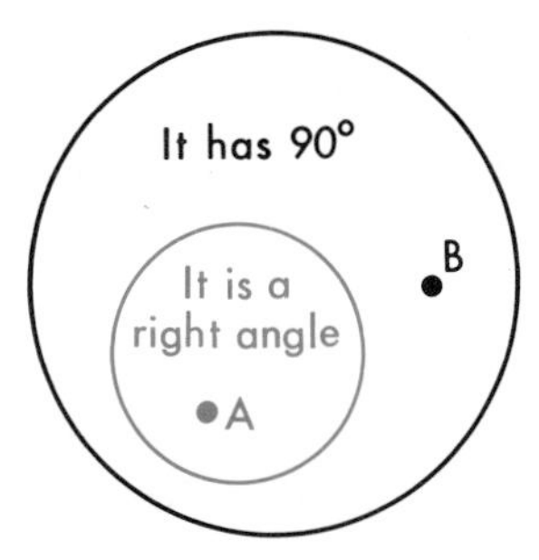

Fig. 10-9. Problem 2.

of 90°, and the B situation, where you have a right angle with another number of degrees. Are there any right angles without 90°? No, there are not. In this case, the small circle completely fills the large circle, so that the necessary and sufficient conditions are the same. In this case, the converse is true:

Original statement: If X is a right angle, X has 90°.
Converse statement: If X has 90°, X is a right angle.

The fact is, that *every* definition is made in such a way that the necessary

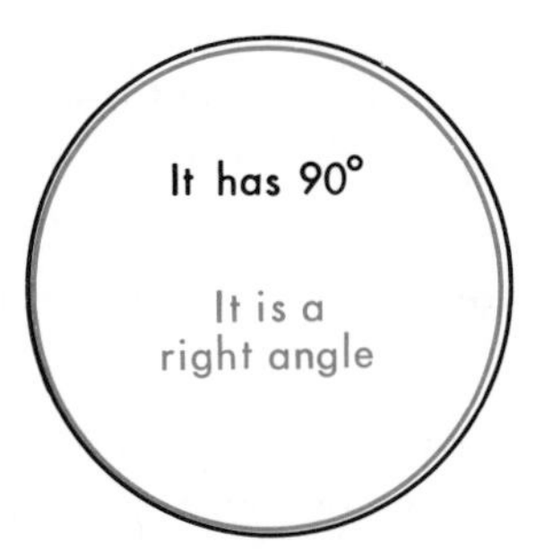

Fig. 10-10. Diagram for a definition.

and sufficient conditions are the same (Fig. 10-10). This means that *the converse of every definition is true.*

Test: Section 4

Part A. State the converses of each of the following. Are they true?

1. If you live in Oshkosh, then you live in Wisconsin.
2. If you live in Boston, then you live in Massachusetts.
3. If you are a man, then you are a human being.
4. If X is a rose, then X is a plant.
5. (Definition) If it is a froom, then it is a gleeb.
6. (Definition) If it is a skree, then it is a zilch.

Part B. In each of the following, write the converse, and tell whether you consider it to be true or false:

1. If a boy studies, then his grades improve.
2. A good person is considerate of the rights of his neighbors.
3. A careful driver will not go 60 miles an hour in traffic.
4. The color, "green," is soothing to the eye.

Part C. Criticize the following arguments:

1. Accept as true the statement that a good citizen votes at election time. Town A and town B each have the same population. In town A, 1000 people voted during the last election, while in town B only 500 voted. Therefore, town A has more good citizens.
2. "I can prove that Australia is a democracy," said Herman. "It has an elective legislative assembly. All democracies have elective legislative assemblies."
3. At Richmond High, all the seniors belong to the dramatic society. Lucius Lofty must be a senior because he belongs to the dramatic society.
4. In State A, all married men with incomes of more than $2500 pay income tax. Mr. Singleton, who pays income tax in that state, and makes more than $2500, must be married.
5. Every good baseball player must have good muscular coordination. John has excellent muscular coordination. He should be a good ball player.
6. In an automobile engine, worn piston rings mean excessive oil consumption. A man finds that his car is using a lot of oil, and concludes that it is due to worn piston rings.

5 THE INVERSE ERROR

"Jean, you must eat your vegetables," said her mother. "Vegetables make you healthy. If you don't eat your vegetables, you won't be healthy!" Jean's mother might have the correct conclusion, but is this a logical argument?

If we diagram the first part of the argument (Fig. 10-11), we can use

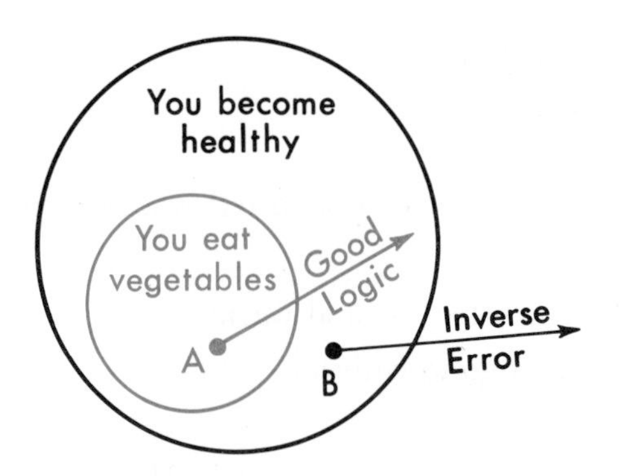

Fig. 10-11. The inverse error.

TV reception is good

It is good weather

A

B

Fig. 10-12. Illustrative problem.

the rule of good logic to say that, "If X eats vegetables, then X will be healthy." *That is all you can say!* The last part of the argument cannot be based on the first part, as you can see from the diagram. The arrow from B leads nowhere at all.

The sentence formed by "denying" the sufficient condition and the necessary condition, is called the *inverse*:

Original statement: If X eats vegetables, X is healthy.

Inverse statement: If X does not eat vegetables, X is not healthy.

Problem: "If it is good weather, TV reception is good." Make a diagram, write the converse, and the inverse.

Solution: See Fig. 10-12.

Converse: If TV reception is good, then it is good weather.
Inverse: If TV reception is poor, then the weather is bad.

Neither of these statements is acceptable as a conclusion.

• Test: Section 5

Part A. State the inverse of each of the following. Is it true?

1 If you live in Oshkosh, then you live in Wisconsin.
2 If you live in Boston, then you live in Massachusetts.
3 If X is a man, then X is a human being.
4 If X is a rose, then X is a plant.
5 If X is a froom, then X is a gleeb. (Definition.)
6 If X is a skree, then X is a zilch. (Definition.)

Part B. In each of the following, write the inverse, and tell whether you consider it to be true or false.

1 If the month is October, the weather will be fair and warm.
2 If Frank passes all his subjects, he will go to college.
3 Youths who participate in sport, are strong.
4 If Fred is a citizen of the United States of America, and is 21 years of age, he may vote.

Part C. Criticize the following arguments:

1 If the cost of living rises, wages should be increased. Therefore, if the cost of living does not rise, wages should not be increased.
2 If you are caught cheating, then you should be punished. Therefore, if you are not caught, you should not be punished.
3 If a Republicrat is elected, prices will rise. Since a Democan was elected, prices will not rise.
4 If any one failed to study hard, he will fail the final examination. Frank studied very hard; he will pass.

6 THE ERROR OF INSUFFICIENT EVIDENCE

It is sad to note that most arguments are not mathematically sound. The following examples show what can happen when there is *insufficient evidence.*

Problem 1. Discuss the argument: This drug cured canker in cats. Therefore, it should cure canker in people.

Discussion. When you have proved that a drug cures canker in cats, that is *all* you have proved. There is no evidence to show that it does or does not cure canker in people. This has to be tested separately, just as the polio vaccine was tested on people. Arguments of this type are sometimes called *argument by analogy.*

Problem 2. Discuss the argument: The Allies were not prepared for World War I or II, but they won. The Allies do not have to be prepared for war. They will win, anyhow.

Discussion. We cannot prove that something will be true in the future just because it was true in the past. Maybe it was just good luck. Arguments of this type are called *hasty generalizations.* It is like the man who has been speeding for twenty years without getting caught. He thinks that he will never get caught, but sooner or later he may.

Problem 3. Discuss the argument: The teacher said, "I have never had a Chinese student in my class, who was not excellent. All Chinese students are excellent."

Discussion. The author of this book agrees with the teacher on the first statement. However, this does not prove a thing about *all* Chinese students. These might have been exceptional cases (we do not really think so). This sort of argument is called *arguing from special cases.*

Here is another example: the fact that any isosceles triangles has two equal angles, does not prove that all triangles have two equal angles.

Problem 4. "Don is tall. He should be a good basketball player."

Discussion. This is called *jumping to conclusions.* You need much more evidence before saying that someone will be a good player!

To summarize, the following types of arguments are not mathematically sound, because they have insufficient evidence.

1. *Arguing by analogy*: where something is true for one thing, but may not be true for another.
2. *Hasty generalizations*: where a little bit of evidence is projected into the future.
3. *Arguing from special cases*: where something true for an exceptional part of a group is held to be true for the entire group.
4. *Jumping to conclusions*: where an important piece of evidence is present, but all the other evidence is missing.

It would be only fair to say that these arguments are not proof, but they are often reasonable. That is, they make a reasonable guess. No mathematician objects to a reasonable guess, if it is made very clear that it *is* just a guess. We cannot prove that the sun will rise tomorrow, but it is a very reasonable guess!

Test: Section 6

Discuss each of the following arguments:

1 John does well in mathematics and therefore will reason well in life situations.

2 The earth and Mars have many characteristics in common. Therefore, there must be life on Mars.

3 John and Mary are both good dancers; therefore, John and Mary should be good skaters.

4 Dentists use a mirror that is bent at the stem. Therefore, the best toothbrush is one in which the bristles are bent away from the stem.

5 The League of Nations failed, therefore the United Nations will fail.

6 You can accomplish more by concentrating your energy on one thing, than by scattering it over several things. It is like the sun's rays; scattered over the earth's surface, they cannot ignite an object, but concentrated by a magnifying glass on one spot, they can start a fire.

7 Gold has been found in the Klondike, at Nome, and in Atlin. Therefore, it is likely to be found in other places in the far North.

8 Corn grew well on this plot last year. It will grow well on the same plot this year.

9 Mr. Jones, who is a successful business man, never went to high school. Therefore, a high school education does not help in business.

10 Three airplanes coming from South American ports to the United States, were found to have carried the yellow fever mosquito. As a result, the United States Government ordered that all such planes be inspected and fumigated.

11 Aspirin is often found to be beneficial in the treatment of headache. Therefore, when afflicted with a headache, use aspirin.

12 In words like *receive, ceiling* and *seize,* the "e" always comes before the "i." Therefore, in all words where "e" and "i" come next to each other, "e" should come first.

13 Man has never found a way to avoid war. Therefore, the efforts of the UN to prevent future wars will be futile.

14 Musicians that I know, are a temperamental group of people. Therefore, any symphony conductor must be temperamental.

15 Every general who became president, was a good president. Therefore, any general would make a good president.

16 Sales in large quantities, lower the cost per unit. Therefore, if you buy stamps in large quantities, you should save money.

17 If we had more playgrounds, there would be less juvenile delinquency.

18 My pencil has gone; someone must have stolen it.

19 May passed me on the street and did not speak to me; I must have done something to make her angry.

20 Diamond and graphite are both pure carbon. The diamond is very valuable, so graphite must be very valuable.

21 Since Harry High was the first-ranking student in his class at medical school, he will be very successful as a doctor.

22 Mr. Brown earned a great amount of money from his law practice; his career was a complete success.

7 THE DOUBLE-TALK ARGUMENT

You have heard of double-talk — where you think the person is saying one thing, when he is actually meaning something else? Well, there are arguments like this, too.

Problem 1. Discuss the argument: The government should not compete with private enterprise. If it did, it might, for example, build power plants to supply electricity. Then there would be competition with private industry which also builds power plants to supply electricity. This is wrong, because the government should not compete with private enterprise.

Discussion. This argument "chases its own tail." As you can see, it starts with a statement, and ends with the same statement. The conclusion may be true or false, but the argument is not logical in any case. This is often called a *circular argument.*

Problem 2. Discuss the argument: "Buy DOOG. DOOG spelled backwards is GOOD."

Discussion. Who cares what it spells? This kind of argument is called *argument by irrelevancy*. Irrelevancy (ĭr•rĕl′*a*-văn•si) is something that has nothing to do with what you are trying to prove.

Problem 3. Discuss the argument: Vote for Jack Freem! He is tall, and good-looking, and he lives on Sycamore Street.

Discussion. Let us suppose that it is true that Jack Freem is tall, and good-looking, and that he lives on Sycamore Street. This series of true statements does not lead to the conclusion that you should vote for him. The statements do not answer the important question, "Why should I vote for him?" This is sometimes called a *non-sequitur argument. Non sequitur* is a Latin phrase meaning "It does not follow!"

Test: Section 7

Discuss each of the following arguments:

1. A safety device was put on this machine a year ago. It was a waste of money, because we have not had an accident since it was put on.
2. Isn't it a coincidence, that the Mississippi River flows by so many important cities?
3. Isn't it lucky that Washington's Birthday always falls on a legal holiday?
4. A group of pupils in school wanted to take a course in advanced general mathematics. They were told by the administration that the course had not been taught, because there was no demand for it. The pupils were told to take some other course.
5. If you are over forty, take ERUP, in the handy, plastic container, and remember, when you read ERUP backwards, it spells PURE.
6. I am going to vote for Hank for president of the council. He is a friend of mine.
7. A father was punishing his son for being late to class so often. The son asked his father whether *he* had not been late to class, too.
8. The following information is known about Miss Smith, the teacher of French at this school: she was born in town, she has traveled in France, majored in French in college, she has taught Latin and English, she is a good disciplinarian, she has a pleasing personality. She should therefore be a good teacher of French.
9. Our basketball team defeated Bellville, and Bellville defeated Lincoln. Therefore, we will defeat Lincoln.
10. Miss Black almost never fails anyone. She must be a good teacher.

11 When I looked for a dozen pairs of compasses which I always keep in my desk, they were missing. Earlier in the day, I saw Miss Mason go down the corridor with some compasses in her hand. Therefore, she took the compasses from my desk.

12 "Well, Joseph, let us look at your report card."

"But, father, don't you think we'd better wait until after dinner? We're having strawberry shortcake for dessert."

"No, no! We'll get it over with now. Hmm! English: 75."

"Well, English comes in the last period, so every Monday I miss a period when the class is excused for assembly."

"I see. And what about this 95 in civics? How did you manage that?"

"Oh, the civics teacher likes me."

8 THE CHAIN OF LOGIC

Now that you have been introduced to so many ways to recognize a *poor* argument, it is time to consider what a *good* argument is. An argument that is logically correct, is said to be *valid.*

We have already mentioned one kind of valid argument (Fig. 10-13).

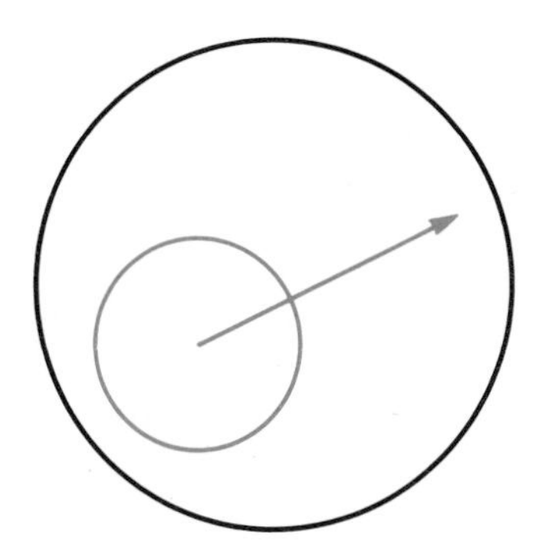

Fig. 10-13. The first link in the chain of logic.

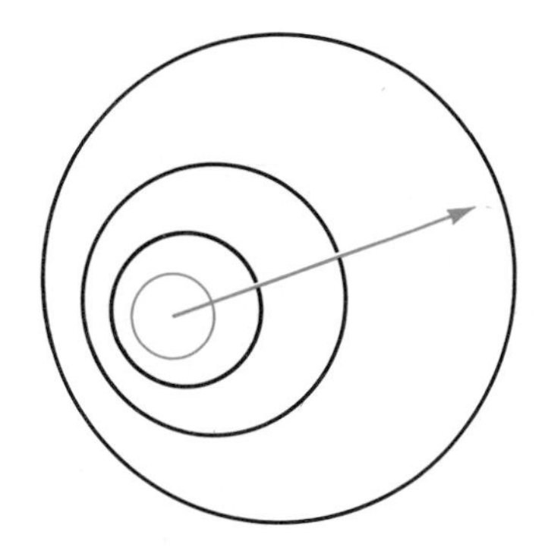

Fig. 10-14. A chain of logic.

That is where the arrow of argument goes from a sufficient condition, to a necessary one.

However, there may be a series of conditions, one inside the other, as shown in Fig. 10-14. This makes a complete, and unbreakable chain of logic. Here is an example:

1. If he is on Broadway, then he is in Manhattan
2. If he is in Manhattan, then he is in New York City
3. If he is in New York City, then he is in New York State
4. If he is in New York State, then he is in the United States of America.

The conclusion from this is:

If he is on Broadway, then he is in the United States of America. Notice that in a chain like this, the *first* sufficient condition leads to the *last* necessary condition. Notice that the necessary condition of the first statement, is the same as the sufficient condition of the second statement, and so on. If this is true, then one circle will always fit inside the next.

Problem 1. What is your conclusion from the following?

If you work hard in school, you get good marks.
If you get good marks, then you have a good record.
If you have a good record, then you graduate with honors.
If you graduate with honors, then you receive the recommendation of the school.
If you receive the recommendation of the school, then you get a good job.
If you get a good job, then you get a good salary.
If you get a good salary, then you buy a car.
If you buy a car, then sooner or later you get a ticket for parking!

Solution: The conclusion is the first sufficient condition, and the last necessary condition:

If you work hard in school, then sooner or later you get a ticket for parking.

The author does not wish to discourage you from working hard in school, so mentions in passing, that the converse and inverse, are not necessarily true. (What are they?)

Problem 2. What is your conclusion from the following?

a If you are in the army, then you are over 18.
b If you are in the army, then you must follow orders.

Solution: We note that the first necessary conclusion, is not the same as the second sufficient condition. This is not a chain of logic. We can draw no conclusion.

Test: Section 8

Part A. Discuss the validity of the following:

1. New York is north of Virginia, and Virginia is north of Florida. Therefore, New York is north of Florida.
2. Lead is heavier than silver, and silver is heavier than feathers. Therefore, feathers are lighter than lead.
3. A cow is larger than a pig, and a giraffe is larger than a pig. Therefore, a giraffe is larger than a cow.
4. Sam is a cousin of Pete, and Pete is a cousin of Eleanor. Therefore, Sam is a cousin of Eleanor.
5. De Gaulle is a Frenchman, and all Frenchmen are Europeans. Therefore, De Gaulle is a European.
6. Lyons is in France, and Paris is in France. Therefore, Paris is in Lyons.
7. This is a metal. All metals are expanded by heat. This is expanded by heat.
8. If litmus paper turns red in a solution, the solution is an acid. This solution did not turn litmus paper red. Therefore, it is not an acid.

Part B. Find the conclusion, if any, for the following:

1. The good die young. He died young.
2. If a man marries, he has troubles. He married.
3. People who go to college are successful. He is successful.
4. If X has a father in business, then X is assured of a job. X has a father in business.

Part C. Find the conclusion, if any, for the following:

1. If you travel much, you get to see the country.
   If you see the country, you notice the different kinds of people.
   If you notice the different kinds of people, you understand that different people have different customs.
   If you understand that different people have different customs, you become tolerant.
   If you become tolerant, you are a better man.
2. If you study mathematics, then you can go to flight school.
   If you can go to flight school, you can become a pilot.
   If you can become a pilot, you can get a commission.

If you can get a commission, you can make the armed services a good career.
If you can make the armed services a good career, then you do not have to worry about finding a job.

9 CIRCUMSTANTIAL EVIDENCE

A district attorney always prefers to convict a person on direct evidence. Once in a while, he finds it possible to use *indirect* or *circumstantial evidence.*

For example, suppose a certain crime could have been committed by A, B, C, or D, but no one else. A has a good alibi. B was in hospital. C was 1000 miles away. Then D must be guilty, even if no one saw him commit the crime.

This is one of the methods of *indirect proof*. It is sometimes called the *method of elimination.* It is quite simple:

First: List all the possibilities.
Second: Cross out all the ones that turn out to be false.
Third: If there is only one remaining possibility, this must be the true one.

This method works only when (1) you can list *all* the possibilities, and (2) you can cross out all but one.

Problem 1. When the TV sound does not come on, what does the technician do?

Solution: There are four possibilities: (1) the plug is defective, (2) the fuse is blown, (3) a tube is out of order, or (4) something is wrong with the circuit. The technician eliminates the easiest ones first. If the first three "check out" as all right, then there must be something wrong with the circuit.

Sometimes, both direct and indirect reasoning are involved, as in the following story:

A man came home and said: "Saw Jim Brady tonight, getting on the train with his bag, just as I got off. Wonder where he was going?

"Chicago," his wife answered.

"How do you know?" the man inquired idly. "Talk to Betty today?"

"No," she said, "but I saw the Brady dog outside about half an hour ago."

"Great Scott! I suppose the dog told you!"

"Don't be silly," his wife replied. "But Betty never lets him out that early except when she's going to the early movie."

"Well . . .?"

"Well," she said, "Betty never goes to the early show except when Jim's away.

She hates to stay home alone evenings, now that they haven't a maid, and the boys aren't there."

"Well . . .?"

"So I knew he must be going somewhere, and the only places he ever goes to, are Washington, Harrisburg, Pittsburgh, and Chicago."

"Well . . .?"

"When he goes to Pittsburgh, he takes the late train so he won't get there too early, and Betty doesn't go to the movies. And he couldn't have been going to Washington, or he'd have taken the other train, not the one you were on."

"Well . . .?"

With perfect reasonableness she replied, "Well, you said he had a bag, so he wasn't going to Harrisburg, because he keeps everything he needs at his sister's there, now that the hotels are so crowded. So I just knew he was going to Chicago."

In the story, the first part is a *chain*, as follows:

If the dog is out, then Betty went to the early movie.

If Betty went to the early movie, then Jim Brady went away.

Therefore, if the dog is out, then Jim Brady went away.

The second part is an *indirect proof* as follows:

Jim Brady went either to Washington, Harrisburg, Pittsburgh, or Chicago.

He did not go to Washington (he would have taken the other train).

He did not go to Pittsburgh (he would have taken the late train).

He did not go to Harrisburg (he would not have taken a bag).

Therefore he went to Chicago.

Test: Section 9

Complete the following arguments:

1 I knew he was either a Frenchman, a Spaniard, or an Italian. When I said, "Comment vous portez-vous?", he looked puzzled. When I said, "Buenos dias," he shook his head. . . . . .

2 The man was killed by a blow from the right, and above his head. One of these three people killed him. The first one could not lift the murder weapon. The second one could not reach high enough, and besides he was left-handed. . . . . .

3 I knew that we had to answer the question by letter *a*, *b*, *c*, or *d*. I was not sure of the right answer, but I knew that *a*, *c*, and *d*, were definitely wrong. . . . . .

4 There was no sign saying "To Detroit" at the crossroads, but it was easy to decide which of the four roads was the right one. The first road was too narrow to be a highway. The second road had a sign which said, "To Mackinaw." The third road was covered with grass which would have been dead if cars had gone over it often enough. . . . .

10 REASONING IN MATHEMATICS

If logic is mathematical, then mathematics should be logical. (This is not a logical statement, but it is common sense.) Can we *prove* things mathematically, instead of relying upon experimentation, which only gives us results within some per cent of error?

Yes, we can. And mathematics consists mostly of proofs of one kind or another. Pure mathematics does not depend on experimentation at all.

The following examples are intended to give you some idea of how mathematicians obtain proofs. It would take years to do a thorough job, but if you get the main idea, this will be sufficient for an informed citizen.

Problem 1. Prove that any pair of opposite vertical angles are equal.

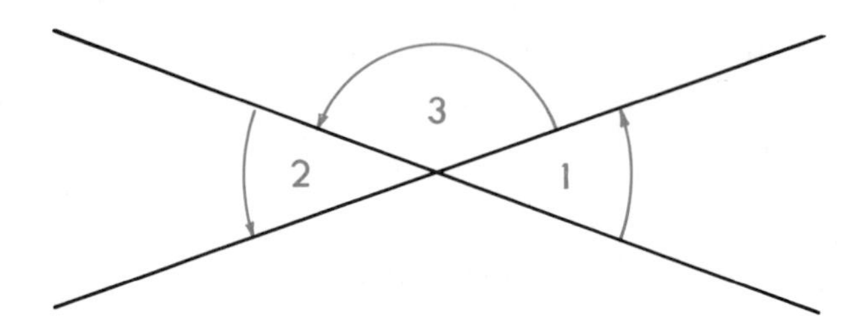

Fig. 10-15. Opposite vertical angles are equal.

Proof: (Fig. 10-15) From the definition of supplementary angles, $\angle 1 + \angle 3 = 180^\circ$. We have already learned that this is *equivalent* to the statement that $\angle 1 = (180^\circ - \angle 3)$. Also, from the definition of supplementary angles, $\angle 2 + \angle 3 = 180^\circ$. The equivalent statement that we want is: $\angle 2 = (180^\circ - \angle 3)$.

Comparing the two equivalent statements, we see that the right members are the same. This means that $\angle 1$, and $\angle 2$, are the same, or $\angle 1 = \angle 2$. This is a *direct* proof.

Problem 2. Prove that if the angles of a triangle are unequal, then the triangle is not an isosceles. (An isosceles triangle is defined as a triangle with at least two equal sides.)

Proof: Either the triangle is isosceles, or it is not. (This lists all the possibilities, in this case, only two.) If it were isosceles, then two angles would be equal (because we know that the base angles of an isosceles triangle are equal). But none of the angles are equal, so it cannot be isosceles (this disposes of the possibility that it is isosceles). The only remaining possibility is that the triangle is not isosceles.

• Test: Section 10

Part A. The following can be proved indirectly:

1 If a quadrilateral has no parallel sides, prove it is not a parallelogram.

2 If a quadrilateral has no parallel sides, prove it is not a trapezoid.

3 If a quadrilateral has no equal sides, prove it is not a rectangle.

4 If a quadrilateral has no equal sides, prove it is not a square.

Part B. The following can be proved directly!

1 Using the fact that a right angle is a 90° angle, prove that all right angles are equal.

2 Using the fact that a straight angle is a 180° angle, prove that all straight angles are equal.

3 Using the fact that the sum of two complementary angles is 90°, prove that complements of the same angle are equal.

4 Using the fact that the sum of two supplementary angles is 180°, prove that supplements of the same angle are equal.

11

MODERN PROBLEMS IN MATHEMATICS

Most of the problems that students study in class, are problems that existed *thousands* of years ago, and were solved at that time one way or another. However, new eras brought about new problems and mathematicians developed new methods for dealing with them. In this chapter, you will be introduced to the theory of *sets,* the theory of *linear programming,* and the theory of *probability.*

1 THE THEORY OF SETS

Any collection of objects, people, or things, is called a *set.* For example: {John, Henry, Mary} is a set. The members of a set are called its *elements,* and the number of elements in a set is called its *cardinal number.* In this case, the cardinal number of the set is *three.*

If there are two or more sets, they may have some elements in common. For example, consider the two sets: {John, Henry, Mary, Jean}, and {Peter, Mary, Joan, Jean and Juan}. Mary and Jean are the *common elements* because they are in both sets, and we may say that these two sets *overlap.*

If two sets overlap, two additional sets are formed: the *intersection set,* and the *union set.*

Definition. The *intersection* set, is the smallest set of all *common* elements.

Definition. The *union set,* is the smallest set of all *different* elements.

Problem 1. Two sets are {Smith, Jones, Brown, Whittaker}, and {Brown, White, Jones, Small}.

a Draw a diagram for the two sets.
b What is the union set?
c What is the intersection set?
d What is the cardinal number of each set?

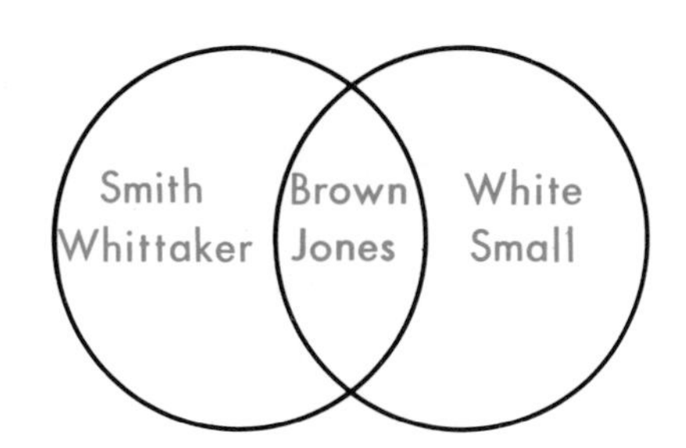

Fig. 11-1. Problem 1.

Solution:

a. See Fig. 11-1.
b. The union set is {Smith, Jones, Brown, Whittaker, White, Small}.
c. The intersection set is {Brown, Jones}.
d. The two original sets have cardinal numbers of four each. The union set has a cardinal number of six. The intersection set has a cardinal number of two.

Problem 2. Two sets are $\{A, R\}$, and $\{X, Y, Z\}$. Draw a diagram, and find the union and intersection sets, and their cardinal numbers.

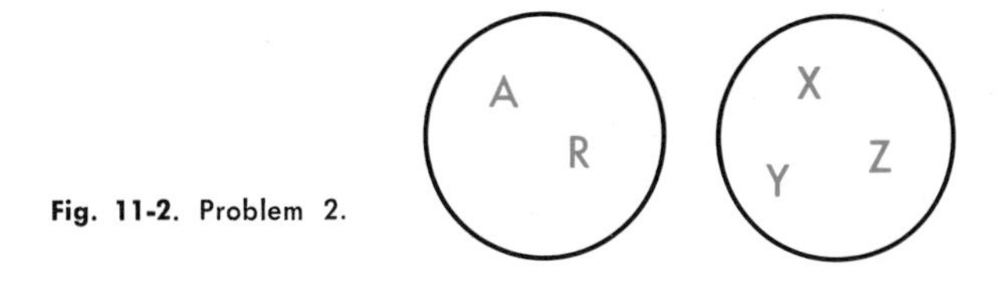

Fig. 11-2. Problem 2.

Solution: The diagram is shown in Fig. 11-2. The union set is $\{A, R, X, Y, Z\}$, and has a cardinal number of five. The intersection set is written ϕ, (Greek letter phi, pronounced *fī*) meaning that it has nothing in it. Its cardinal number is *zero* (0).

Problem 3. Two sets are $\{P, Q,\}$, and $\{A, P, B, Q\}$. Draw a diagram, and find the union and intersection sets, and their cardinal numbers.

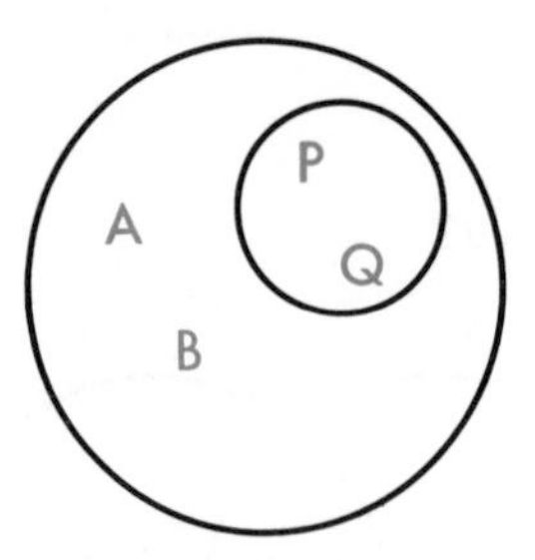

Fig. 11-3. Problem 3.

Solution: The diagram is shown in Fig. 11-3. The union set is $\{A, B, P, Q\}$, and has a cardinal number of four. The intersection set is $\{P, Q\}$, and has a cardinal number of two.

Problem 4. Three sets are $\{M, N, P, Q, V\}$, $\{M, R, S, N, T\}$, and $\{N, A, B, M, V, T\}$. Draw a diagram, and find the union and intersection of the three sets.

Solution: The diagram is shown in Fig. 11-4. The union set is $\{P, Q, R, S, M, N, V, T, A, B\}$. Its cardinal number is ten. The intersection set is $\{M, N\}$. Its cardinal number is two.

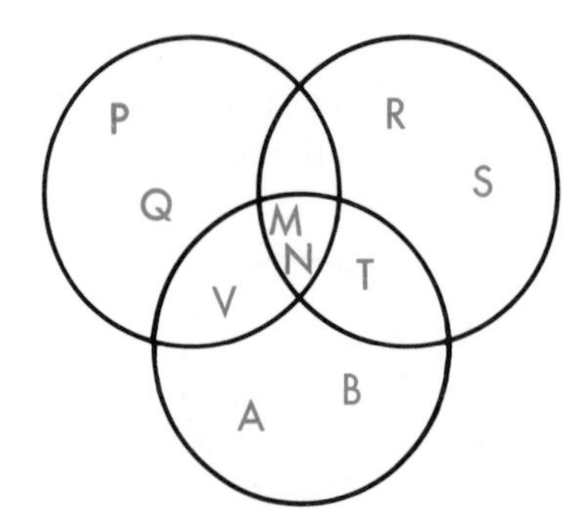

Fig. 11-4. Problem 4.

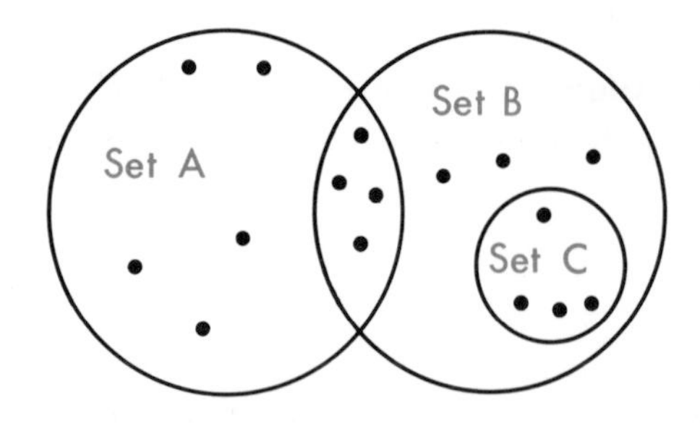

Fig. 11-5. Problem 5.

Problem 5. In Fig. 11-5, each point represents an element of a set. Find the cardinal number of each set, and of the union and intersection of the sets.

Solution: Set A has 9 elements. Set B has 11 elements. Set C has 4 elements. The union has 16 elements. The intersection of the three sets has 0 (zero) elements.

Test: Section 1

Part A. Draw diagrams, and find the union, and the intersection, of the following sets.

1 $\{A, B, C\}, \{B, C, D\}$
2 $\{F, X, L\}, \{X, L, P\}$
3 $\{A, B\}, \{C, E, M\}$
4 $\{P, Q\}, \{D, R, S\}$
5 $\{A, B, C\}, \{C, B, A\}$
6 $\{M, N, R\}, \{R, N, M\}$
7 $\{A, B, C, D\}, \{B, C\}$
8 $\{R, S\}, \{P, Q, R, S\}$
9 $\{A, B\}, \{B, C\}, \{C, D\}$
10 $\{M, N, R\}, \{N, R, S\}, \{R, S, T\}$

Part B. In each of the following, find the number of elements in each set (including the union, and intersection sets). Each "dot" represents an element.

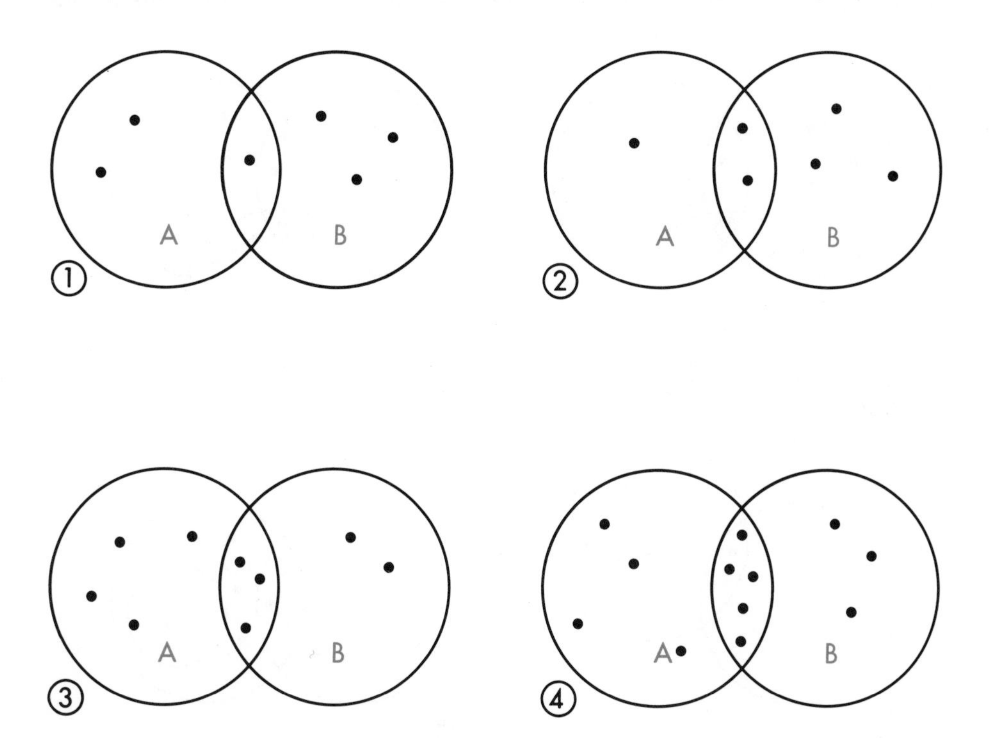

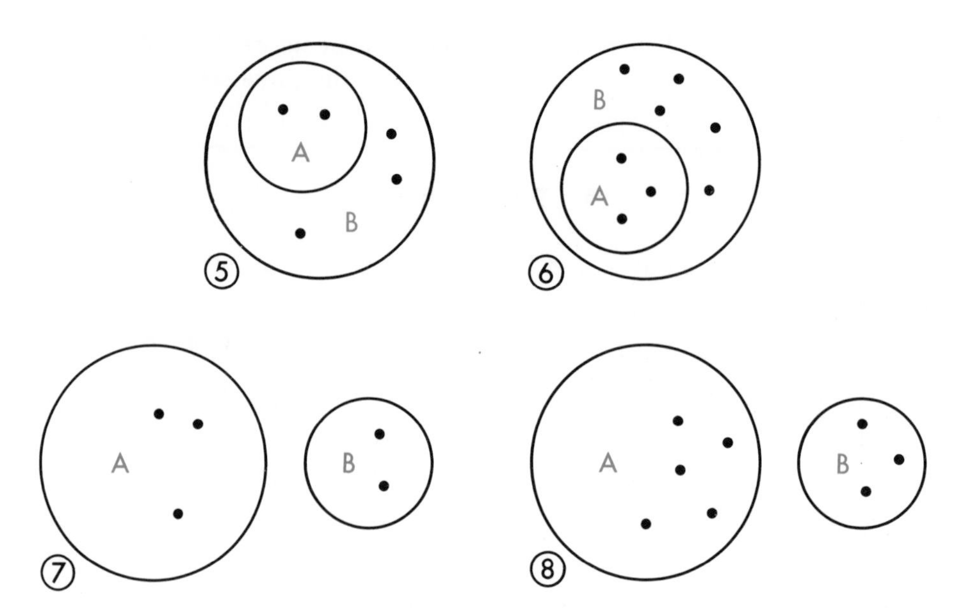

Part C. In each of the following, find the number of elements in each set (including the union, and intersection sets). Each "dot" represents an element.

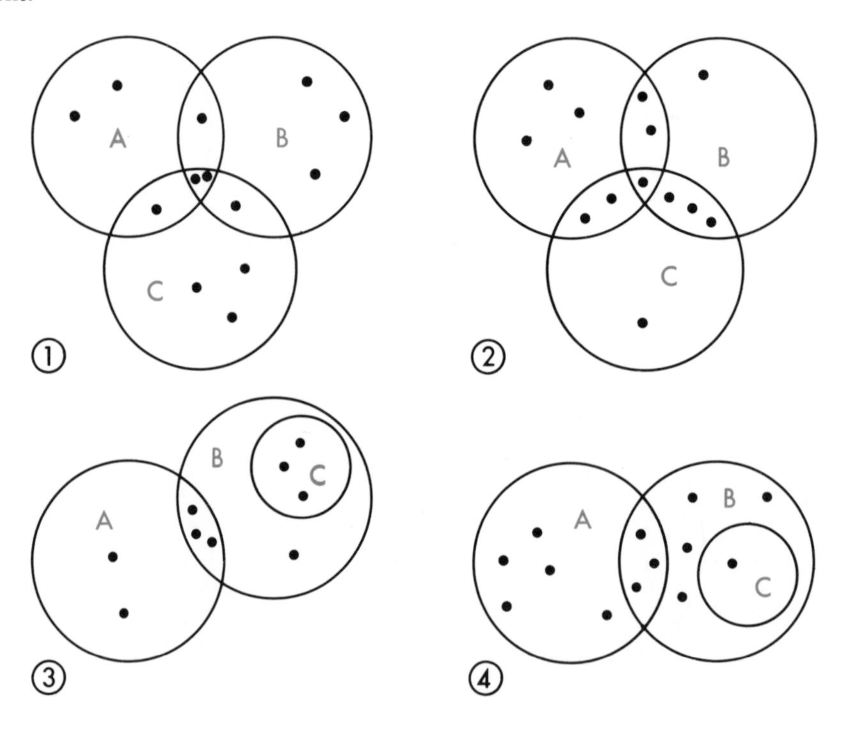

2 INCOMPLETE POLLS

The theory of sets is easily applied to the problem of "squeezing" extra information out of a poll. The best way to show you how this is done is to do a couple of problems.

Problem 1. An investigator was paid 50¢ per person to ask how many liked the policy of the Republicrats, and how many liked the policy of the Democans. He reported that 27 liked the Republicrats, 31 liked the Democans, and 8 of these liked both. How much money did he earn?

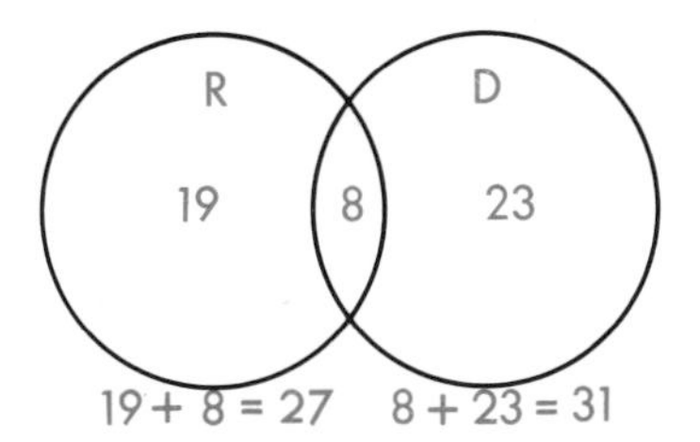

Fig. 11-6. Problem 1.

Solution: (Fig. 11-6) A diagram shows that there were only 19 + 8 + 23 = 50 elements in the union set. He earned $25.

Problem 2. A market investigator found that in a study of 1000 people, 816 bought utilities stock, 723 bought automation stock, and 645 bought transportation stock. Of these, 562 bought both utilities and automation, 463 bought both utilities and transportation, and 479 bought both automation and transportation. How many bought all three?

Solution: Figure 11-7 shows the number of elements in the "large" sets. Figure 11-8 shows the number of elements in the sets of "pairs." What we are interested in, is the intersection set, which is labeled X.

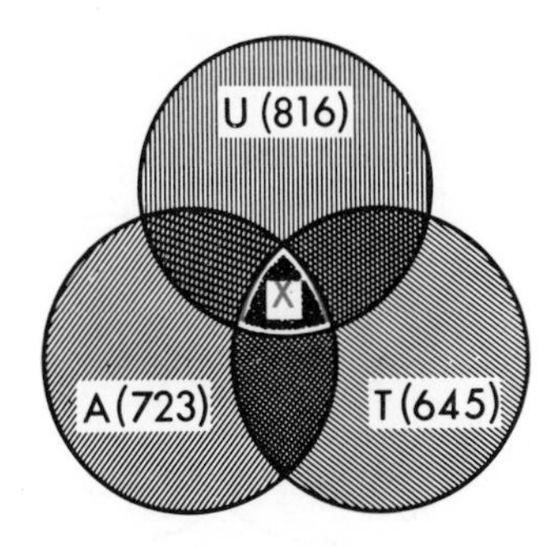

Fig. 11-7. Elements in the "large" sets.

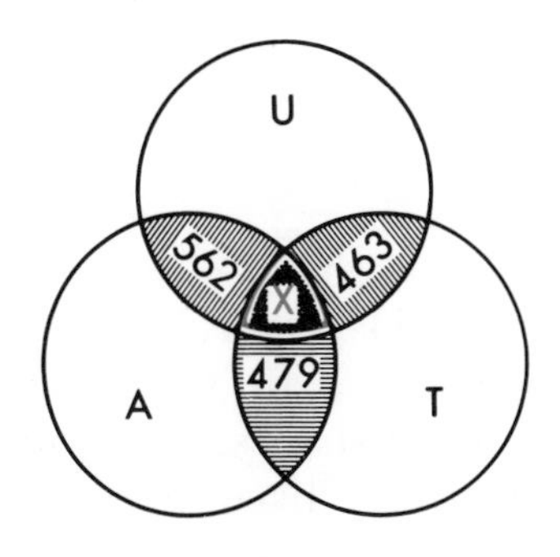

Fig. 11-8. Elements in the sets of pairs.

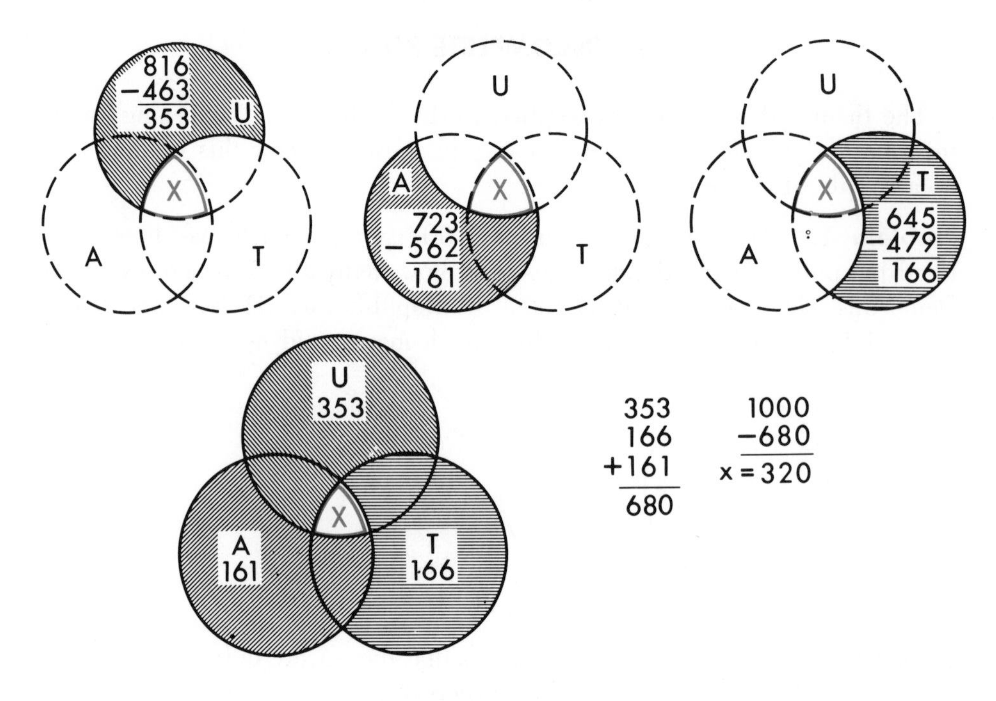

Fig. 11-9. Separating the sets to find set X.

If we separate the sets very carefully, as in Fig. 11-9, we find that the three separated sets account for $353 + 166 + 161 = 680$ of the elements. All the other elements, $1000 - 680 = 320$, must be in X.

In other words, 320 people bought all three stocks.

Test: Section 2

Part A.

1 In a poll, 11 people voted that they liked English, 15 voted that they liked social studies, and 5 of them said that they liked both. If everyone voted, how many people were interviewed?

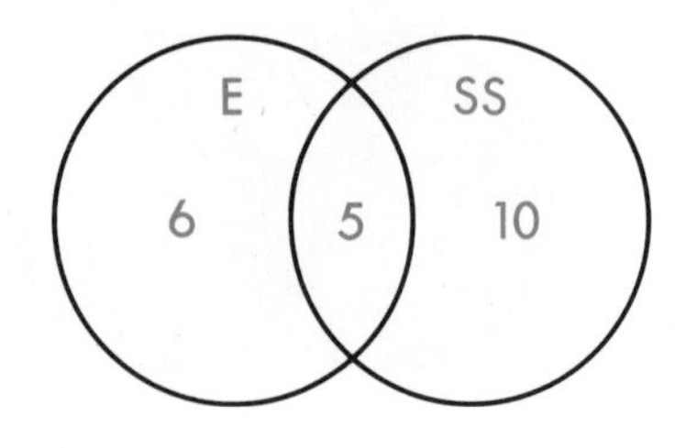

2 In a certain class, 21 boys wore bow ties, 19 wore white shirts, and three of these wore both white shirts and bow ties. How many boys were there?

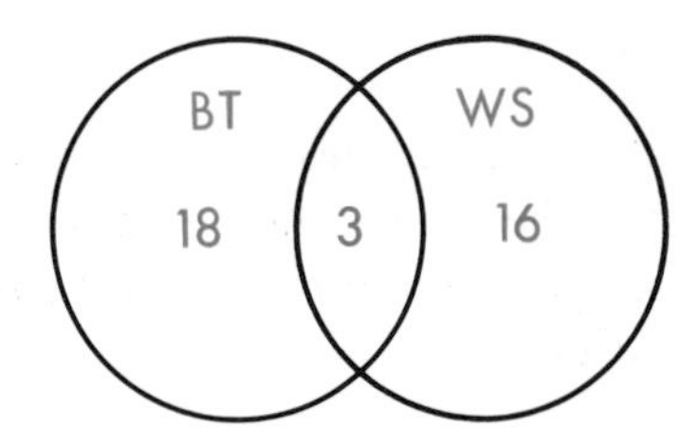

3 A small lunchroom serves one, or two vegetables to customers, as they request. On a certain day, the counterman served 16 orders of beans, and 14 orders of carrots; he noticed that 4 of these had both beans and carrots. How many customers were there?

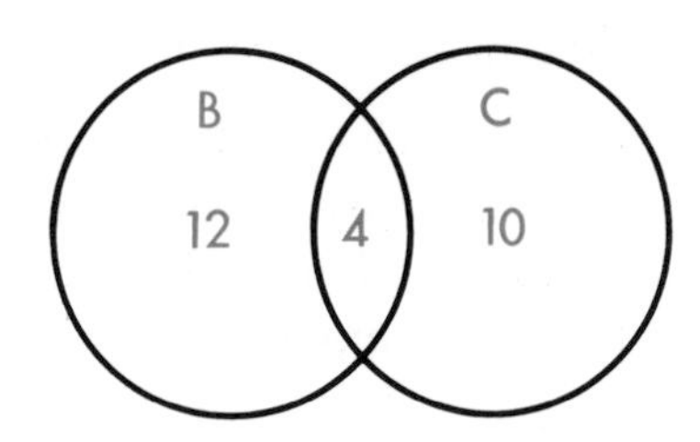

4 A dealer found that 25 of his customers looked at 4-door cars, and 18 looked at 2-door cars. Fourteen of them looked at both. How many customers were there?

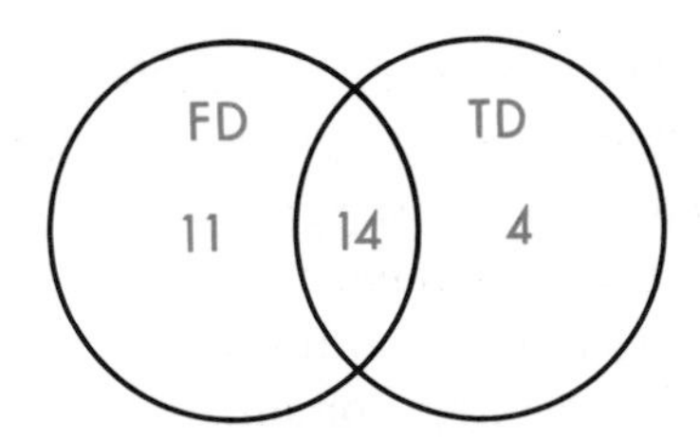

Part B. Make your own diagrams for the following:

1 A questionnaire study showed that 19 people liked Brand A, 18 liked Brand B, and 20 liked Brand C. Five of these people liked A and B, 8 liked B and C, and 7 liked A and C. Two people liked all three. How many people were there?

2 A travel bureau reported that on a certain day, 63 people inquired about trips to Europe, 52 people inquired about trips to the West Indies, and 87 people inquired about trips within the U.S.A. Some inquired about more than one trip; 27 inquired about both Europe and the U.S.A.; 25 about the West Indies and the U.S.A.; and 12 about both the West Indies and Europe. Ten people inquired about all three. How many people asked questions that day.

Part C.

1 A social studies class was asked to interview 52 businessmen to find out whether they liked to advertise in the school paper (set A), the school magazine (set B), or in the school yearbook (set C). The results were as follows:

A: 35	B: 23	C: 28
A and B: 15	A and C: 13	B and C: 11

How many businessmen liked to advertise in all three?

2 Forty-six chemical samples were tested for arsenic (As), lead (Pb), and iron (Fe). It was found that 27 had As, 25 had Pb, and 16 had Fe. Of these, 8 had both As and Pb, 7 had As and Fe, and 10 had Pb and Fe. How many had As, Pb, and Fe together?

3 POLYGON GRAPHS

The next modern problem which we will discuss is solved by a method called *linear programming*. Before going into this, you will have to learn how to make *polygon graphs*.

You will remember that we have already learned how to make a great many types of graphs. Figure 11-10 reviews some of these.

By making combinations of these, we obtain what are called *polygon graphs*.

Problem. Make a graph of

$$\begin{cases} y \geqq 1 \\ y \leqq 10 \\ x \geqq 2 \\ x \leqq 8 \\ y \leqq 13 - x \end{cases}$$

and find the coordinates of the "corners" (or, *vertices*).

Solution: (Fig. 11-11) First, we plot $y = 1$, $y = 10$, $x = 2$, $x = 8$, $y = 13 - x$. The polygon enclosed by parts of these lines satisfies all the conditions of the problem. The vertices are $A(2, 1)$, $B(2, 10)$, $C(3, 10)$, $D(8, 5)$, and E $(8, 1)$.

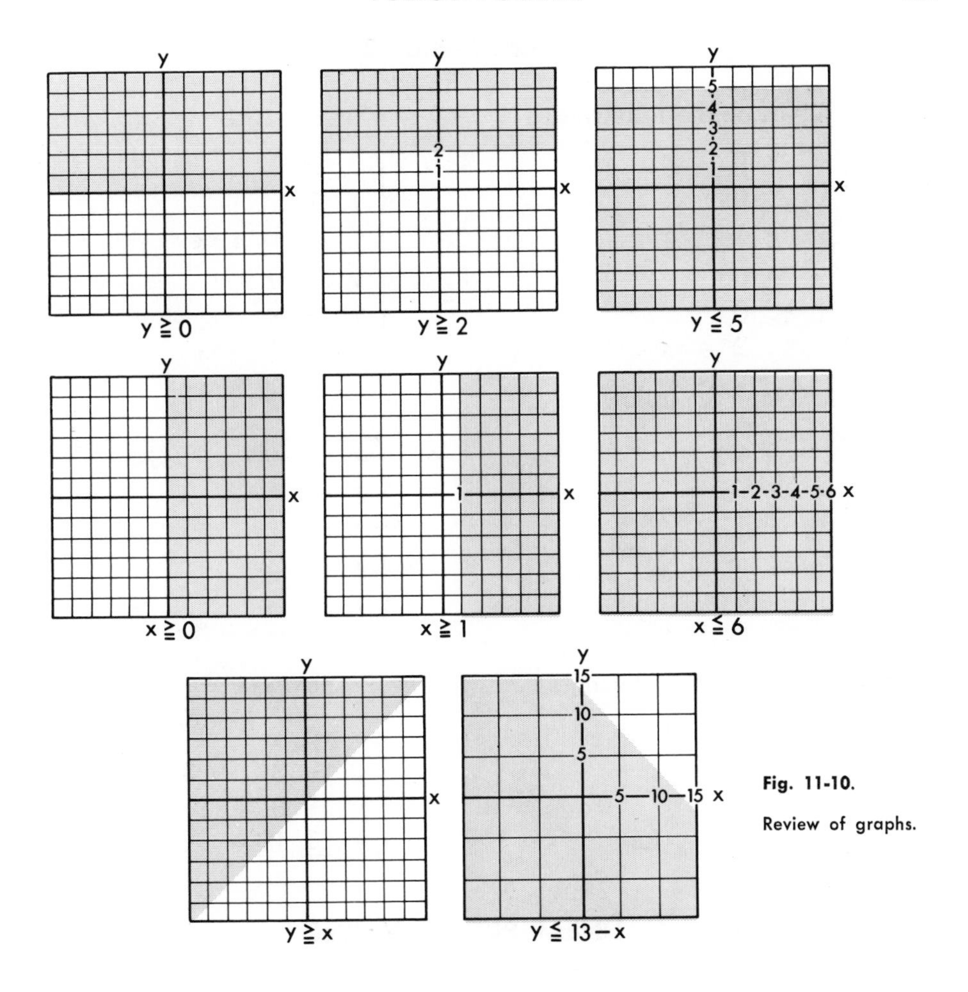

Fig. 11-10.

Review of graphs.

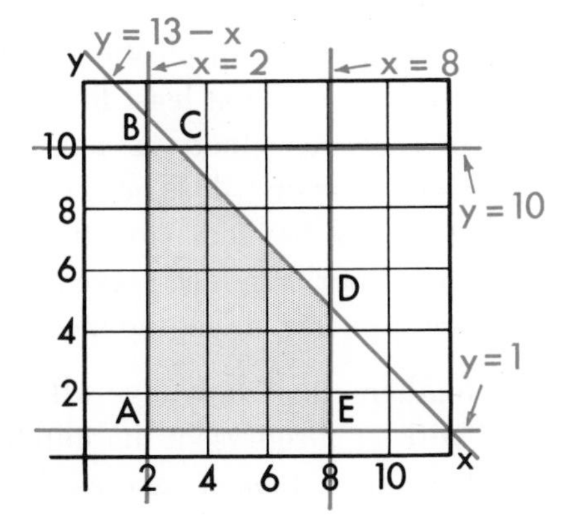

Fig. 11-11.

Ilustrative problem.

• Test: Section 3

Part A. Graph the following:

1 $\begin{cases} y \geqq 0 \\ x \geqq 0 \\ y \leqq 1 - x \end{cases}$

2 $\begin{cases} y \geqq 0 \\ x \geqq 0 \\ y \leqq 2 - x \end{cases}$

3 $\begin{cases} y \geqq 0 \\ y \leqq x \\ y \leqq 1 - x \end{cases}$

4 $\begin{cases} y \geqq 0 \\ y \leqq x \\ y \leqq 2 - x \end{cases}$

Part B. Graph the following:

1 $\begin{cases} y \geqq x \\ y \leqq 2x \\ y \leqq 3 - 2x \end{cases}$

2 $\begin{cases} y \geqq x \\ y \leqq 3x \\ y \leqq 5 - x \end{cases}$

3 $\begin{cases} y \geqq 2x \\ y \leqq 4x \\ y \leqq 7 - 2x \end{cases}$

4 $\begin{cases} y \geqq 2x \\ y \leqq 3x \\ y \leqq 6 - 3x \end{cases}$

Part C. Graph the following:

1 $\begin{cases} y \geqq x + 1 \\ y \leqq 2x - 1 \\ y \geqq 7 - x \\ y \leqq 18 - 3x \end{cases}$

2 $\begin{cases} y \geqq x - 1 \\ y \leqq 3x - 3 \\ y \leqq 8 + x \\ y \leqq 12 - x \end{cases}$

4 LINEAR PROGRAMMING

The following two problems show how mathematicians answer the question, "How can I get the most for my money?"

Problem 1. Adam McLane is conducting a campaign for election as senior president. The *facts* are as follows: (1) He must provide at least five posters. (2) He cannot have more than 15 posters, because there is not enough space to hang them. (3) He wants at least one banner. (4) The school rule is that you cannot hang more than 18 posters and banners (together). (5) Each poster convinces 11 people. (6) Each banner convinces seven people. How many of each, banners and posters, should he use, to get the most votes?

Solution: First, we must translate into mathematical language all the information about posters and banners. We will let x represent the number of posters, and y, the number of banners. Then the statements are as follows:

Statement	*Translation*
1	$x \geqq 5$
2	$x \leqq 15$
3	$y \geqq 1$
4	$x + y \leqq 18$

Now, *all* the points *on*, and *inside* the polygon graph (Fig. 11-12), satisfy

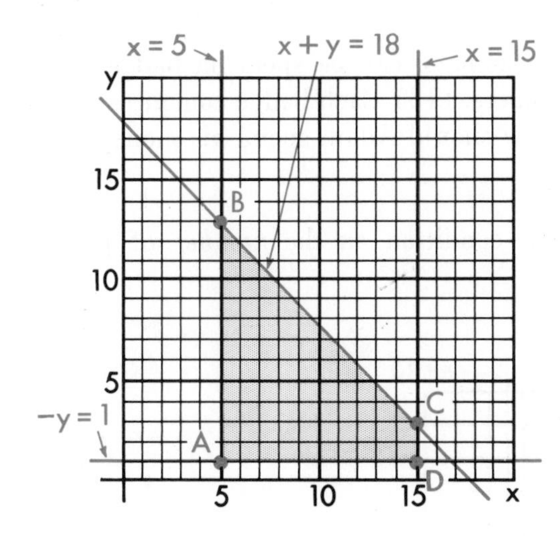

Fig. 11-12. Problem 1.

the four rules about number of items. Which is the best? We shall have to make use of a rule proved by mathematicians:

Rule for Best Choice. Test only the vertices of the polygon, to find the best and worst points. (This is simplified, but it will do for our purposes. There are other points just as good, in some cases.)

Now we use facts 5 and 6, to find out how many people are convinced at each corner. Table I (p. 362) shows the situation at the corners.

From the table, the best choice is to put up 15 posters, and 3 banners.

Problem 2. Adam McLane then finds out that there are additional rules to the six named in Problem 1. They are: (7) He is allowed to spend $25 for posters, banners, and badges. (8) The posters cost $1 each. (9) The banners cost 50¢ each. (10) The badges cost 10¢ each. (11) Whatever he

TABLE I

Vertex	Posters	Banners	People Convinced by Posters	People Convinced by Banners	Total Number of People Convinced
A	5	1	55	7	62
B	5	13	55	91	146
D	15	1	165	7	172
C	15	3	165	21	186

does not spend on posters and banners, can be spent on badges. (12) He does not want more than ten banners. (13) Each badge convinces one person (the one who is wearing it). How should Adam spend his money?

Solution: The only additional condition on the *number* of posters and

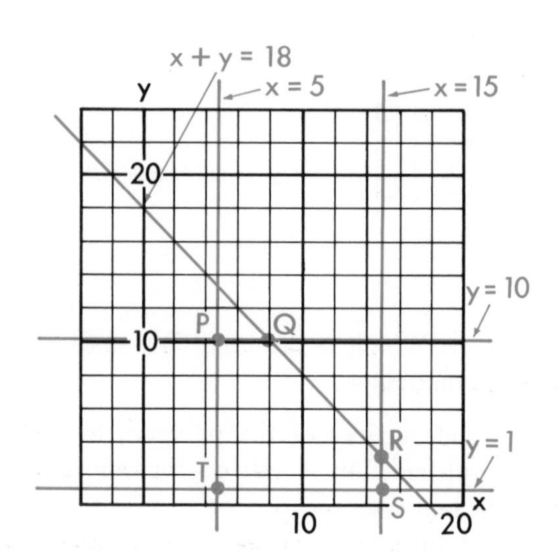

Fig. 11-13. Problem 2.

banners, is No. 12, which tells us that $y \leqq 10$. Adding this to the graph, we obtain Fig. 11-13.

Now the vertices are $P(5, 10)$, $Q(8, 10)$, $R(15, 3)$, $S(15, 1)$, and $T(5, 1)$. Let us see how much each of these "corners" cost, so that we can find out how many badges Adam can buy. Table II shows this information:

TABLE II

Vertex	Cost of Posters	Cost of Banners	Money Used on Posters and Banners	Money Left for Badges	Number of Badges to Buy
P	$5	$5	$10	$15	150
Q	$8	$5	$13	$12	120
R	$15	$1.50	$16.50	$ 8.50	85
S	$15	$0.50	$15.50	$ 9.50	95
T	$5	$0.50	$5.50	$19.50	195

Now let us see how many voters are convinced at each vertex:

TABLE III

Vertex	Convinced by Posters	Convinced by Banners	Convinced by Badges	Total Number Convinced
P	55	70	150	275
Q	88	70	120	278
R	165	21	85	271
S	165	7	95	267
T	55	7	195	257

According to Table III, Adam's best bet is to get eight posters, ten banners, and 120 badges.

Notice the steps in doing a problem of this kind. *First,* translate into mathematical language all the *number facts* about *two* of the things involved. Then, draw the polygon graph. *Last,* calculate the situation at each corner, and take the one which fits the problem best.

Test: Section 4

Part A.

1 Henry has two tests to study for, and has only two hours (120 minutes) of study time. He must use at least 15 minutes for subject X, but he cannot stand more than 60 minutes of this. He must spend at least 20 min-

utes on subject Y, but it does not pay him to use more than 90 minutes on this subject. (So far, $x \geqq 15$, $x \leqq 60$, $y \geqq 20$, $y \leqq 90$, $x + y \leqq 120$.) His average in subject X is 70%, and he figures that for every minute that he studies for this subject he will raise his average by one third of a point. In subject Y, he has an average of 65%, and he figures that every minute of study will raise his average in this subject by one fifth of a point.

a. Make a polygon graph.
b. Find the coordinates of the corners.
c. For each corner, find the new mark in subjects X, and Y.
d. Which combination of study periods will give him the best average in both subjects?

2 John Smith is considering stock X and stock Y. He must not spend more than \$1000. ($x + y \leqq 1000$). He must buy at least \$100 worth of stock X ($x \geqq 100$), but not more than \$600 worth ($x \leqq 600$). He must buy at least \$200 worth of stock Y ($y \geqq 200$), but not more than \$800 worth ($y \leqq 800$). Every \$100 share of stock X pays \$8 dividend, and every \$50 share of stock Y pays \$9.

a. Make a polygon graph.
b. Find the coordinates of the vertices.
c. For each corner, find the amount of dividend.
d. What should John Smith buy?

Part B.

1 In Question 1, Part A, Henry suddenly remembers that he has a little test in subject Z. His average in this subject is now 90%, but for every minute he studies, he will push his average in the subject up by 0.1%. Remembering that he has 120 minutes altogether, whatever he does not spend on subjects X and Y, he can spend on subject Z.

a. Using the same graph, calculate the number of minutes on subjects X, Y, and Z.
b. Find the new marks for each corner
c. What is the best distribution of study time for the three subjects?

2 In Question 2, Part A, John Smith finds stock Z, which pays \$10 per \$100 invested. Whatever is not used in stocks X and Y, can be used in stock Z.

a. Using the graph of Question 2, (Part A), calculate the number of dollars spent on X, Y, and Z.
b. Find the total dividend for each corner.
c. What is the best distribution of money, now?

Part C.

1 Mary has been told that she must take pills for a serious illness. In each month, she needs at least 20 units of X, but not more than 50 units. She needs 10 units of Y, but not more than 40 units. She should have at least 40 units of X, and Y, together.

a. Make the polygon graph to represent these facts.
b. If X costs \$1 per unit, and Y costs \$2 per unit, what is the cheapest satisfactory combination?

2 An advertiser has \$50,000 to spend on advertising, ($x + y \leqq 50{,}000$), with at least \$40,000 for newspapers and TV ($x + y \geqq 40{,}000$). He will spend at least \$10,000 on newspapers (X), but not more than \$25,000. He will spend at least \$20,000 on TV (Y), but not more than \$30,000. He will not spend on TV more than twice what he spends on newspapers ($y \leqq 2x$). Whatever he does not spend on TV and newspaper advertising, he can use for radio advertising (Z). Each \$1000 spent on newspapers brings 100 customers. Each \$1000 spent on TV brings 120 customers. Each \$1000 spent on radio, brings 115 customers. How should he spend his money?

5 DICE COMBINATIONS

Students are always surprised to find that mathematicians are interested in studying dice throwing, coin-tossing, poker, and other, more complicated games of chance. There is nothing to be surprised about. Life is a series of events affected by chance. A mathematician merely tries to make some sense out of life, by finding out as much as he can about the way chance operates.

The easiest game to start with is the dice game. In this game, two dice are shaken (or shuffled) and thrown onto a hard surface. When they bounce back, each die rolls *at random*. When it stops rolling, the top face may show anything from a *one* to a *six*. The numbers showing on both dice are now added. The possible results are shown in the following addition table (which should remind you of the clock mathematics we started the book with!).

	+	1	2	3	4	5	6
		Second Die					
	1	2	3	4	5	6	7
	2	3	4	5	6	7	8
	3	4	5	6	7	8	9
First Die	4	5	6	7	8	9	10
	5	6	7	8	9	10	11
	6	7	8	9	10	11	12

As you can see, there are $6 \times 6 = 36$ ways the dice can settle down. We say that:

$$\textit{Total ways} = 36$$

You can also see that each die is equally likely to turn up 1, 2, 3, 4, 5, or 6; but the combinations are *not* equally likely. There is little *chance* or *probability* of getting a 2, because there is only one way to get it, and that is when each die turns up 1. There is a good *chance* or *probability* of getting a 7, because there are many ways of getting it. If you look at the table, you will see that you can get it by $6 + 1$, $5 + 2$, $4 + 3$, $3 + 4$, $2 + 5$, or $1 + 6$. The ways you get what you are looking for, are called *favorable ways,* so we say

$$\textit{Favorable ways} \text{ (to get a 7)} = 6$$

A mathematician measures chance or probability by dividing one of these by the other:

Definition. Probability (or, chance) $= \dfrac{\textit{Favorable ways}}{\textit{Total ways}}$

Problem 1. What is the chance of rolling a 7?

Solution: There are six ways of rolling a 7, so that the chance is $\frac{6}{36}$, or $\frac{1}{6}$. This means that a 7 should turn up about once in six throws. Sometimes mathematicians express this in per cent form. One sixth is about 17%, so we can say that the probability of rolling a 7 is about 17%, or 17 out of a hundred times.

Sometimes we wish to find the probability of *either* of two events. The procedure is the same:

Problem 2. What is the probability of rolling either a 7 or an 11?

Solution: There are six ways of rolling a 7, and two ways of rolling an 11. This makes eight *favorable ways* in all. The probability is $\frac{8}{36}$, or $\frac{2}{9}$. Two times out of nine, the dice should come up either 7 or 11. This is about 22% probability.

Test: Section 5

Part A. Using the table, how many (favorable) ways are there of rolling the number given below? (Remember, that is the sum of both dice!) What is the probability of rolling this?

1 2 **2** 3 **3** 4 **4** 5 **5** 6
6 8 **7** 9 **8** 10 **9** 11 **10** 12

Part B. How many ways are there of rolling either of the two numbers given below? What is the probability of rolling them?

1 5 or 7 **2** 8 or 3 **3** 2 or 12
4 6 or 9 **5** 4 or 8 **6** 2, 4, 6, 8, 10, or 12
7 3, 5, 7, 9, or 11 **8** 3, 6, 9 or 12 **9** 4, 8, or 12
10 5 or 10

Part C. Make a table which shows (in per cent form) the probability for each sum:

Sum:	2	3	4	5	6	7	8	9	10	11	12
Probability:						?					

Now take a pair of dice and throw them 100 times. Keep a record of the sums, and see whether your answers check within 2%.

6 TOSSING COINS

A coin has a *head* and a *tail.* There are a *total* of two ways a single coin can turn up when you toss it. The probability of a head is $\frac{1}{2}$, and the probability of a tail, is also $\frac{1}{2}$, provided that it is a *fair coin.*

Now, suppose you toss it twice. Then you can get two heads (HH), a tail and a head (TH), a head and a tail (HT), or two tails (TT). The diagram (inset) is called a *tree,* and is used by mathematicians to show all the possibilities.

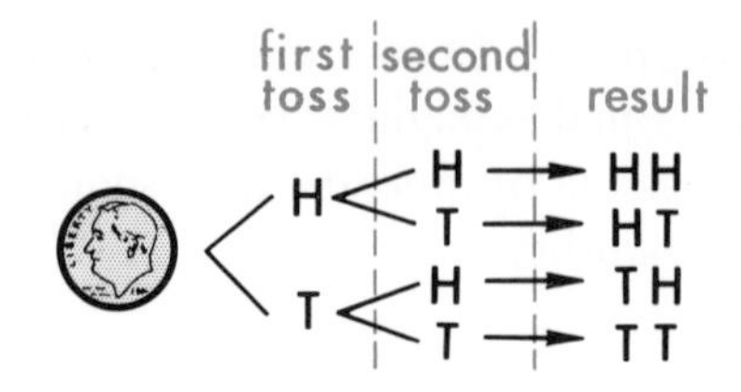

Problem 1. In tossing a coin twice, what is the chance of getting (a) two heads; (b) a tail and a head?

Solution: From the diagram, the total number of ways is four (see the "result" column of the tree). There is *one* way of getting two heads, so the probability is $\frac{1}{4}$ (or, 25%). There are *two* ways of getting a head and a tail (either order), so the probability is $\frac{2}{4}$ (or 50%).

From a mathematical viewpoint, it makes no difference whether you toss *one* coin *twice,* or *two* coins *once.* You just get the results faster, when you use two coins. The diagram is labeled differently.

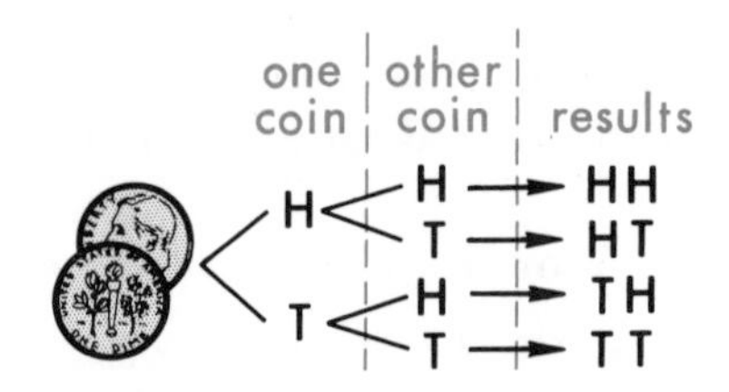

If you toss *three* coins at the same time, the diagram becomes:

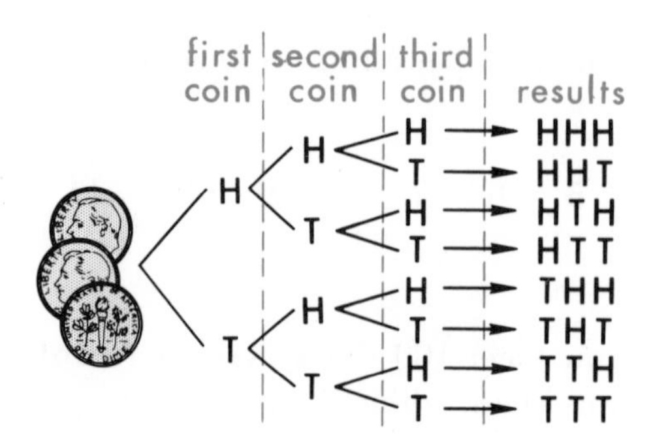

Problem 2. Make a complete table of probabilities for tossing three coins.

Solution: There are eight ways (total) listed in the results column. Some of them look different, but we count them as the same in tossing coins: *HHT*, *HTH*, *THH*, are all considered two heads and a tail, so there are three ways of getting this result. The probability for two heads and a tail is therefore $\frac{3}{8}$ (or, about 38%). This means that when you toss three coins, you should get two heads and a tail about three times out of every eight tosses. The following table shows the complete calculation for three coins:

Coins	*Favorable Ways*	*Probability (fraction)*	*Probability (per cent)*
3 heads	1	$\frac{1}{8}$	12.5%
2 heads, 1 tail	3	$\frac{3}{8}$	37.5%
1 head, 2 tails	3	$\frac{3}{8}$	37.5%
3 tails	1	$\frac{1}{8}$	12.5%

Problem 3. What is the probability of getting *at least* two heads, when three coins are tossed?

Solution: This can happen when you have two heads and a tail, or three heads. From the diagram (or the table) there are four favorable ways. The probability is therefore, $\frac{4}{8}$ (or 50%).

Test: Section 6

Part A. Continue the tree to four coins, and find out how many of the tosses will be (a) four heads; (b) three heads and a tail; (c) two heads and two tails; (d) one head and three tails; and (e) four tails.

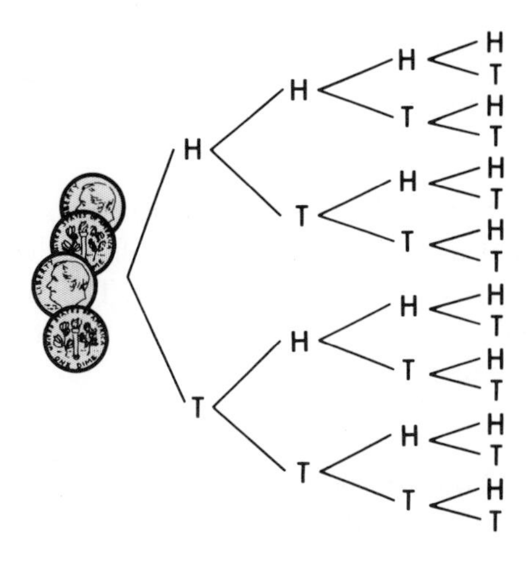

1. What is the probability of getting two heads and two tails?
2. What is the probability of getting all heads?
3. What is the probability of getting at least two tails?
4. What is the probability of getting at least one head?

Part B. Continue the tree to five coins, and make a table of ways. Now find the probability of each of the following:

1 Five heads
2 Four heads, one tail
3 Three heads, two tails
4 Two heads, three tails
5 One head, four tails
6 Five tails
7 At least three heads
8 At least two tails

Part C. Projects.

1 Experiment with four coins to see how closely your predictions are followed. Each person in the class should do at least 20 tosses, and all the results should be put together in one table.

2 Now experiment with five coins, and see how well your predictions are followed.

7 SHUFFLING

You would be very surprised if you shuffled a deck of cards, and someone then guessed the exact order they were in, without looking. Do you know what the probability of this is? It is about 1 in 80,000,000,000,000,000,000, 000,000,000,000,000,000,000,000,000,000,000,000,000,000,000 (an *eight* followed by 67 zeros). This big number represents the total number of ways of shuffling 52 poker cards.

To learn how this was calculated, let us limit ourselves to a small pack of cards.

Suppose we have *two* cards, an ace, and a king. Then, after shuffling, we may come up with *AK* or *KA*. The diagram shows a tree for the two possible results.

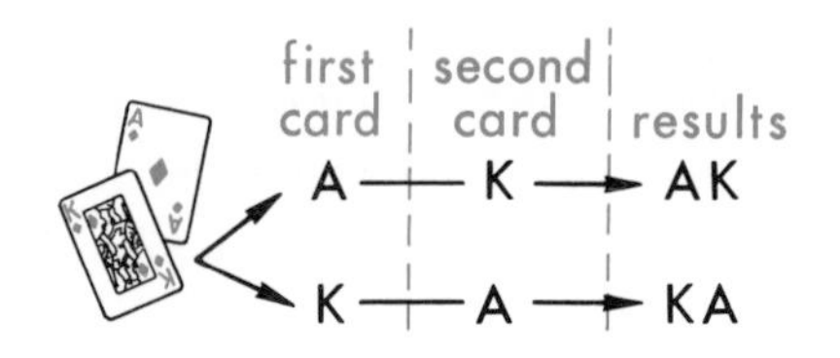

You will see that there are two shuffles for two cards. (If you guessed, you would be right $\frac{1}{2}$ the time.)

Suppose we have three cards: *AKQ*. The possibilities are:

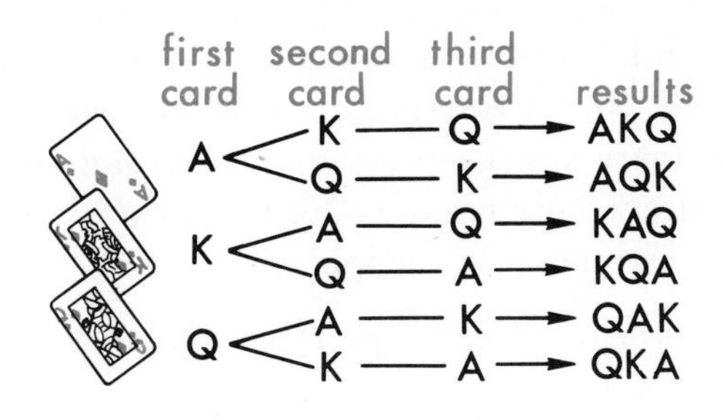

As you can see, there are *six* ways for *three* cards. A guess would be right $\frac{1}{6}$ of the time.

Now, suppose we have four cards: *AKQJ*. The tree is:

As you can see, there are *twenty-four* ways for *four* cards.

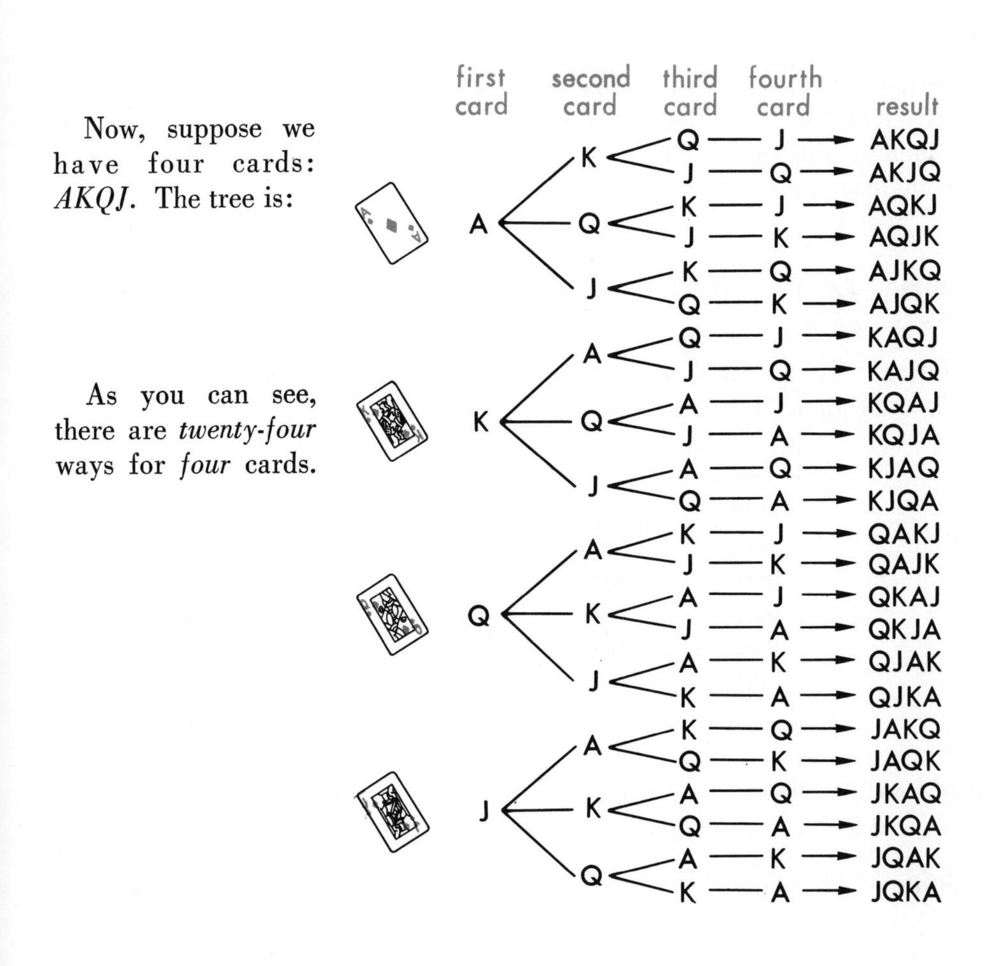

As you get to more cards, the "tree" method becomes a little bit troublesome. There is a faster way to figure out the "number of ways." Let us go back to the case of *AKQ*. When you finish shuffling these, the *first* card may be either ace, king, or queen. In other words, there are *three* ways for the *first* card. Now there are two cards left. The second card may be either of the two, so there are *two* ways for the *second* card. The third is whatever is left, so there is only *one* way for the *third* card.

The general principle when there is a succession of events is as follows:

Principle for Independent Successive Events. Multiply the numbers of ways.

Using this principle, the number of ways to shuffle three cards is $3 \times 2 \times 1 = 6$.

Problem 1. How many ways can four different cards be shuffled?

Solution: In the result, the first card can be any one of *four*, the second card can be any one of the *three* remaining, and so on. The number of ways of shuffling four cards is $4 \times 3 \times 2 \times 1 = 24$, which agrees with the result we obtained from the tree method.

Problem 2. How many ways can the letters *a*, *b*, *c*, and *d*, be written? Show the ways.

Solution: This is another shuffling problem, and the answer is $4 \times 3 \times 2 \times 1 = 24$ ways. Here they are:

abcd	bacd	cabd	dabc
abdc	badc	cadb	dacb
acbd	bcad	cbad	dbac
acdb	bcda	cbda	dbca
adbc	bdac	cdab	dcab
adcb	bdca	cdba	dcba

Problem 3. Sandra has five perfume bottles to arrange in a row on her vanity table. In how many ways can this be done?

Solution: Shuffling, the answer is $5 \times 4 \times 3 \times 2 \times 1 = 120$ ways.

Test: Section 7

Part A. In how many ways can the following numbers of cards be shuffled, if they are all different?

1 5 2 6 3 7 4 8 5 9 6 10

Part B.

1 A shopkeeper wishes to place five different items in his window, in a straight line. How many different ways can this be done?

2 The chairman of a class committee decides to arrange four posters on the front board, before a discussion. How many ways are there?

3 An election board is working on the listing of six political parties on a ballot. How many different ways are there of listing these?

4 A player in a word game has before him seven blocks, with different letters on them. How many different arrangements are there, of the seven letters?

8 EQUAL-SUIT GAMES

In some card games, like *Casino*, all suits are the same, so that one king is the same as another, in actual play. How many ways can you shuffle three kings, a queen, and a jack?

You might think that there are $5 \times 4 \times 3 \times 2 \times 1 = 120$ ways, but there are actually only *20* ways, because the three kings are considered the same:

KKKQJ	KQJKK	KKQKJ	QKJKK	QKKJK
KKKJQ	KJQKK	KKJKQ	JKQKK	JKKQK
KKQJK	QJKKK	KQKJK	KQKKJ	QKKKJ
KKJQK	JQKKK	KJKQK	KJKKQ	JKKKQ

Note that: $$\frac{5 \times 4 \times 3 \times 2 \times 1}{3 \times 2 \times 1} = 20 \text{ ways.}$$

A little experimentation will convince you that if some of the items are repeated, you have to divide for every repeated item. If an item appears twice, you divide by (2×1). If it appears four times, you divide by $(4 \times 3 \times 2 \times 1)$. This is proved in a subject called *advanced algebra.*

Problem 1. How many ways are there of shuffling three aces, two queens, and a ten, if all the suits are the same?

Solution: There are six cards. Using the rule for repetition:

$$\text{No. of ways} = \frac{6 \times 5 \times \overset{2}{\cancel{4}} \times \cancel{3} \times \cancel{2} \times \cancel{1}}{(\cancel{3} \times \cancel{2} \times 1) \times (\underset{1}{\cancel{2}} \times \cancel{1})} = 60 \text{ ways}$$

Problem 2. If you shuffle three aces, two queens, and a ten, what is the chance of getting a queen first?

Solution: There are many ways of figuring this out. Here is one of them. There are six cards, and two of them are queens. The first card can come up in *six* ways, of which *two* are queens. We are not interested in the other cards. The probability is $\frac{2}{6}$, or about 33%.

Test: Section 8

Part A. In how many ways can the following be shuffled? In each of these problems, disregard the suits.

1 Two kings and three queens.

2 Three tens and four twos.

3 One seven and five jokers.

4 Two jacks and four aces.

Part B.

1 A grocer has ten boxes of cereal, seven of one kind, and three of another. How many different arrangements can he make on a shelf?

2 How many different looking ways can a set of twins, and a set of triplets be seated, if the twins and triplets are each identical?

3 How many different ways are there of arranging the ten letters: aaeeeiiouu?

4 How many different ways are there of arranging the eight letters: mmaaathh?

5 How many ways are there of arranging three identical pennies, and four identical nickels?

6 How many ways are there of arranging two identical roses, five identical lilacs, and two identical gardenias?

Part C.

1 In $A1$, (*Part A*, Q. 1) what is the probability of getting a king first?
2 In $A2$, what is the chance of getting a ten first?
3 In $A3$, what is the probability of getting a joker last?
4 In $A4$, what is the probability of getting an ace last?
5 In $A3$, what is the probability of getting two jokers first?
6 In $A4$, what is the probability of getting two aces first?

9 PICK A CARD

Pam took a deck of 52 poker cards, shuffled them, and spread them in her hand. "Pick two cards," she said to her brother, Lance.

Problem 1. What is the probability that Lance will pick two kings?

Solution: There are four kings in the deck, so the chance that the first card will be a king, is $\frac{4}{52}$. On the second draw, the first draw being successful, there are three kings left in the 51 cards, so the chance of getting a king is $\frac{3}{51}$. Using the rule for *successive independent events*, the probability of getting two kings is $\frac{4}{52} \times \frac{3}{51} = \frac{12}{2652}$, which is approximately 45 chances in 10,000.

For your convenience in doing these problems, the following table is sometimes useful:

	Product	*Approximate Reciprocal*
52	52	0.0192
52 × 51	2652	0.000377
52 × 51 × 50	132,600	0.000,007,54
52 × 51 × 50 × 49	6,497,400	0.000,000,154
52 × 51 × 50 × 49 × 48	311,875,200	0.000,000,003,21

Using this table, $\frac{12}{2652} = 12 \times 0.000{,}377 = 0.004{,}524$, or about 45 in 10,000 (which agrees with the previous result).

Problem 2. What is the chance of getting the king of spades, followed by the king of clubs, when you draw from a full deck?

Solution: There is only one way to get the king of spades, and only one way to get the king of clubs, so the probability is:

$$\frac{1}{52} \times \frac{1}{51} = \frac{1}{2652} = 1 \times 0.000{,}377 = 0.000{,}377$$

or about 38 chances out of 100,000.

Problem 3. What is the chance of getting five cards of a red suit, when you draw from a full deck?

Solution: There are 26 red cards in the deck of 52 cards.

$$\frac{\overset{1}{\cancel{26}}}{\underset{2}{\cancel{52}}} \times \frac{\overset{1}{\cancel{25}}}{51} \times \frac{\overset{1}{\cancel{24}}}{\underset{2}{\cancel{50}}} \times \frac{23}{49} \times \frac{\overset{11}{\cancel{22}}}{\underset{\underset{1}{\cancel{2}}}{\cancel{48}}} = \frac{253}{9996} = \text{approx. } 0.025$$

or, 25 chances out of one thousand.

• Test: Section 9

Find the probability of the following, assuming that you start with a full poker deck of 52 cards.

1 Drawing three aces.

2 Drawing two jacks.

3 Drawing the ten, jack, and queen of spades.

4 Drawing the two of spades, and the ten of diamonds.

5 Drawing four cards of a black suit.

6 Drawing two cards of a red suit, followed by three cards of a black suit.

7 Drawing one card of a red suit, followed by two cards of a black suit.

8 Drawing one card of a black suit, followed by two cards of a red suit.

9 Drawing a five-card flush (all cards in the same suit). (*Hint*: There are 52 ways of drawing the first card, but once this is drawn, there are only 12 ways of matching it on the second draw, 11 ways of matching the third card, and so on.)

10 Drawing any five-card flush, ace high, with the ace first. (*Hint*: There are four ways of picking the ace, but once this is picked, there are only 12 ways of matching the second card, 11 ways of matching the third card, and so on.)

10 COMPLICATED GAMES

To end the book with a real "bang!", let us investigate a complicated game. Complicated games are more like the ones that turn up in military strategy, in stock maneuvers, and in other "life" games.

Problem. The game is as follows: First, you toss a coin. If the coin turns up heads, you roll a pair of dice. You win if it comes up 6 or 7. If the coin turns up tails, you draw a card from a full poker deck. You win if the card is a picture card. What is your chance of winning this game?

Solution: These complicated games are solved by tree diagrams, using the rule of *successive independent events.* The tree is as follows:

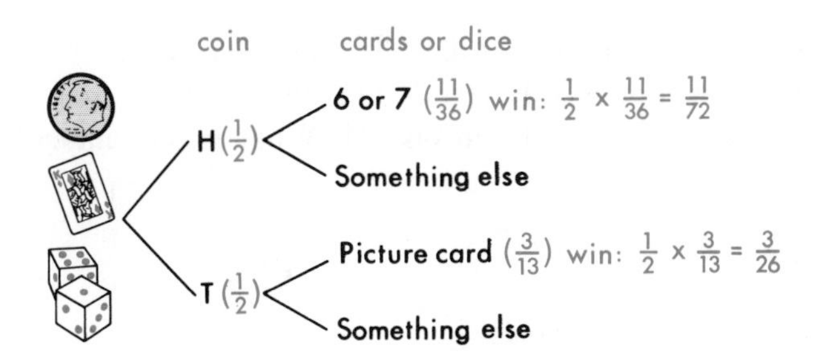

Adding the winning probabilities, we get $\frac{11}{72} + \frac{3}{26}$, which is approximately $0.153 + 0.115 = 0.268$ This gives you about a 30% chance of winning. To put it another way, you would win 30 games out of a hundred. For the game to be *fair,* the pay-off for a win should be figured out so that 30 wins, will balance 70 losses. For example, if the game costs \$30 every time you lose, it should pay \$70 every time you win. In this way, $30 \times \$70 = \$2100 = 70 \times \$30$.

Test: Section 10

Part A.

1 In this game, you toss a coin first. If it turns up heads, you draw a card from *AAKKK*. You win, if you draw an ace. If it turns up tails, you draw a card from *AQQQQ*. You win, if you draw an ace. What is your chance of winning?

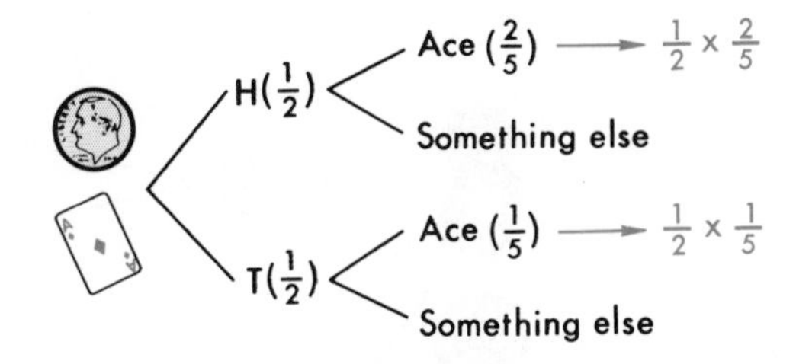

2 In this game, you draw a card from *AKQJ*. If you draw the king, you toss a coin; heads wins. If you do not draw the king, you toss two coins at the same time. Double-heads wins. What is your chance of winning?

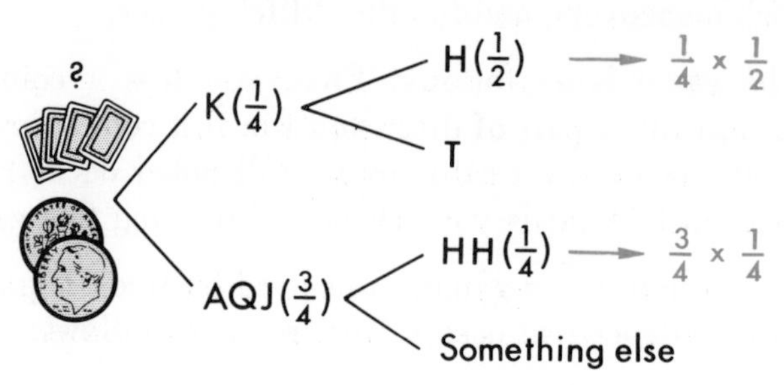

3 In this game, you roll a pair of dice. If you get a 7, then you roll the dice again, and win on a 5. If you do not get a 7 on the first roll, then you roll the dice again, and win on a 4. What is the chance of winning?

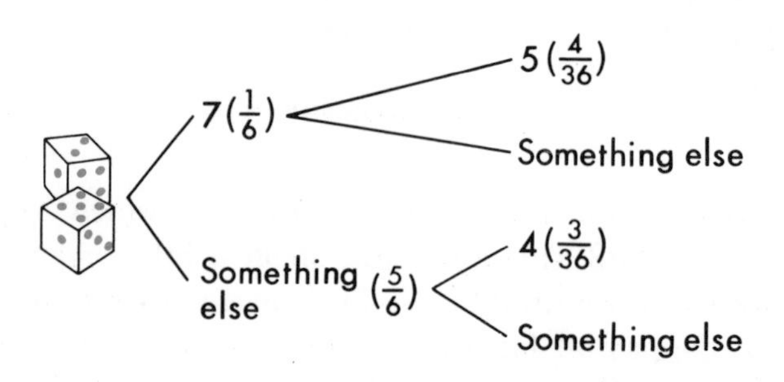

4 In this game, you draw a card from a full poker deck. If it is a ten, then you toss a coin; heads wins. If it is not a ten, then you toss two coins at the same time. To win, you must get at least one head. What is your chance of winning?

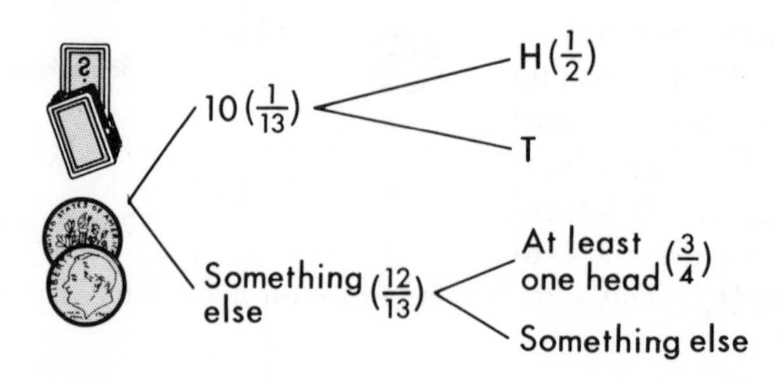

Part B. Make your own tree diagrams, and solve the problems.

1 In this game, you toss a coin. If it turns up heads, then you draw one card from *JQK;* jack wins. If it turns up tails, then you draw two cards from *JQK*. King and queen (in either order) wins. What is your chance of winning?

2 In this game, first you roll a pair of dice. If it turns up 7, then you toss a coin, and heads wins. If it turns up anything but 7, then you toss two coins at the same time. You need at least one tail to win. What are your chances of winning?

3 There are three balls in an opaque jar; one is red, and two are white. You reach in and take a ball. If it is *red,* you reach into a second jar with three red balls, and two white balls. A second red ball wins. If the first ball was *white,* you reach into the second jar *twice.* You need *two more white balls* to win. What are your chances of winning?

4 You toss a coin. If it is heads, you draw from a poker deck. Any picture card wins. If it is tails, you draw from a pinochle deck. Any picture card wins. What is the chance of winning? (A pinochle deck has two cards of each suit as follows: 9, 10, J, Q, K, A.)

Number	Square	Square Root	Number	Square	Square Root	Number	Square	Square Root
1	1	1.000	**51**	2,601	7.141	**101**	10,201	10.050
2	4	1.414	**52**	2,704	7.211	**102**	10,404	10.100
3	9	1.732	**53**	2,809	7.280	**103**	10,609	10.149
4	16	2.000	**54**	2,916	7.348	**104**	10,816	10.198
5	25	2.236	**55**	3,025	7.416	**105**	11,025	10.247
6	36	2.449	**56**	3,136	7.483	**106**	11,236	10.296
7	49	2.646	**57**	3,249	7.550	**107**	11,449	10.344
8	64	2.828	**58**	3,364	7.616	**108**	11,664	10.392
9	81	3.000	**59**	3,481	7.681	**109**	11,881	10.440
10	100	3.162	**60**	3,600	7.746	**110**	12,100	10.488
11	121	3.317	**61**	3,721	7.810	**111**	12,321	10.536
12	144	3.464	**62**	3,844	7.874	**112**	12,544	10.583
13	169	3.606	**63**	3,969	7.937	**113**	12,769	10.630
14	196	3.742	**64**	4,096	8.000	**114**	12,996	10.677
15	225	3.873	**65**	4,225	8.062	**115**	13,225	10.724
16	256	4.000	**66**	4,356	8.124	**116**	13,456	10.770
17	289	4.123	**67**	4,489	8.185	**117**	13,689	10.817
18	324	4.243	**68**	4,624	8.246	**118**	13,924	10.863
19	361	4.359	**69**	4,761	8.307	**119**	14,161	10.909
20	400	4.472	**70**	4,900	8.367	**120**	14,400	10.954
21	441	4.583	**71**	5,041	8.426	**121**	14,641	11.000
22	484	4.690	**72**	5,184	8.485	**122**	14,884	11.045
23	529	4.796	**73**	5,329	8.544	**123**	15,129	11.091
24	576	4.899	**74**	5,476	8.602	**124**	15,376	11.136
25	625	5.000	**75**	5,625	8.660	**125**	15,625	11.180
26	676	5.099	**76**	5,776	8.718	**126**	15,876	11.225
27	729	5.196	**77**	5,929	8.775	**127**	16,129	11.269
28	784	5.292	**78**	6,084	8.832	**128**	16,384	11.314
29	841	5.385	**79**	6,241	8.888	**129**	16,641	11.358
30	900	5.477	**80**	6,400	8.944	**130**	16,900	11.402
31	961	5.568	**81**	6,561	9.000	**131**	17,161	11.446
32	1,024	5.657	**82**	6,724	9.055	**132**	17,424	11.489
33	1,089	5.745	**83**	6,889	9.110	**133**	17,689	11.533
34	1,156	5.831	**84**	7,056	9.165	**134**	17,956	11.576
35	1,225	5.916	**85**	7,225	9.220	**135**	18,225	11.619
36	1,296	6.000	**86**	7,396	9.274	**136**	18,496	11.662
37	1,369	6.083	**87**	7,569	9.327	**137**	18,769	11.705
38	1,444	6.164	**88**	7,744	9.381	**138**	19,044	11.747
39	1,521	6.245	**89**	7,921	9.434	**139**	19,321	11.790
40	1,600	6.325	**90**	8,100	9.487	**140**	19,600	11.832
41	1,681	6.403	**91**	8,281	9.539	**141**	19,881	11.874
42	1,764	6.481	**92**	8,464	9.592	**142**	20,164	11.916
43	1,849	6.557	**93**	8,649	9.644	**143**	20,449	11.958
44	1,936	6.633	**94**	8,836	9.695	**144**	20,736	12.000
45	2,025	6.708	**95**	9,025	9.747	**145**	21,025	12.042
46	2,116	6.782	**96**	9,216	9.798	**146**	21,316	12.083
47	2,209	6.856	**97**	9,409	9.849	**147**	21,609	12.124
48	2,304	6.928	**98**	9,604	9.899	**148**	21,904	12.166
49	2,401	7.000	**99**	9,801	9.950	**149**	22,201	12.207
50	2,500	7.071	**100**	10,000	10.000	**150**	22,500	12.247

NOTE: *Answers to selected, and in general odd-numbered problems only, are given here.*

Answers to Chapter 1

Introducing: *MATHEMATICS*

Section 1

A (1) IIII∩∩∩ IIII∩∩∩ 𓍢𓍢𓍢 (3) c; (5) b; (7) $10,000

B (1) To find the number of volts produced in a network supplied by a battery, multiply the number of amperes (current) by the number of ohms (resistance) in the circuit.

(3) *See Chapter 5*; (5) *See Chapter 7.*

C (1) *See Chapter 8*; (3) No! *See Chapter 10*; (5) 15 posters and three banners; (7) b; (9) About 69 times out of a million.

Section 2

B (1) 3573; (3) 3027; (5) 27,246; (7) 40,012;
(9) 5,237,815.29

C (1) 271; (3) 258

Section 3

A (3) About 8; (5) $30, 6%

B (1) 310; (3) 311; (5) 268; (7) 231; (9) 3061

Section 4

B (1) 3800; (3) 4964; (5) 5913; (7) 3530; (9) 3177

Section 5

A (1) *Add* 287 to the present year.

B (1) 35; (3) 217; (5) 346; (7) 312; (9) 314

Section 6

B (1) 4396; (3) 5996; (5) 6644; (7) 1038; (9) 3993

Section 7

B (1) 543; (3) 4466; (5) 4606; (7) 41,172; (9) 23,625

Section 8

B (1) 125,454; (3) 112,024; (5) 73,920 (7) 28,804
(9) 658,600

Section 9

B (1) 240; (3) 109; (5) 580; (7) 964; (9) 2331

Section 10

B (1) $237\frac{3}{7}$; (3) $435\frac{2}{9}$; (5) $503\frac{3}{46}$; (7) $707\frac{14}{63}$; (9) $2473\frac{11}{43}$

The Oldest Skill: COUNTING

Section 1

A (1) 12,164; (3) 1864

B (1)

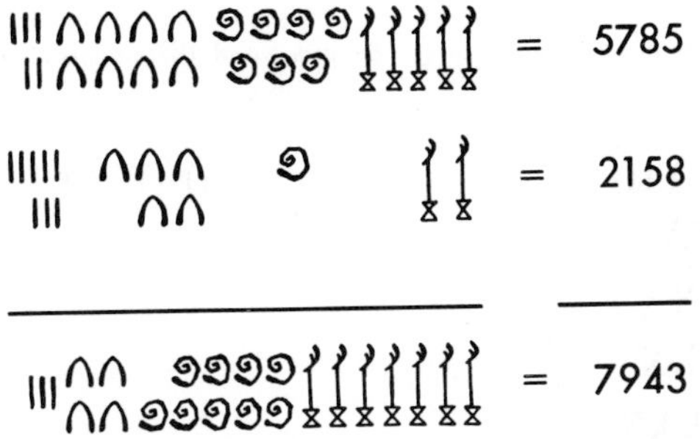

= 5785

= 2158

= 7943

Fig. 2-1-B1. Adding 5785 and 2158 in (a) Egyptian and (b) modern numerals.

(3) (a)

CCXVI	
CLVII	
CCCLXVVIII	= CCCLXXIII

(b) 373

(5) (a)

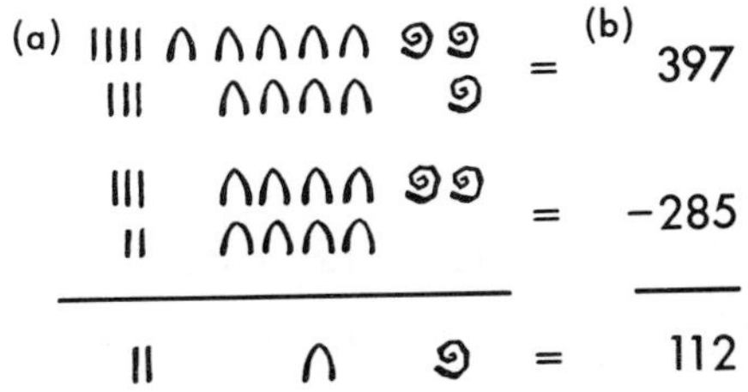

(a) = (b) 397

= −285

= 112

Fig. 2-1-B5. Subtracting 285 from 397 using (a) Egyptian and (b) modern numerals.

(7) (a)

CCCLVIII	=	CCLLXXXXXVIII
	−	CC L XXV
		L XXX III

(b) 83

C (1)

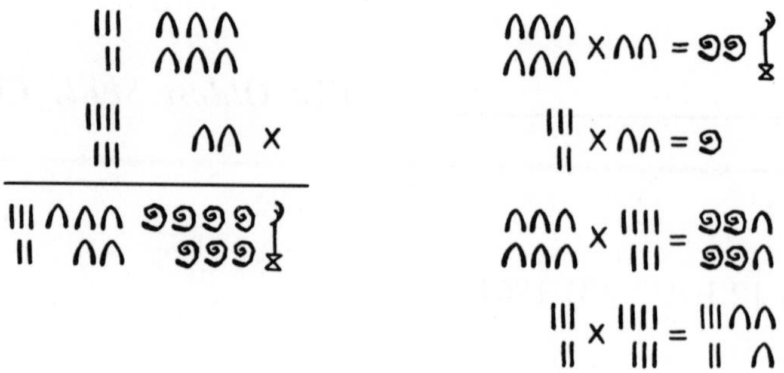

Explanation

Fig. 2-1-C1. Multiplying 65 by 27 in (a) Egyptian and (b) modern numerals.

(3) (a)

$$\begin{array}{r} \text{XXXXVIII} \\ \times\ \text{XXXV} \\ \hline \text{CCXXXX} \\ \text{MCCCCXXXX} \\ \hline \text{M D C LXXX} \end{array}$$

(b) 1680

Explanation:

$$\begin{aligned} \text{V} \times \text{III} &= \text{XV} \\ \text{V} \times \text{V} &= \text{XXV} \\ \text{V} \times \text{XXXX} &= \text{CC} \\ \text{XV} + \text{XXV} + \text{CC} &= \text{CCXXXX} \\ \text{XXX} \times \text{III} &= \text{LXXXX} \\ \text{XXX} \times \text{V} &= \text{CL} \\ \text{XXX} \times \text{XXXX} &= \text{MCC} \\ \text{MCC} + \text{CL} + \text{LXXXX} &= \text{MCCCCXXXX} \end{aligned}$$

Section 2

A (1)

+	0	1	2	3
0	0	1	2	3
1	1	2	3	0
2	2	3	0	1
3	3	0	1	2

(2) $(2 + 3) = 1$, $(3 + 2) \pm 1$

(3) $(1 + 2) + 3 = 3 + 3 = 2$
$1 + (2 + 3) = 1 + 1 = 2$

(4) $0 + 0 = 0$, $1 + 0 = 1$,
$2 + 0 = 2$, $3 + 0 = 3$

(5) Negatives of 0, 1, 2, 3 are 0, 3, 2, 1

Section 3

A (1) (*a*) 4, (*b*) 1; (2) (*a*) 1, (*b*) 4; (3) (*a*) 3, (*b*) 2;
(4) (*a*) 1, (*b*) 2; (5, 6) Commutative principle;

(7) $(4 \times 2) \times 3 = 3 \times 3 = 4$
$4 \times (2 \times 3) = 4 \times 1 = 4$ Associative principle;

(8) $(3 \times 3) \times 2 = 4 \times 2 = 3$
$3 \times (3 \times 2) = 3 \times 1 = 3$ Associative principle

C (1)

×	0	1	2	3	4	5	6
0	0	0	0	0	0	0	0
1	0	1	2	3	4	5	6
2	0	2	4	6	1	3	5
3	0	3	6	2	5	1	4
4	0	4	1	5	2	6	3
5	0	5	3	1	6	4	2
6	0	6	5	4	3	2	1

Section 4

A (1) 3; (3) 9; (5) 13; (7) 15; (9) 1100; (11) 0101;
(13) 1111; (15) 0010

B (1)
```
 01001
 01100
 10101  (= 21)
```

(3)
```
      0111
   ×  1010
      0000
     0111
    0000
   0111
   1000110  (= 70)
```

C (1)
```
   10
 - 01
   01  (= 1)
```

(3)
```
  11001   (= 25)
 -10101   (= 21)
  00100   (=  4)
```

Section 5

A (1) (*a*) $-5 < 0 < 1 < 3 < 6 < 8 < 11 < 12$

(3) (*a*) $-2 < 0 < 1 < 3 < 4 < 6 < 7 < 9$

(5) (*a*) $-9 < 0 < 5 < 11 < 15 < 17$

(7) 7 tens, 5 ones, 6 tenths, 8 hundredths

(9) 1 hundred, 3 tens, 8 ones, 5 tenths, 0 hundredths

(11) 3 hundreds, 1 ten, 8 ones, 9 tenths, 1 hundredth

B (1) (*a*) $-0.7 < -0.15 < 0.02 < 3 < 5$

(3) (*a*) $-0.5 < -0.05 < 0.06 < 0.6 < 3$

(5) 3 millions, 5 hundred thousands, 0 ten thousands, 1 thousand, 0 hundreds, 3 tens, 3 ones, 1 tenth, 8 hundredths, 8 thousandths

(7) 0 ones, 0 tenths, 0 hundredths, 1 thousandth, 4 ten-thousandths, 4 hundred-thousandths, 5 millionths

Section 6

A (1) -2; (3) -10; (5) $+3$; (7) 164.14; (9) 906.899; (11) 508.62

B (1) $+7$; (3) -20; (5) -6; (7) $+2$

C (1) -1.1; (3) -12.5; (5) $+1.1$

Section 7

A (1) $+2$; (3) $+6$; (5) $+19$; (7) $+22$; (9) -13; (11) -14; (13) -5; (15) 0

B (1) $18 - 5 = 13$; (3) $4 + 8 = +12$; (5) $13 - 6 = +7$; (7) $-2 + 9 = +7$

Section 8

A (1) $+300$; (3) $+78$; (5) -300; (7) -78; (9) -300; (11) -78; (13) $+300$; (15) $+78$

B (1) $+31.96$; (3) -12.69; (5) -46.97; (7) $+43.71$

Section 9

A (1) $\frac{1}{7}$; (3) $\frac{1}{15}$; (5) $-\frac{1}{3}$; (7) $-\frac{1}{4}$; (9) $\frac{3}{2}$; (11) $\frac{7}{5}$; (13) $-\frac{5}{6}$; (15) $\frac{11}{15}$; (17) 4; (19) 3; (21) -4; (23) -3; (25) -4; (27) -3; (29) $+4$; (31) $+3$

B (1) $\frac{2}{3} \times \frac{4}{3} = \frac{8}{9}$; (3) $\frac{4}{5} \times \frac{21}{8} = 2\frac{1}{10}$; (5) $-\frac{8}{9}$; (7) $-2\frac{1}{10}$; (9) $-\frac{8}{9}$; (11) $-2\frac{1}{10}$; (13) $\frac{8}{9}$; (15) $2\frac{1}{10}$

C (1) $\frac{2}{5}$; (3) $\frac{4}{17}$; (5) $\frac{5}{2} \times \frac{4}{23} = \frac{10}{23}$; (7) $\frac{61}{8} \times \frac{1}{4} = 1\frac{29}{32}$

Section 10

B (1) $120 + 24 = 144$; (3) $80 + 56 = 136$; (5) $300 + 75 = 375$; (7) $2200 - 22 = 2178$; (9) $8000 - 8 = 7992$

Section 11

(1) 3.963×10^3; (3) 5.747×10^7; (5) 2.9003×10^4; (7) 2.38854×10^5; (9) 1.86×10^5; (11) 864,000; (13) 74,900; (15) 142,000,000; (17) 1250; 240; (19) 1087

Answers to Chapter 3

MATHEMATICS OF SCIENCE AND INDUSTRY

Section 1

A = approximate, E = exact.

A (1) A; (3) E; (5) E; (7) E; (9) A; (11) E; (13) A; (15) A; (17) A; (19) A

Section 2

The first figure given is the *precision*, the second figure is the *doubt.*

A (1) 0.1 ft., 0.05 ft.; (3) 0.01°, 0.005°; (5) 1 min., $\frac{1}{2}$ min.; (7) 0.001 in., 0.0005 in.; (9) 0.1 sq. in., 0.05 sq. in.

B (1) 0.01 ft., 0.005 ft.; (3) 1 sec., $\frac{1}{2}$ sec.; (5) 0.01 sq. mi., 0.005 sq. mi.; (7) $\frac{1}{2}$ in., $\frac{1}{4}$ in.; (9) $\frac{1}{8}$ sq. in., $\frac{1}{16}$ sq. in.

C (1) $5\frac{1}{2}$ in. has a precision of $\frac{1}{2}$ in. and is in doubt by $\frac{1}{4}$ in.
$5\frac{4}{8}$ in. has a precision of $\frac{1}{8}$ in., and is in doubt by $\frac{1}{16}$ in.
(3) $2\frac{1}{2}$ hr. has a precision of $\frac{1}{2}$ hr., and is in doubt by $\frac{1}{4}$ hr.
2 hr. 30 min. has a precision of 1 min., and is in doubt by $\frac{1}{2}$ min.

Section 3

(1) 0.625; (3) 0.6875; (5) 3.28125; (7) 5.53125; (9) 10.328125; (11) $\frac{3}{8}$; (13) $\frac{5}{16}$; (15) $2\frac{31}{32}$; (17) $5\frac{23}{32}$; (19) $6\frac{45}{64}$

Section 4

A (1, 3, 5, 7, 9) In each case, all but the last digit is *sure*; the last figure is an indication of the precision, i.e. 0.1, 0.01, etc., and the measurement may be in error by one half the precision.

B (1) 85.2 mi.; (3) 950.6 yd.; (5) 71.18 in.; (7) 27°; (9) 24 hr.

C (1) 0.38; (3) 0.56; (5) 0.09; (7) 0.714; (9) 0.266

Section 5

A (1) 199.1762 → 199.18 ft.; (3) 312.17 → 312.2 in.; (5) 58.89 → 58.9 mi.; (7) 114.3651 → 114.365 hr.; (9) 30.7498 → 30.75 ft.

B (1) 48.85″ → 48.9″

C (1) 11.4375 → 11.4 in.; (3) 17.65625 → 17.66 in.

Section 6

A (1) 7.75 → 7.8; (3) 7.2384 → 7.24;
(5) 4.158 → 4.2; (7) 52.6560 → 52.7;
(9) 0.720244 → 0.720

B (1) 564.0 → 564 man-hours; (3) 1590.4 → 1590 watts (3 s.f.);
(5) 6904.65 → 6900 mi. (3 s.f.)

Section 7

(1) 1.3809 lb. (3) 6.95 mi.;
(5) 18.5889 ... → 18.59 mpg.; (7) 176.395 . . . → 177 ohms;
(9) 615.2905 . . . → 615 mph

Section 8

A (1) $\frac{2}{3}$; (3) $\frac{3}{4}$; (5) $\frac{8}{9}$; (7) $\frac{4}{9}$; (9) $\frac{8}{3}$ or $2\frac{2}{3}$

B (1) $\frac{5}{8}$; (3) 1; (5) $\frac{10}{33}$; (7) $-\frac{1}{4}$; (9) $+\frac{1}{6}$;

C (1) $\frac{27}{2}$ or $13\frac{1}{2}$; (3) $40\frac{1}{2}$; (5) $1\frac{3}{5}$; (7) -6; (9) $+2\frac{1}{10}$

Section 9

A (1) $\frac{5}{8}$; (3) 1; (5) $\frac{10}{33}$; (7) $-\frac{1}{4}$; (9) $+\frac{1}{6}$

B (1) $1\frac{3}{5}$; (3) $8\frac{1}{2}$; (5) $\frac{13}{24}$; (7) $-2\frac{4}{9}$; (9) $\frac{1}{10}$

C (1) $7\frac{1}{9}$; (3) 27; (5) $2\frac{2}{21}$; (7) $-\frac{15}{16}$; (9) $+3\frac{1}{2}$

Section 10

A (1) 2; (3) $1\frac{1}{7}$; (5) -1; (7) $-\frac{1}{10}$; (9) -1

B (1) $1\frac{1}{4}$; (3) $-\frac{1}{15}$; (5) $-\frac{11}{16}$; (7) $\frac{11}{16}$; (9) $\frac{9}{28}$

C (1) LCD = 20, $-1\frac{13}{20}$; (3) LCD = 24, $6\frac{11}{24}$;
(5) LCD = 60, $3\frac{2}{5}$; (7) LCD = 30, $2\frac{19}{30}$;
(9) LCD = 105, $2\frac{2}{35}$;

TWO-DIMENSIONAL NUMBERS

Section 1

A

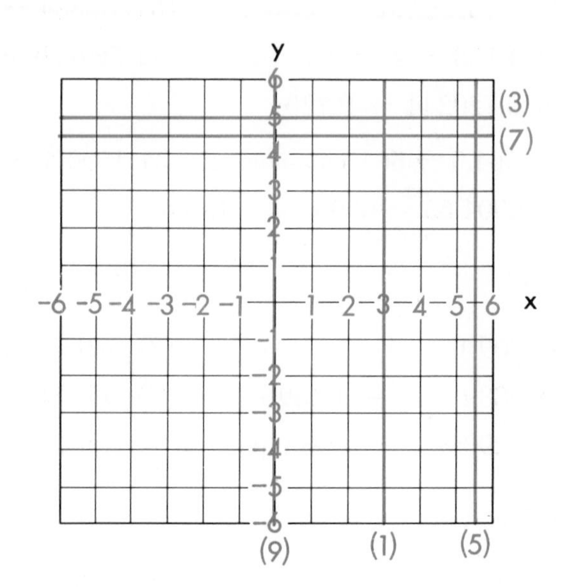

Fig. 4-1-A.

Lattice for Test Questions in Part A.

B (*a*) (1, 1) I; (*c*) (−3, 4) II; (*e*) (−5, −4) III;
(*g*) (1, −4) IV; (*i*) (4, 0) I and IV; (*k*) (0, −2) III and IV

C

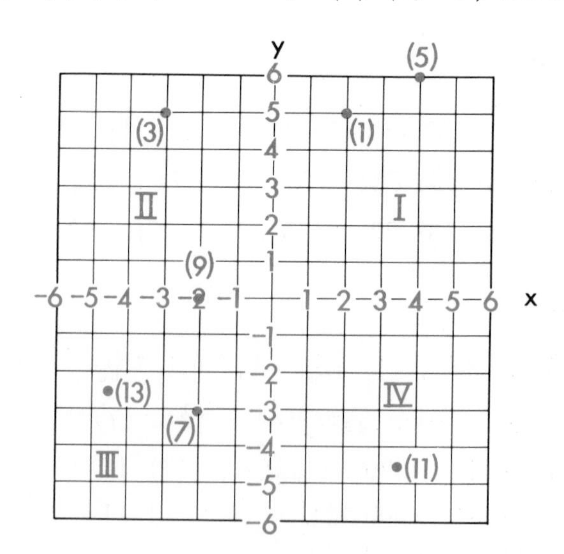

Fig. 4-1-C.

Lattice for Test Questions in Part C.

Section 2

A The vertex (corner) points are as follows:

(1)

x	-4	-2	5	3
y	-2	3	3	-2

(3)

x	-1	-1	4	4
y	-3	2	2	-3

(5)

x	-4	-2	4
y	-3	3	-3

(7)

x	-4	-4	5
y	-3	4	-3

B

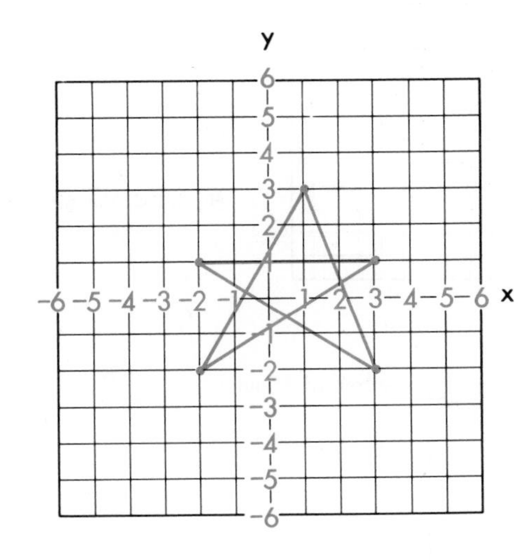

Fig. 4-2-B1. The five-pointed star.

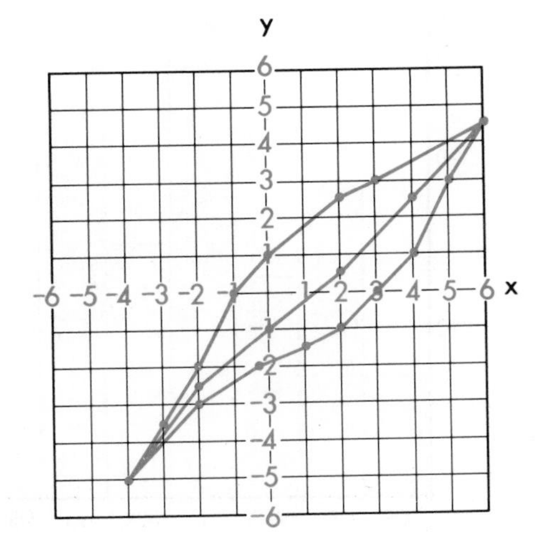

Fig. 4-2-B3. The leaf.

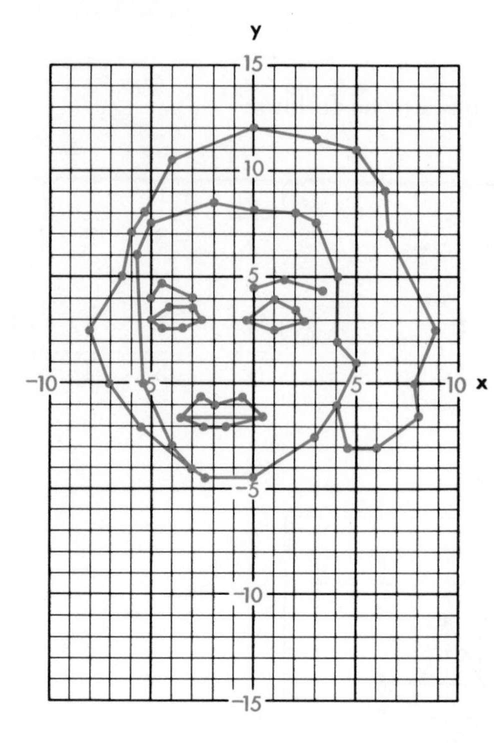

Fig. 4-2-C. The girl's face.

Section 3

B

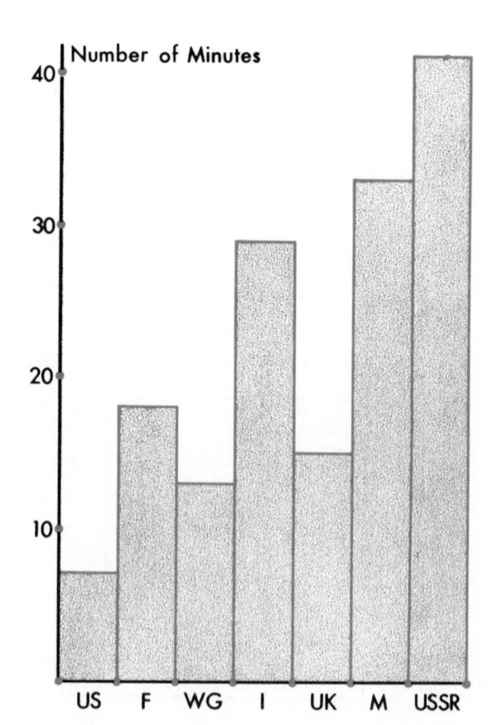

Fig. 4-3-B1.

Bar graph of average working time for money to buy a quart of milk.

C (*a*) (1) Elementary 26.3 million
Secondary 7.1 million
College 2.5 million

Section 4

A (1) 1 million; (3) 40 million; (5) 115 million; (7) 62 million; (9) 15 million

B (1) 170 million; (3) 200 million

C (1) *See graph*; (2, 3) This depends upon the graph

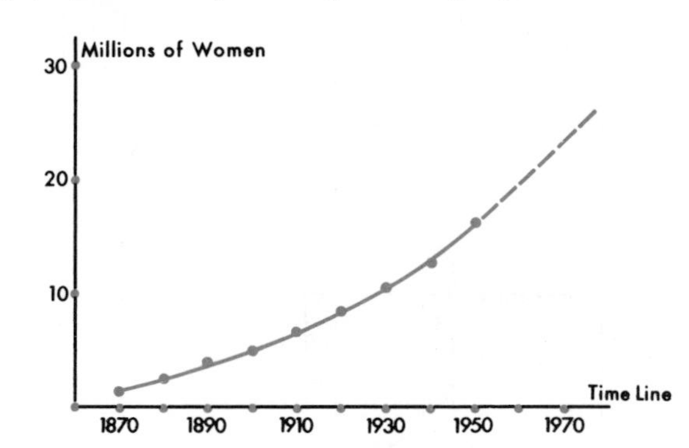

Fig. 4-4-C1. Time-change graph of women in the working population of the USA.

Section 5

A (1) 7; (3) 16; (5) 25; (7) 16; (9) 9

B (1)

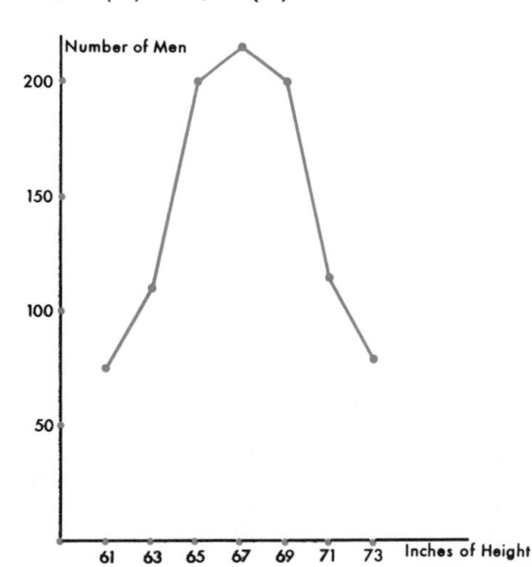

Fig. 4-5-B1. Distribution of height among 1000 men.

C (1) (Graph not shown.)

(1)

Midpoint	55	65	75	85	95
Per cent	7.4	18.5	37.0	33.3	3.7

Section 6

A

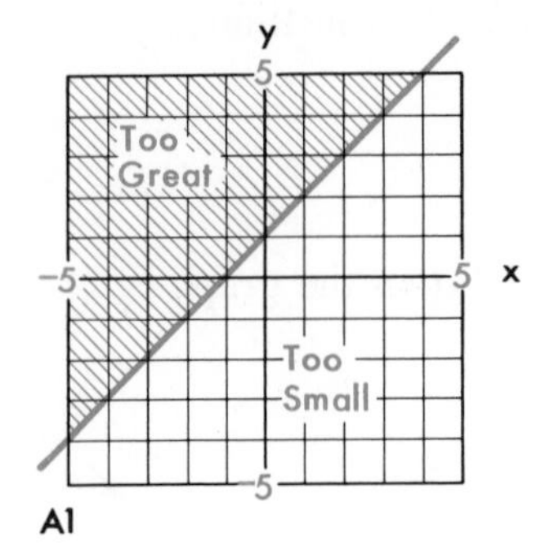

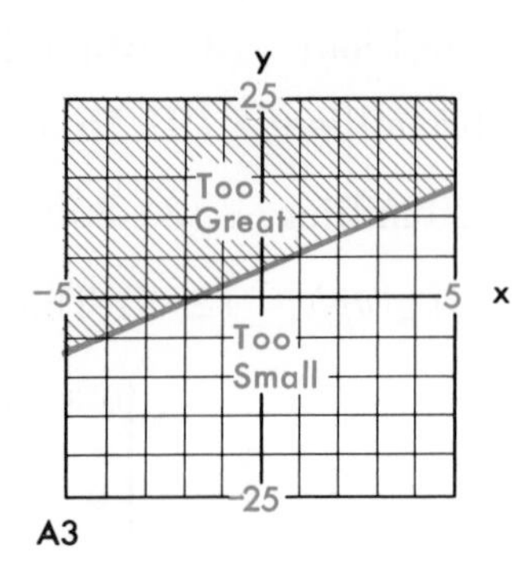

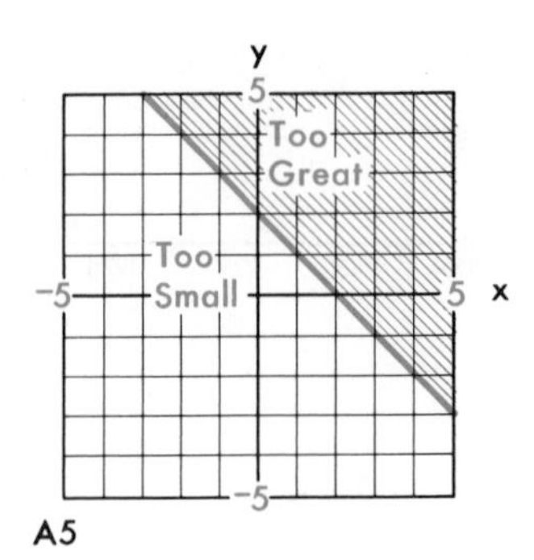

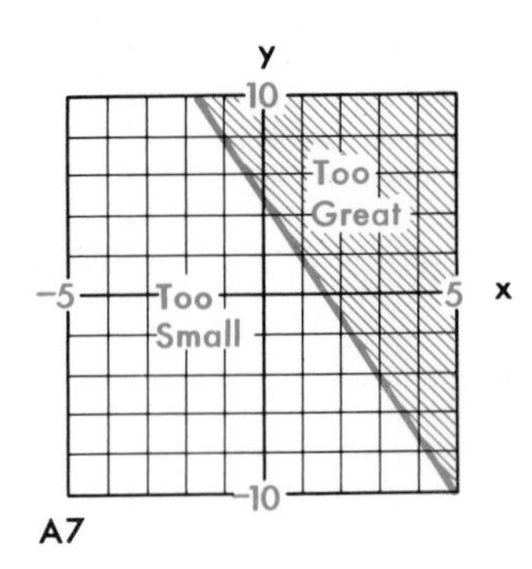

Fig. 4-6A. Graphs for Test Problems 1, 3, 5, and 7.

B (*a*) (1) $y = x$; (3) $y = 2x$; (5) $y = 2x - 1$

Section 7

A (1)

x	−3	−2	−1	0	1	2	3
y	−15	−10	−5	0	5	10	15

(3)

x	−3	−2	−1	0	1	2	3
y	6	4	2	0	−2	−4	−6

(5)

x	-3	-2	-1	0	1	2	3
y	-16	-11	-6	-1	4	9	14

(7)

x	-3	-2	-1	0	1	2	3
y	5	3	1	-1	-3	-5	-7

(9)

x	-3	-2	-1	0	1	2	3
y	-4	-2	0	2	4	6	8

B (*a*) (1) $y = 3x$; (3) $y = -4x$; (5) $y = 2x + 2$;
(7) $y = 2(x + 2)$

Section 8

A Using only the number *3* in (*a*) and *4* in (*b*).

(1) (*a*) Using *3*: $12y + 3 = 24x + 3$; $12y - 3 = 24x - 3$

(*b*) Using *4*: $48y = 96x$; $3y = 6x$

(3) (*a*) $24y + 3 = 36x + 3$; $24y - 3 = 36x - 3$

(*b*) $96y = 144x$; $6y = 9x$

(5) (*a*) $6y + 3 = 12x + 3$; $6y - 3 = 12x - 3$

(*b*) $24y = 48x$; $\frac{6}{4}y = 3$

(7) (*a*) $y + 3 = 10x + 3$; $y - 3 = 10x - 3$

(*b*) $4y = 40x$; $\frac{1}{4}y = \frac{10}{4}x$

(9) (*a*) $2y + 3 = -3x + x$; $2y - 3 = -3x - 3$

(*b*) $8y = -12x$; $\frac{2}{4}y = -\frac{3}{4}x$

B (1) $y = x - 5$; (3) $y = x + 2$; (5) $y = x + 5$;
(7) $y = 6x$; (9) $y = -x$;

C (*a*) (1) $y = 2x - 4$; (3) $y = 3x + 4$; (5) $y = 3x + 1$;
(7) $y = 3x + 1$; (9) $y = 4x - 3$

Section 9

A (Formula only) (1) $y = x^2$; (3) $y = 3x^2$

B (Tables of values only)

(1)

x	-3	-2	-1	0	1	2	3
y	8	3	0	-1	0	3	8

(3)

x	-3	-2	-1	0	1	2	3
y	15	5	-1	-3	-1	5	15

C (Solved formula only)

(1) $y = x^2 - 1$; (3) $y = 2x^2 - 3$

Section 10

A (1) $x = 2, y = 2$; (3) $x = 4, y = 9$; (5) $x = 2\frac{1}{2}, y = -5\frac{1}{2}$

B (1) $(3, 9)$ or $(-2, 4)$; (3) $(2\frac{1}{2}, 12\frac{1}{2})$ or $(-1, 2)$

C *See graphs.*

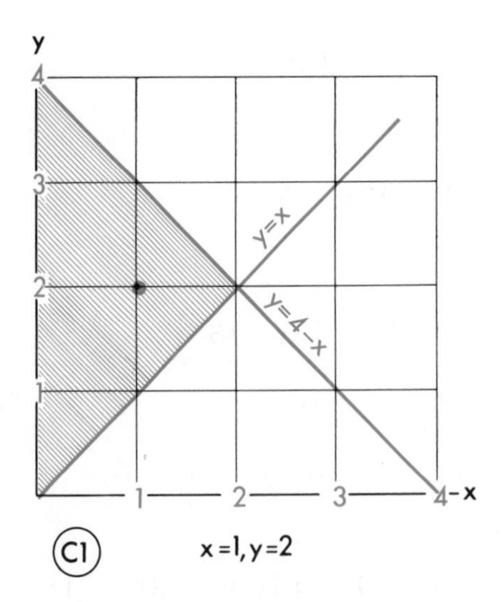

Fig. 4-10-C1. Graph for Test Problem C1.

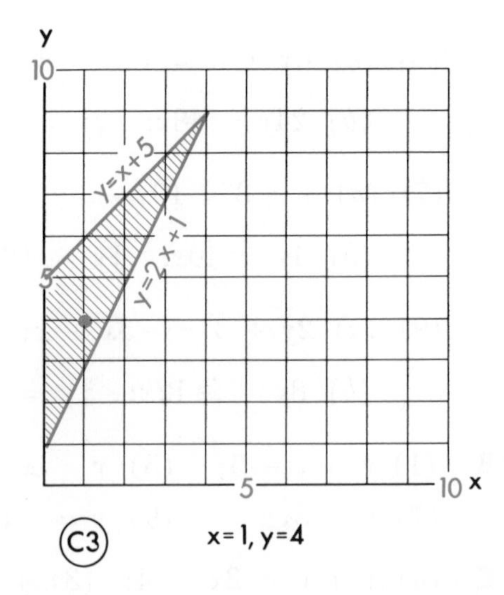

Fig. 4-10-C3. Graph for Test Problem C3.

NUMBER PUZZLES

Section 1

A (1) 3; (3) 5; (5) 6

B (1) 3; (3) 2

C (1) 7; (3) 1

Section 2

A (1) $x + 17$; (3) $x + 8$; (5) $x - 11$;
(7) $x - 6$; (9) $8x$; (11) $\frac{2}{3}x$ or $\frac{2x}{3}$

B (1) $x + 7 = 9$; (3) $2x = x - 5$;
(5) $3x + 4 = 16$; (7) $2x + 5 = 3x - 2$

Section 3

A (1) 4; (3) 3

B (1) $x + 8 = 12, x = 4$; (3) $x + 2 = 7, x = 5$;
(5) $x - 8 = -2, x = 6$; (7) $x - 5 = -8, x = -3$

C (1) 1; (3) $\frac{5}{4}$; (5) -1; (7) $\frac{7}{20}$; (9) $3\frac{11}{15}$; (11) -2

Section 4

A (1) 5; (3) 3

B (1) 6; (3) 5

C (1) $\frac{2}{7}$; (3) $\frac{3}{4}$; (5) $\frac{1}{10}$

Section 5

A (1) $\frac{1}{5}$; (3) $\frac{3}{2}$; (5) $\frac{2}{5}$; (7) $\frac{6}{17}$; (9) $-\frac{2}{5}$

B (1) 2; (3) 6; (5) 18

C (1) 9; (3) 10; (5) $1\frac{1}{7}$; (7) 2

Section 6

A (1) 2; (3) 3; (5) 2

B (1) $5x - 4 = 11, x = 3$; (3) $8x + 1 = 41, x = 5$

(5) $3 + 4x = 5, x = \frac{1}{2}$

C (1) $\frac{1}{2}$; (3) $\frac{7}{12}$; (5) $\frac{5}{9}$; (7) $3\frac{1}{2}$

Section 7

A (1) $2(x + 1) = 6$; (3) $8(x - 4) = 56$;

(5) $3(x + 2) = 21$; (7) $4(x - 3) = 16$

B (1) $3(x + 5) = 5(x - 3)$; (3) $8(x - 3) = 5(x + 6)$;

(5) $2(3x + 1) = 8(x - 4)$ (7) $5(3x - 1) = 4(2x + 4)$

C (1) $3(x + 1) + 4 = 5(2x - 1) - 23$;

(3) $2(2x + 1) - 1 = 3(3x - 1) - 16$

Section 8

A (1) 2; (3) 11; (5) 5; (7) 7

B (1) 15; (3) 18; (5) 17; (7) 3

C (1) 5; (3) 4

Section 9

A (1) 5, 10; (3) 4, 12; (5) 2, 5; (7) 10, 16; (9) 2, 8

B (1) 3, 5; (3) 5, 11

C (1) 2, 7; (3) 11, 8

Section 10

A (1) 5, 6; (3) 10, 11, 12; (5) 11, 12, 13, 14

B (1) 18, 20; (3) 31, 33; (5) 20, 22, 24, 26;
(7) 13, 15, 17, 19; (9) No such numbers exist

C (1) 89, 93, 97; (3) 603, 609, 615

Answers to Chapter 

FORMULA PROBLEMS

Section 1

A (1)

$m + n$	4	7	10	13	17	21
$m - n$	-2	-3	-4	-5	-7	-9

(3)

$a + b$	-3	7	-1	11	-3
$a - b$	1	-3	7	-3	13

(5)

$2f$	2	4	6	8	10
$3g$	-6	24	12	15	15
$2f + 3g$	-4	28	18	23	25
$2f - 3g$	8	-20	-6	-7	-5

B (1) $3x - y$; (3) $3p - r$; (5) $7x - 2y$; (7) $a + 4x$;
(9) $4h$, or $4h + 0k$; (11) $-9n + 4p$; (13) $y + z = 5x - 2$;
(15) $2p = 2m + 18$; (17) $0 = -4x - 14$; (19) $0 = -3r + 12$

C (1) $\frac{1}{3}(3n) = n$; (3) $\frac{1}{2}(2n + 6) = n + 3$

Section 2

A (1) $m = 2p$, or $p = \frac{1}{2} m$;
(3) $s = p + 1$, or $p = s - 1$;
(5) $b = 2t - 1$, or $t = \frac{1}{2} (b + 1)$, or $t = \frac{1}{2}b + \frac{1}{2}$

B (1) $r = p^3$; (3) $a = b^3 + 1$; (5) $w = t^2 + 1$

C (1) $c = a + b$, or $a = c - b$, or $b = c - a$;

(3) $p = mn$, or $m = \frac{p}{n}$, or $n = \frac{p}{m}$

Section 3

A Your guesses may be as good as the following:
(1) $m = p$; (3) $t = s + 1$; (5) $w + z = 2$

B Your guesses may be as good as the following:
(1) $t = b^2$; (3) $w = d^2 + 1$

C In (1) and (3), your guesses may be as good as those given here:
(1) $p = m + n$; (3) $ab = c$; (5) 1.5 volt, 0.5 amp., 3.0 ohms;
(7) 4 volts, 2 amps., 2 ohms; (9) 3 volts, 3 amps., 1 ohm

Section 4

A (1) 16.3 ohms; (3) 19.5 in. (5) 0.9995 in.

B (1) 8.7175 → 8.72 sq. in.;
(3) 17.4515 → 17.5 sq. in.;
(5) 150 miles (2 s.f.); (7) 31.50 → 32 volts; (9) $187.50

C (1) 14.107 . . . → 14%; (3) 2.459 . . . → 2.46;
(5) $8\frac{1}{3}$ board feet; (7) 125.60 → 130 in./min. (2 s.f.)

Section 5

A (1) 300 ohms; (3) 1 in./ft.; (5) 320 foot-pounds (2 s.f.)

B (1) 2318.4 → 2300 ft. (2 s.f.); (3) 45 hp

C (1) 10; (3) 11 ohms; (5) 8.9 seconds

Section 6

A (1) 5.6 ohms; (3) 17 ft; (5) 52.5 yd.;
(7) 1.9516 in.; (9) 0.5000 in.

B (1) 3.00 hrs.; (3) 71 mph.; (5) 13.2 in.;
(7) 45.01 yd.; (9) 5 yr.; (11) 4%

C (1) 114 foot-pounds; (3) 9.2 ft.,; (5) 0.23 in.

Section 7

A F = false.
(1) F; (3) F; (5) Not a proportion;
(7) Not a proportion; (9) Not a proportion;
(11) (*a*) Middles are 8 and 9; (13) (*a*) Middles are 11 and 27

B (1) 9; (3) 22; (5) 15; (7) 36

C (1) $7\frac{1}{2}$; (3) $9\frac{1}{3}$; (5) $12\frac{1}{2}$; (7) $41\frac{1}{4}$

Section 8

A (1) $37.50; (3) 8.333 . . . → $8.34; (5) 11.2 → 11 items;
(7) 4.28 . . . → 4 items

B (1) 685.7 rpm; (3) 23.75 → 23 teeth; (5) 371.4 . . . → 371 rpm;
(7) 2.18 in.

C (1) 1840 qt.; (3) 245 cc; (5) 15,000 foot-pounds;
(7) 210 lb.; (9) 200 lb., (2 s.f.)

Section 9

A D = direct proportion, I = indirect proportion.

(1) $D, P = 2M$; (3) $D, T = 4S$; (5) $I, N = \frac{8}{A}$;

(7) $I, R = \frac{60}{C}$

B (1) $A = kB$; (3) $M = \frac{k}{P}$; (5) $N = kT$;

(7) $B = \frac{k}{Y}$; (9) $F = kma$; (11) $E = \frac{kv^2}{g}$

C (1) For *fixed velocity*, energy is *directly* proportional to mass.

(3) For *fixed volume*, pressure is *directly* proportional to the absolute temperature.

(5) Pressure is *directly* proportional to *absolute temperature* and *inversely* proportional to *volume*.

Section 10

A (1) $A = 2w$; (3) $C = 5r$; (5) $E = \frac{1}{4}R$;

(7) $G = \frac{18}{m}$; (9) $I = \frac{24}{L}$; (11) $M = \frac{12}{n^2}$

B In the following, only answers to part (d) are given:

(1) $A = 6L$; (3) $M = 7T$; (5) $R = \frac{24}{U}$; (7) $L = \frac{72}{W}$

C In the following, only the formula for answering is given:

(1) $F = \frac{2}{3}a$; (3) $R = \frac{10{,}000}{T}$; (5) $I = \frac{36}{d^2}$; (7) $S = 3D^2$

(The exact formula for No. 7 is $S = \pi D^2$, where π is approximately 3.14.)

THE MATHEMATICS LABORATORY

Section 2

	Total	*Average*	*Difference*	*Per Cent Error*
(1)	15.8	3.95	0.05	1.3
(3)	86.10	17.22	2.78	14
(5)	24.4	2.44	0.06	2.4

Section 3

A (1) Acute; (3) Right; (5) Obtuse; (7) Reflex; (9) Reflex

Section 4

A (1) 70°; (3) 30°; (5) 150°; (7) 80°; (9) 62.5°

Section 5

C

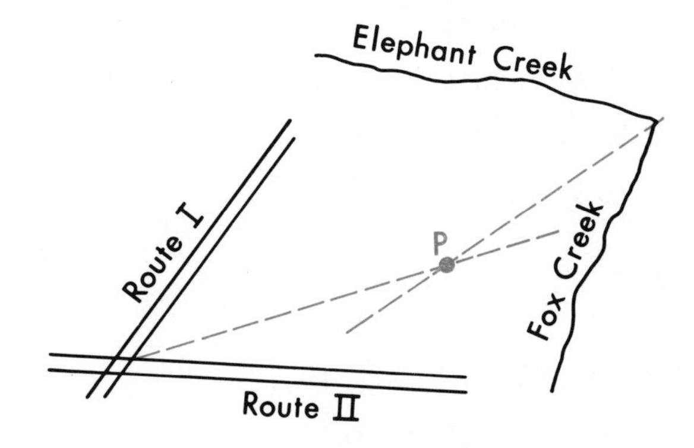

Fig. 7-5-C1. Best place for the factory.

GEOMETRICAL FIGURES

Section 2

A (1) 900°; (3) 1260°; (5) 135°; (7) 144°

Section 3

C (2) $EB = 12$

Section 4

B (1) $\angle 1 = 90°$

C (1) Central, 40°; (3) Inscribed, 40°; (5) Chord-chord, 60°;
(7) Secant-secant, 45°

Section 5

B (1) 25 sq. in.; (3) 24 sq. in.; (5) 32 sq. units;
(7) 40 sq. units; (9) 39 sq. units; (11) 78.550 → 78.6 sq. in.

C (1) 14.3448 → 14.3 sq. units;
(3) 25.9182 → 25.9 sq. units;
(5) 21.8708 → 21.9 sq. units;
(7) 23.4170118 → 23.4 sq. mi.

Section 6

A (1) $1\frac{1}{2}$, $1\frac{1}{2}$; (3) 3, 4; (5) $22\frac{1}{2}$, $33\frac{3}{4}$, 15;
(7) Ratio = 0.353, sides are 6.4, 12, 6.4

B R = ratio.
(1) $R^2 = 4.00 : 1$, area = 108 sq. units;

(3) $R = 0.614$, $R^2 = 0.377$, area = 3.2 sq. units;

(5) $R = 3.00$, $R^2 = 9.00$, area = 255 sq. units

Section 7

A (1) 150 cu. units; (3) 375 cu. units; (5) 240 cu. units;

(7) 1030 cu. units (3 s.f.)

B (1) Rectangular prism, 504 cu. units;

(3) Triangular prism, base = 27.6 sq. units, volume 193 cu. units;

(5) Cylinder, base = 12.568 sq. units, volume = 214 cu. units

Section 8

A In cubic units:

(1) 125; (3) 125; (5) 80.0; (7) 342

B Areas in square units, volumes in cubic units:

(1) Base = 28.0, volume = 84.0; (3) Base = 27.6, volume = 110;

(5) Base = 12.57, volume = 71.2

Section 9

(1) 4.19 cu. in.;

(3) $d^3 = 91.13$, $V = 47.7$ cu. in.;

(5) $d^3 = 244.1$, $V = 128$ cu. in.;

(7) $d^3 = 658.5$, $V = 345$ cu. in.;

(9) $d^3 = 1728$, $V = 905$ cu. ft.

Section 10

R = ratio of sides.

(1) $R = 2.00 : 1$, $R^3 = 8.00 : 1$, $V = 1600$ cu. in. (3 s.f.)

(3) $R = 0.500$, $R^3 = 0.125$, $V = 18.8$ cu. in.

(5) $R = 0.250$, $R^3 = 0.0156$, $V = 15.6$ cu. in.

Answers to Chapter 9

INDIRECT MEASUREMENT

Section 1

A (1) Elevation; (3) Depression; (5) Elevation;
(7) Depression

B You can check your measurements by asking the custodian engineer to look at the building blueprints and give you the correct answer.

Section 2

A (1) 17.3 → 17 ft. 4 in.; (3) 11.25 → 11 ft. 3 in. (2 s.f.)
(5) 11.6 → 11 ft. 7 in. (2 s.f.)

Section 3

You can check your measurements by comparing the results with those obtained by other students.

Section 4

A (1) 38 yd.; (3) 10.2 → 10 ft. 2 in.;
(5) 28.8 → 28 ft. 10 in.; (7) 171.8 → 172 ft.

B (1) 92 ft.; (3) 57 ft.

Section 5

A (1) $14.44 + 27.04 = 41.48$, $(7.1)^2 = 50.41$

$$\text{Per cent error} = \frac{100 \times 8.93}{46} = 19\%$$

This is not a right triangle.

(3) $4.8400 + 3.2400 = 8.0800, (2.76)^2 = 7.6176$

$$\text{Per cent error} = \frac{100 \times 0.4624}{7.8488} = 6\%$$

This is not a right triangle

B

(1) $36.0000 + 289.0000 = 325.0000, (18.1)^2 = 327.61$

$$\text{Per cent error} = \frac{100 \times (327.61 - 325.00)}{326} = 0.8\%$$

(3) $53.29 + 94.09 = 147.38, (12.1)^2 = 146.41$

$$\text{Per cent error} = \frac{100 \times 0.97}{147} = 0.7\%$$

(5) $306.25 + 265.69 = 571.94, (23.9)^2 = 571.21$

$$\text{Per cent error} = \frac{100 \times 0.73}{572} = 0.1\%$$

(7) $3994.24 + 11664 = 15658, (125)^2 = 15625$

$$\text{Per cent error} = \frac{100 \times 33}{15642} = 0.2\%$$

Section 6

A (1) $x^2 = 41.00, x = 6.4$
(3) $x^2 = 128.50, x = 11.3$ or 11.4
(5) $x^2 = 30.24, x = 5.5$
(7) $x^2 = 858.69, x = 29.3$

B (1) 10; (3) 50; (5) 12.0; (7) 5.88

C (1) 13.7 → 13 ft. 8 in.; (3) 27 in.

Section 7

B (1) $\sin 10^\circ = 0.17$, $\tan 10^\circ = 0.18$
(3) $\sin 40^\circ = 0.64$, $\tan 40^\circ = 0.84$
(5) $\sin 60^\circ = 0.87$, $\tan 60^\circ = 1.73$

Section 8

A (1) 0.2588, 0.2679; (3) 0.5150, 0.6009;
(5) 0.7880, 1.2799; (7) 0.9563, 3.2709;
(9) 0.3584, 0.3839

B (1) 18°; (3) 10°; (5) 5°; (7) 56°;
(9) Closer to 16°; (11) Closer to 80°

C The first number is the ratio, the second the nearest angle given in the table.
(1) 0.600, 37°; (3) 0.583, 30°; (5) 0.532, 32°;
(7) 1.22, 51°; (9) 0.757, $90^\circ - 49^\circ = 41^\circ$

Section 9

(1) 60°, 160.5172 → 160
(3) 40°, 432. 1365 → 432
(5) 20°, 22.364650 → 22.4
(7) 17°, 0.498291 → 0.498

Section 10

(1) 60°, 153.5 → 154;
(3) 40°, 360.6108 → 361;
(5) 20°, 23.801 . . . → 23.8;
(7) 12°, 1.666 . . . → 1.67

Answers to Chapter 10

ADVERTISEMENTS, EDITORIALS, and LOGICAL THINKING

Section 3

A (1) All; (3) All; (5) Some; (7) Some

C (1) If it is a piece of iron, then it is a metal.

(3) If he is a teacher, then he was once a student.

(5) If it is a bird, then it may or may not fly.

(7) If she is a girl, then she may or may not be pretty.

(9) If it is a mushroom, then it may or may not be inedible.

Section 4

A *T* means that this is a *true* logical conclusion, *F* means that it is not.

(1) If you live in Wisconsin, then you live in Oshkosh, *F*.

(3) If you are a human being, then you are a man, *F*.

(5) If it is a gleeb, then it is a froom, *T*.

B The following may be true or false *in fact,* but they are not *logically* true.

(1) If a boy's school grades improve, then he is studying.

(3) If a person will not drive over 60 miles per hour in traffic, then he is a careful driver.

Section 5

A *T* means that this is a *true* logical conclusion, *F* means that it is not.

(1) If you do not live in Oshkosh, then you do not live in Wisconsin, *F*.

(3) If *X* is not a man, then *X* is not a human being, *F*.

(5) If *X* is not a froom, then *X* is not a gleeb. This is *T*. (Note that

the converse *and inverse* of a definition are always logically true.)

B The following *may* or *may not* be true *in fact,* but they are *not logically true.*

(1) If the month is not October, then the weather will not be fair and warm.

(3) If youths do not participate in sports, they are not strong.

Section 8

A V = valid, I = invalid. (1) V; (3) I; (5) V; (7) V

B (1) None; (3) None

C (1) If you travel much, you are a better man.

Section 10

B (1) If $\angle 1 = 90°$ and $\angle 2 = 90°$, then $\angle 1 = \angle 2$.

(3) Let $\angle 3$ be the angle in common. Then, in one case, $\angle 1 + \angle 3 = 90°$, and in the other case $\angle 2 + \angle 3 = 90°$. The equivalent statements are: $\angle 1 = 90° - \angle 3$, and $\angle 2 = 90° - \angle 3$. Therefore, $\angle 1 = \angle 2$.

Answers to Chapter 11

MODERN PROBLEMS IN MATHEMATICS

Section 1

A The *first set* given is the *union,* the *second set* is the *intersection.*

(1) {A, B, C, D}, {B, C}; (3) {A, B, C, E, M}, ϕ;

(5) {A, B, C}, {A, B, C}; (7) {A, B, C, D}, {B, C};

(9) {A, B, C, D}, ϕ

B In the following, the four numbers are (a) the cardinal number of set A; (b) the cardinal number of set B; (c) the cardinal number of the union; and (d) the cardinal number of the intersection.

(1) 3, 4, 6, 1; (3) 7, 5, 9, 3;

(5) 2, 5, 5, 2; (7) 3, 2, 5, 0

C In the following, the five numbers are (a) the cardinal number of set A; (b) the cardinal number of set B; (c) the cardinal number of set C; (d) the cardinal number of the union of the three sets, and (e) the cardinal number of the intersection of the three sets.

(1) 6, 7, 7, 13, 2; (3) 5, 7, 3, 9, 0

Section 2

A (1) 21; (3) 26

B (1) 39

C (1) 5

Section 3

A *See graphs.*

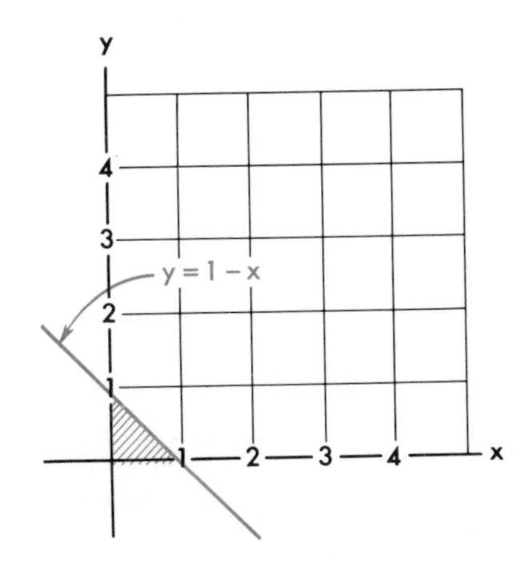

Fig. 11-3-A1. Polygon graph for Problem A1.

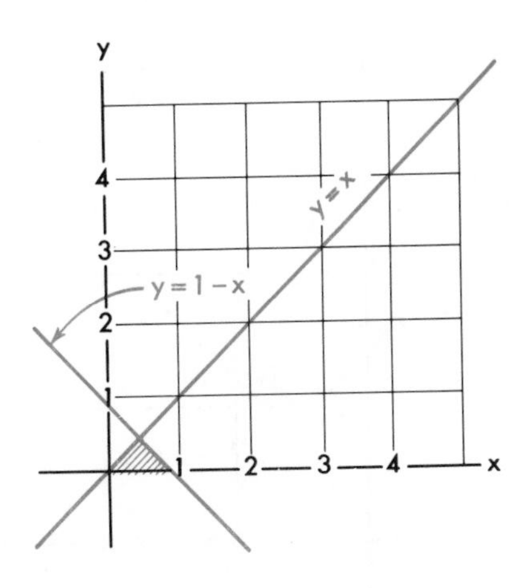

Fig. 11-3-A3. Polygon graph for Problem A3.

B *See graphs below.*

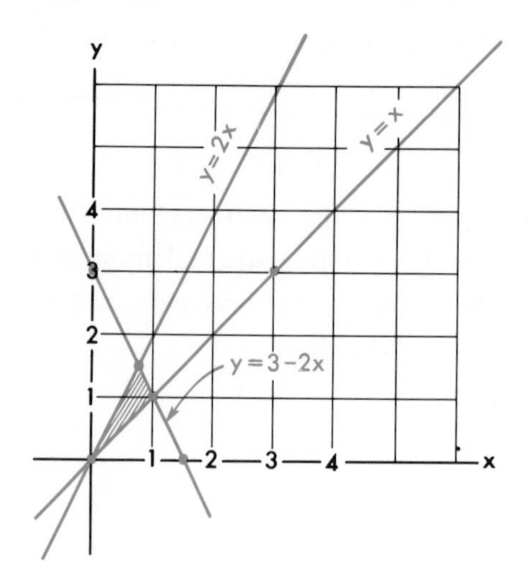

Fig. 11-3-B1. Polygon graph for Test Problem B1.

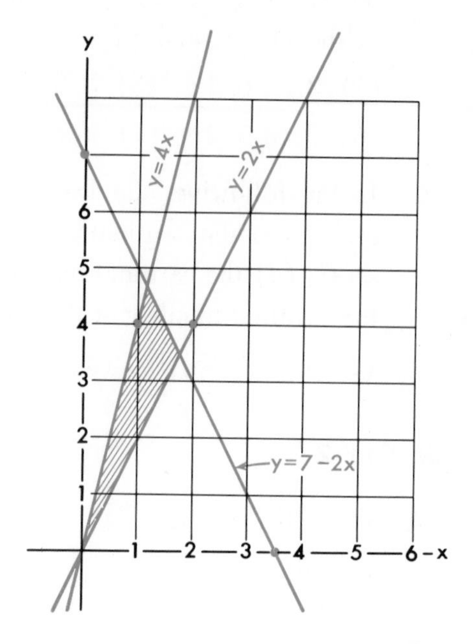

Fig. 11-3-B3. Polygon graph for Test Problem B3.

C *See graph below.*

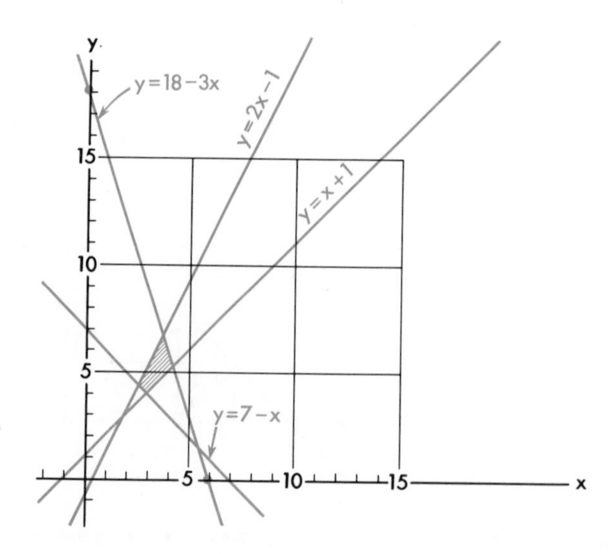

Fig. 11-3-C1.

Polygon graph for Test Problem C1.

Section 4

A (1) *See graph.* The table is as follows:

Vertex	X	Y	New Averages Subject X	Subject Y
P	15	20	75%	69%
Q	15	90	75%	83%
R	30	90	80%	83%
S	60	60	90%	77%
T	60	20	90%	69%

The best strategy is probably the one at S.

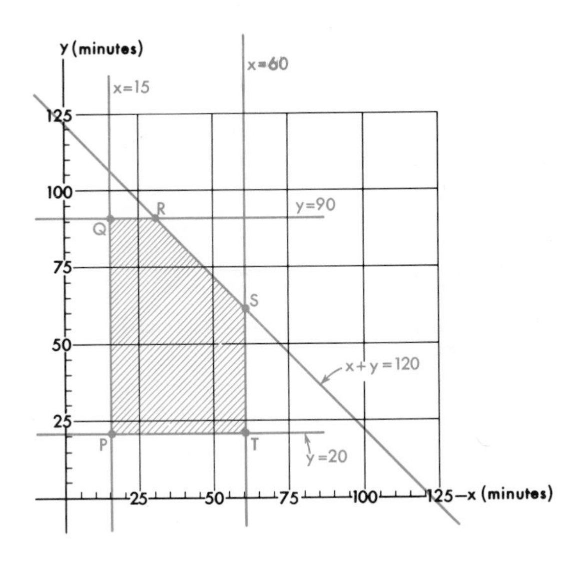

Fig. 11-4-A1.

Polygon graph for Test Problem A1.

B (1) The new table is as follows:

Vertex	X	Y	Z	New Averages Subject X	Subject Y	Subject Z
P	15	20	85	75%	69%	98.5%
Q	15	90	15	75%	83%	91.5%
R	30	90	0	80%	83%	90.0%
S	60	60	0	90%	77%	90.0%
T	60	20	40	90%	69%	94.0%

The best overall strategy is still at vertex S. (*See Fig. 11-4-A1.*)

C (1) *See graph.* The table is as follows:

Vertex	X(Units)	Y(Units)	Cost		
			X	Y	Total
P	20	20	$20	$40	$ 60
Q	20	40	$20	$80	$100
R	50	40	$50	$80	$130
S	50	10	$50	$20	$ 70
T	30	10	$30	$20	$ 50

The cheapest combination is at vertex T.

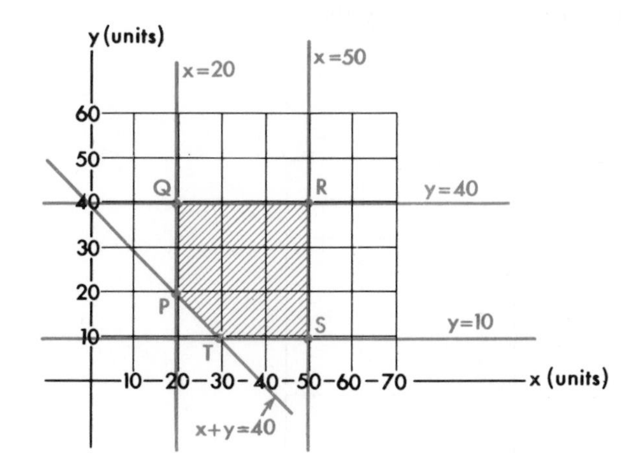

Fig. 11-4-C1. Polygon graph for Test Problem C1.

Section 5

A (1) 1, 2.78%; (3) 3, 8.33%; (5) 5, 13.89%; (7) 4, 11.11%; (9) 2, 5.56%

B (1) 10, 27.78%; (3) 2, 5.56%; (5) 8, 22.22%; (7) 18, 50.00%; (9) 9, 25.00%

Section 6

A (1) $\frac{6}{16}$ = 37.5%; (3) $\frac{11}{16}$ = 68.75%

B (1) 3.125%; (3) 31.25%; (5) 15.625%; (7) 50.00%

Section 7

A (1) 120; (3) 5040; (5) 362,880

B (1) 120; (3) 720

Section 8

A (1) 10; (3) 6

B (1) 120; (3) 75,600; (5) 35

C (1) $\frac{2}{5}$; (3) $\frac{5}{6}$; (5) $\frac{5}{6} \times \frac{4}{5}$

Section 9

(1) $\frac{4}{52} \times \frac{3}{51} \times \frac{2}{50}$; (3) $\frac{1}{52} \times \frac{1}{51} \times \frac{1}{50}$;

(5) $\frac{26}{52} \times \frac{25}{51} \times \frac{24}{50} \times \frac{23}{49}$; (7) $\frac{26}{52} \times \frac{26}{51} \times \frac{25}{50}$;

(9) $\frac{52}{52} \times \frac{12}{51} \times \frac{11}{50} \times \frac{10}{49} \times \frac{9}{48}$

Section 10

A (1) $\left(\frac{1}{2} \times \frac{2}{5}\right) \times \left(\frac{1}{2} \times \frac{1}{5}\right) = 30\%$

(3) $\left(\frac{1}{6} \times \frac{4}{36}\right) + \left(\frac{5}{6} \times \frac{3}{36}\right) =$ approximately 8.80%

B (1)

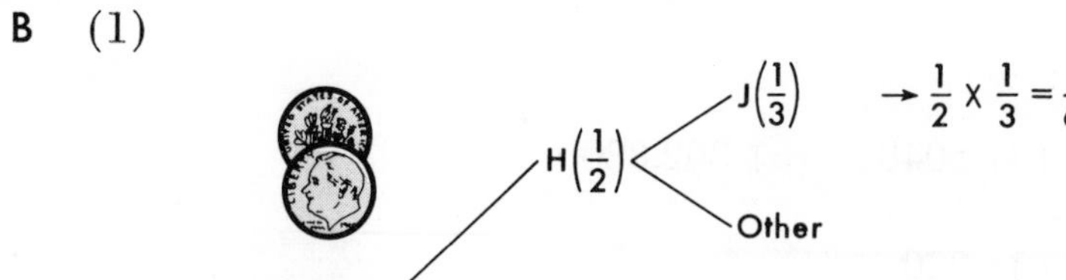

Fig. 11-10-B1. Tree diagram for Test Problem B1.

(3)

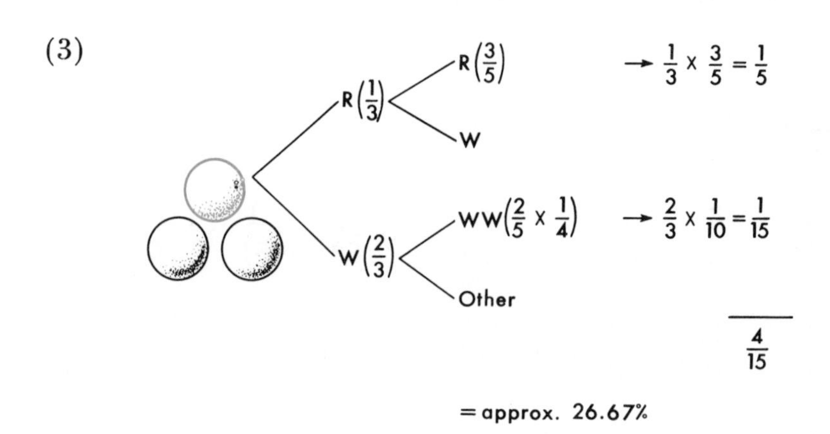

Fig. 11-10-B3. Tree diagram for Test Problem B3.

INDEX